Collier's *Junior* Classics

Series Editor
Margaret E. Martignoni

Series Titles	*Volume Editors*
A, B, C: GO!	**Rosemary E. Livsey**
ONCE UPON A TIME	**Elizabeth H. Gross**
MAGIC IN THE AIR	**Mary V. Gaver**
JUST AROUND THE CORNER	**Alice Brooks McGuire**
IN YOUR OWN BACKYARD	**Marian C. Young**
HARVEST OF HOLIDAYS	**Ruth Weeden Stewart**
LEGENDS OF LONG AGO	**Jane Darrah**
ROADS TO GREATNESS	**Louise Galloway**
CALL OF ADVENTURE	**Charlemae Rollins**
GIFTS FROM THE PAST	**Elenora Alexander**

roads to GREATNESS

A completely new selection of outstanding children's stories and poems compiled for enrichment reading by a distinguished editorial board of children's librarians.

Series Editor
MARGARET E. MARTIGNONI
Former Superintendent
Work with Children
Brooklyn Public Library

Editor-in-Chief
DR. LOUIS SHORES
Dean, Library School
Florida State University

Managing Editor
HARRY R. SNOWDEN, JR.

Volume Editor
LOUISE GALLOWAY
Assistant Professor
Library School
Florida State University

Collier's *Junior* Classics Series

THE CROWELL-COLLIER PUBLISHING COMPANY • NEW YORK

Roads to Greatness

Library of Congress Catalog Card Number 61-17993
Printed in the United States of America
Eleventh Printing

Introduction

Collier's Junior Classics Series

We are children only once, and then only for a few brief years. But these are the most impressionable years of a lifetime. Never again will the world and everything in it be so eternally new, so filled with wonder. Never again will physical, mental, spiritual growth be so natural and unavoidable. During these years, habits become ingrained, tastes are developed, personality takes form. The child's whole being is geared toward learning. He instinctively reaches out for truth and, having no prejudices, seizes upon that which is good, just, beautiful. For these reasons, a child deserves what Walter de la Mare has called "only the rarest kind of best."

What do we mean by "best" in a book for children? Best books reflect universal truths with clarity and artistry. Such books reveal that man is essentially good and that life is infinitely worth living. They do not deny the existence of evil, but rather emphasize man's thrilling struggle against evil through faith, courage, and perseverance. They awaken the young reader's imagination, call forth his laughter as well as his tears, help him to understand and to love his fellow man. The reading of such books constitutes a rich heritage of experience which is every child's birthright.

The librarian-editors of *Collier's Junior Classics* have combed the best children's books of the past and present to assemble in a single series a sampling of the finest literature for boys and girls. High standards have been maintained for the art work also, which in most instances has been taken from the original book. No attempt has been made to cover all fields of knowledge or to include factual material for its own sake. The emphasis here is on good literature, chiefly fiction and biography, folk lore and legend, and some poetry. Special attention is given to the American scene and American democratic ideals, but many selections cover other cultures, geographical areas, and historical periods.

The purpose of *Collier's Junior Classics* is to introduce boys and girls to some of the best books ever written for children, to stimulate young readers to seek for themselves the books from which the selections have been drawn as well as other good books of similar appeal, and to encourage children to become discriminating, thoughtful, life-time readers. Author, title, and publisher are given at the foot of the page on which each selection opens. This enables readers to ask for the complete book at a library or bookstore. When necessary, brief introductions set the scene for the selection, while follow-up recommendations, complete with publishers' names, appear at the end of most stories.

Collier's Junior Classics is a series of ten individually indexed volumes. A, B, C: GO! has been lovingly compiled for the youngest, and consists of nursery rhymes, favorite folk tales, best-loved poems, and stories for reading aloud. Four volumes have been assembled for the intermediate group: ONCE UPON A TIME, a wonderous collection of fables, world folk tales, and modern fairy tales; MAGIC IN THE AIR, selections from great masterpieces of fantasy; JUST AROUND THE CORNER, excerpts from warm-hearted stories of other lands; and IN YOUR OWN BACKYARD, selections from stirring books about our own country. Four additional volumes cater to the interests of more mature boys and girls: GIFTS FROM THE PAST, memorable selections from world classics; LEGENDS OF LONG AGO, selections from great myths, epics, and American tall tales; ROADS TO GREATNESS, excerpts from biographies of some of the greatest men and women of the world; and CALL OF ADVENTURE, selections from action and suspense stories of today and yesterday. Finally, and most unusual of all, is the volume entitled HARVEST OF HOLIDAYS, a feast of stories, poems, documents, and factual material about twenty-two American national and religious holidays. Although perhaps of greatest interest to the intermediate group, HARVEST OF HOLIDAYS will intrigue and delight all ages.

The tables of contents for the ten volumes read like an all-time Who's Who of distinguished writers. A brief mention of only a few of these authors would include such names as Lewis Carroll, Kenneth Grahame, Charles Dickens, Mark Twain, Louisa May Alcott, Pearl Buck, Laura Ingalls Wilder, Eleanor Estes, Genevieve Foster, Robert Louis Stevenson, Robert McCloskey, Valenti Angelo, Carl Sandburg, A. A. Milne, Eleanor Farjeon, Elizabeth Enright, and Margaret Wise Brown. Among the illustrators, many of whom are also authors, are to be found the Petershams, the d'Aulaires, Wanda Gág, Louis Slobodkin, Helen Sewell, Lois Lenski, Roger Duvoisin, Maurice Sendak, Kurt Wiese, Marguerite de Angeli, Steele Savage, Howard Pyle, Lynd Ward, James Daugherty, Arthur Rackham, Fritz Kredel, and Gustave Dore.

Collier's Junior Classics is intended primarily for the home, although libraries will find the series valuable for browsing as well as for introducing children to many different books. Because each book is an individual volume, complete with its own index, it can be shelved where the librarian believes it will be most useful to the children.

No pains have been spared to make the individual volumes a series of stepping stones to all that is best in the magic world of children's books.

Margaret E. Martignoni
SERIES EDITOR

Contents

Roads to Greatness

A sandy-haired lad scuffed along the streets of Hannibal, Missouri, kicking a stone as he walked. Suddenly his attention was captured by a scrap of paper blowing in the wind. The boy chased and caught the paper. It was a page from a biography of Joan of Arc that told how Joan was tormented and tortured in the Tower of Rouen in France. The boy had never heard of Joan of Arc, but the text of the torn page sparked his interest. He hunted for other books about her. The more he read, the more he wanted to read. He was fascinated by her unrelenting faith, intrigued by her courage, indignant over the injustices she suffered. The boy was Sam Clemens, known to the world as Mark Twain.

Sam Clemens courted the Maid of Orleans all his life. Because of her, he became an avid reader. Through her came the seeds for many ideas that were later to blossom forth in his books. And in 1896, he published his own biography of Joan of Arc.

Good biographies have guided aspiring artists to their own Sistine Chapels, they have created thousands of nurses in the image of Florence Nightingale, and guided statesmen towards lofty goals. In biographies we can be anyone—Lou Gehrig hitting the ball over the center-field fence, Madam Curie on the brink of discovery. Through biography we learn that heroes are people—that they have self-doubts, that they make mistakes, and that they must learn to accept failures and to benefit from them.

ROADS TO GREATNESS presents people from all walks of life. You will read of the pressures that drove Michelangelo, the devotion that characterized the career of ballerina Anna Pavlova. You will see the mischievous Tom Sawyer in the life of his creator, Sam Clemens. Perhaps you will be sparked by one of the people in this volume. Perhaps you will go on to read the book that has been excerpted. Then, for you, as for young Clemens, the hunt will have begun.

LOUISE GALLOWAY
Assistant Professor,
Library School,
Florida State University

ROBERT E. LEE

A Soldier Is Made

BY HENRY STEELE COMMAGER

Illustrations by Lynd Ward

The great Southern general Robert E. Lee (1807-1870) has retained a respect and love comparable to Lincoln's over the century since the Civil War. Lincoln, indeed, held so high a regard for Lee that at the onset of war he asked him to command the Union army. Lee decided that duty demanded his support of the South. As a patriotic American, he felt much as Washington must have when he undertook the break with Britain.

IT was something to be born a Lee, in Virginia. All through the South there were great families that dominated society—and politics and war too—but nowhere was there a greater or a prouder family than the Lee. For over a hundred years the Lees played a leading part in the history of the Old Dominion. They had been Governors and Councillors and Burgesses. They had served the King, had fought in the Revolution, sat in the Continental Congress, and represented their country at foreign courts. They had been great planters, great statesmen, great soldiers. Two Lees had written their names on the Declaration of Independence, under the flourishing signature of John Hancock—but Lees needed no flourish to their names! "I know of no country that can produce a family all distinguished as clever men, as our Lees," said Washington, who knew them well.

A sort of Lee cousinship spread like a network over the whole state. Little Robert Edward didn't know it yet, but he was cousin to the Carters and the Randolphs, the Tazewells and

the Peytons, the Blands and the Corbins, the Fitzhughs and the Nicholases and a dozen others. And there wasn't a great plantation in the whole Tidewater where the Lees weren't welcome.

He had been born in mid-winter of 1807, at Stratford, in the same room in which two signers of the Declaration of Independence had been born. What a wonderful place Stratford was—a great brick house, sitting low on the land, with massive walls four feet thick, with two immense chimneys, larger than any others to be found in the whole of America, and with a promenade on the roof from which you could see the broad shining Potomac River. There was an elegant ballroom, the handsomest, it was said, in all Virginia, and each of the other rooms—there were seventeen in all—was painted a different color. There was a blue room and a white room, a green room and a cherry room, and each with a fireplace big enough to hide in. From the walls hung portraits of ancestors frowning down, or smiling, as they chose, in their stiff, formal clothes and their powdered wigs.

And Stratford was more than a house; it was a whole village, with cook houses and an office and a schoolroom, and stables all close to the big house, and the Negro quarters off at a distance, but not too far for adventure. Best of all for a boy were the acres and acres of land, shaded by great poplars and oaks and sugar maples and cedars. A little way off was shallow Pope's Creek to wade in, and the Potomac with the great sailing boats going up and down.

He was the third boy, and was named Robert Edward, after his mother's brothers. She was a Carter, and if there was any family in Virginia that could hold its own with the Lees, it was the Carters. Grandfather Charles Carter—himself son of a planter so rich and splendid that he had been called "King" Carter—lived at Shirley on the James River, and during his boyhood Robert spent more time at Shirley than at Stratford. Shirley was almost as famous as Stratford, and even more elegant: people came from far and wide to see the wonderful staircase that seemed to hang suspended in the air, and to see the painting of General Washington by the Philadelphia artist, Charles Peale, that hung so proudly in the drawing room. The Carter clan was even more wide-flung than the Lee: grandfather Carter had had no less than twenty-one children, and most of them had large families in turn, so wherever you went visiting in Virginia you ran into a Carter cousin—at Ravenswood and at Chatham and at Nomini Hall and Roswell, and so many others you could scarcely remember them all.

Yes, it was something to be born a Lee and to have a Carter mother. But it was hard to be a poor relation. Robert's father was the famous "Light-Horse Harry." He had been a hero in the Revolution, and Governor of Virginia, and General Washington admired him. But Light-Horse Harry's career was all in the past—and his fame and fortune too. He would still ride off at the head of the little army that put down the so-called "Whiskey Rebellion"; he would still serve in Congress, and propose the famous resolution to Washington—"first in war, first in peace, and first in the hearts of his countrymen." But, after all the glamor of the Revolution and the Governorship, Light-Horse Harry found it hard to settle down to the humdrum life of a planter. He just wasn't meant for the quiet life. Soon he owed money, lots of it, and he thought the easiest way to get out of debt was to speculate. He bought shares in canal companies that never built canals and he bought western lands that proved worthless. He sold off some of his lands; he mortgaged his farms; he tried new business deals and new borrowings, but all in vain. Soon he was barricading himself from the people he owed, while the plantation at Stratford went to rack and ruin. He couldn't escape his creditors forever though, and one day, when Robert was only two years old, they came and put his father in debtor's jail. That was a curious practice of those days which did no good either for debtor or for creditor. If Anne Carter Lee hadn't had a little money of her own, things would have gone hard with the little family.

As it was they went badly enough. Light-Horse Harry managed to get out of jail in a year or so, but that didn't help much. It was clear that he would have to give up Stratford, now neglected and shabby, the garden overgrown with weeds, most of the Negroes gone. As a final gesture Anne Carter Lee with her little boy went out in the garden and planted a chestnut tree. Then the family set off for near-by Alexandria. Robert was just four years old, and he was never again to live in the great house or play beneath the towering trees.

Yet it wasn't a bad move—even from Robert's point of view. The little brick house on Cameron Street in Alexandria was pleasant enough, especially with some of the elegant furniture that had been brought from Stratford. The gardens were handsome and spacious, and Robert particularly liked the big snowball bushes. And there were two horses in the stables, so that of a Sunday Mrs. Lee and her children—there were two little girls now—were able to ride out in proper style.

Alexandria, too, was very much like home. It was filled with aunts and uncles and cousins, and no less than twenty of Light-Horse Harry's old soldiers lived there. All of these were proud to welcome their former commander and his family, and most of them were ready enough to tell young Robert stories of the exploits of "Lee's Legion." So Robert heard about men who were already legends—Marion the Swamp Fox, Sumter the Partisan Leader, the noble Marquis de Lafayette, and many others.

Mostly, though, the talk was about George Washington—or got around to him—for the spirit of Washington was everywhere

in the old city. Wherever Robert went he saw houses and churches and taverns that brought up Washington's name. Here was the Masonic Lodge to which Washington had belonged, and the old Carlyle House where Braddock's expedition against the Indians had been organized. Here was Gadsby's Tavern, where Washington had met so often with his fellow-revolutionists, still doing business. Here was the Friendship Fire Company, with a fire "engine" given by the General. Sundays Robert went to Christ's Church and his mother would point out Washington's pew.

Across the broad Potomac was the new city which bore Washington's name, a straggling unfinished collection of houses, strung out along muddy lanes where pigs and cattle jostled the Congressmen. It was not nearly as handsome a town as Alexandria. Also, not far down the river was Mount Vernon where Washington had lived, and on pleasant spring days Robert and his mother would drive down there and look at the stately white-pillared mansion and the lovely lawns sloping down to the river. Up the Potomac just a few miles was the imposing new house called Arlington which George Washington Custis had built—Custis who was the adopted son of the first President of the Country.

Robert also heard stories of the Revolution from his father and his uncles and cousins, and sometimes his father read aloud from the History of the War that he was writing. That war was already a bit dim and awe-inspiring, like Washington himself.

Soon young Robert was to have a taste of war at first hand. In 1812 the United States and England fought a second time. Robert's half-brother, Henry, marched off to Canada, as smart as you please in a major's uniform, and there was recruiting and mustering in of soldiers in Alexandria, as elsewhere. One hot summer day, when Robert was seven, he heard an explosion from the fort below Alexandria, and the next day there was the British fleet, its blue-coated sailors tumbling about the streets while their Commodore forced the city fathers to pay tribute as a price for sparing the town. That the Commodore meant business was clear enough, for the British had set Washington itself afire just three days earlier. Alexandria paid up, and was spared.

For a boy of seven all this was exciting enough, especially the fires in Washington that he could see from across the river. But soon the British left and were forgotten, and life went on its familiar way. It was, on the whole, a very pleasant way, pleasanter, certainly, than Stratford with its poverty. In the summertime Robert swam in the Potomac or visited his mother's kin at Shirley or Chatham; in the fall and winter he often went hunting, following the hounds afoot all through a frosty day. Perhaps it was more fun outdoors than in. For Robert's father was still dodging his creditors, still talking about his grievances, still scribbling away on his book. Meantime he was planning to get away to the West Indies or South America if he could. He found it hard to settle down to the humdrum existence of a sleepy little town.

One July day in 1812, just after the war with England had begun, Light-Horse Harry set off for near-by Baltimore to visit his friend, Alexander Hanson. Robert waved good-bye to him as he set off, a distinguished old man, elegantly dressed in a tall white hat and a long coat, with a white stock at his throat. The next Robert and his mother heard of him was that he was lying dead in a Baltimore jail. It wasn't quite true, but it was almost that bad. Somehow, no one knew quite how, he had got mixed up in a fight—he couldn't resist a fight. Gradually the whole story came out, and it was one that made people hang their heads in shame. Alexander Hanson edited a newspaper which was against the war with England. The rabble of Baltimore thought this disloyal, and set out to punish him. It was while Lee was visiting him, that the mob swarmed down on Hanson's house, thirsting for blood. Lee thought that he knew how to handle a mob: a few shots would do the trick. But alas, a few shots simply maddened the mob. Just when things got serious, the militia arrived, and took Lee and Hanson and their friends to the city jail for protection. It proved a poor protection. The mob followed them, broke into the jail, attacked Lee and Hanson with clubs and knives, and left them for dead. Lee survived, but from then on he was broken in health and in spirit. More dead than alive, he made his way back home where his wife and children nursed him back to health.

Ironically enough President Madison now offered him a

major-generalship in the armies fighting the old enemy. But Lee's fighting days were over. All he wanted was to get away to some warm climate where he could regain his health and find peace. President Madison was willing to help him, and after a while passage was arranged—on an English boat, of all things. So one warm summer day in 1813 Anne Carter and her five children stood on the quay at Alexandria and waved a sorrowful farewell as Light-Horse Harry sailed by on his way to the Barbadoes.

Robert never saw his father again. For six years the old General wandered from island to island in a vain search for health. Every so often there would be letters with strange postmarks, and Robert's mother would read to her sons the stilted phrases which concealed so much anxiety and pride. "Self-command is the pivot upon which the character, fame, and independence of us mortals hang," or "fame in arms, or art, however conspicuous, is naught unless bottomed on virtue." Sometimes he would ask directly about the children. "Robert was always good," he wrote. "Does he strengthen his native tendency?"

That was an easy question to answer. Yes, Robert was always good, so good that if it hadn't been for his native manliness, he might have turned into a prig. More and more he took over management of the larder, the garden, the horses—Mrs. Lee was becoming every day more of an invalid, and his sister Anne, too, was sickly, while Mildred was too little for anything but play. Carter, the oldest of the boys, was off at Harvard, and soon the next brother, Sidney Smith, went to sea as a midshipman. That left Robert pretty much in charge. In the quaint phrase of the time, he "carried the keys."

Meantime there was the serious business of an education—serious indeed for a boy whose family standards were so high, and whose prospects were so poor. For a time Robert had gone to one of the Carter schools; the family connection was so large that they kept up one school for the Carter girls and one for the boys. When he was thirteen his mother sent him to the Alexandria Academy—General Washington had been one of the trustees—where a genial Irishman named William Leary drilled him in Greek and Latin and mathematics. This would have prepared him for college, but there wasn't enough money for college. Brother Sidney Smith had made himself a career in the Navy; why shouldn't Robert have a career in the Army? Clearly, if he was to be a soldier, the place for him was the Military Academy at West Point. And to West Point he determined to go.

The first problem was to get into the Academy. The requirements for admission were easy enough, ludicrously easy by modern standards. Applicants had to be between the ages of fourteen and twenty, at least four feet nine inches tall, free from physical defects, able to read and write, and competent in arithmetic! Robert could meet these all right. He was seventeen years old, almost six feet tall, in perfect health, and as well educated as almost any boy of his age.

The real difficulty was to get an appointment from the Secretary of War who, at this time, was John C. Calhoun of South Carolina. Competition was sharp, especially in the South, where it was a tradition that the sons of gentlemen go into the Army. Yet Robert's chances were good. It was not only that he was a handsome and likeable young man, well trained in the classics and in mathematics. That helped, of course. Rather it was that he had behind him the powerful Lee connection, and all their friends. And there were many who remembered Light-Horse Harry's services to his country, and who were eager to extend a helping hand to his son. So Robert was able to submit to the Secretary of War not only the usual recommendations from friends and teachers, but letters from no less than five Senators and three Congressmen! Whether it was these letters, or the Lee name, or young Robert himself, we do not know, but in March 1824 Robert E. Lee was informed that he had been appointed to the United States Military Academy at West Point.

On a warm June day in 1825 Lee stepped aboard a gleaming white paddle-wheeler—perhaps it was the *Chancellor Livingston* or the *James Kent*, or even the new *Richmond*—and steamed up the Hudson to West Point. It was only fifty-some miles from New York to the Point, but the trip took half a day, and there was plenty of time to admire the scenery, as lovely as any in the country. It was all new to Robert, yet not wholly strange, not unlike the upper Potomac, which he knew well—

the broad blue river, on one side the steep Palisades, on the other trim lawns running down to the water's edge, and handsome mansion houses. The steamer stopped when it came opposite the Point, swinging back and forth in the current. A little skiff put out from the pier, and the lads who were going to the Academy climbed down the rope ladder and into the boat, and were rowed to shore, Robert among them.

Set in a great bend of the Hudson, the Point was as beautiful then as now. It was hemmed in on two sides by the majestic river; to the south stretched the Highlands, while Storm King Mountain, its summit often hidden in clouds, dominated the north. The magnificence of the natural setting brought out in sharp contrast the shabbiness of the Academy itself. As Lee came up the steep path from the river pier, he saw a group of ugly stucco buildings, squatting on a narrow, treeless plateau.

There were the North and South Barracks, which housed the four-hundred-odd cadets, the main Academy building, a long mess hall—also used as a hotel for visitors—and, scattered around the grounds, a group of smaller buildings almost as ugly as the main ones.

Living conditions, Lee quickly learned, were as meager as the buildings. In the summertime Lee and his fellow cadets lived in tents, in what was called—in honor of the President then in the White House—Camp Adams. The rest of the year Lee lived in the old barracks. His room was small, bare, and uncomfortable, heated only by a tiny fireplace, and he had to share it with two or three other lads. Here he studied, in such time as was allowed him, by the flickering light of candles; here he slept, unrolling his mattress on a cold floor. The food, too, as Lee soon learned, was very different from the rich and varied fare he was used to at home. The Academy chef, a thrifty soul, filled his victims up on porridge, bread, soup, and potatoes, with bacon and mutton and beef only on rare occasions. It was, all in all, pretty grim.

Plebe Lee fell quickly into the routine of the Academy. Reveille sounded at sunrise; then came drill and parade for an hour or so; breakfast; five hours of classes and study; an hour for dinner; two more hours of study; two hours for drill; supper, study, and inspection. Taps were sounded at nine-thirty, and lights out at ten. It was all quite strenuous, but once Lee got the hang of it, he managed easily enough. There was not much time for play, and no organized sports at all. Saturday afternoons and Sundays the cadets could swim in the Hudson, or walk to near-by Buttermilk Falls, or find a few hours for reading, and perhaps for visitors.

Life, as Lee soon learned, was hedged around with endless rules and regulations. Woe betide the cadet who forgot them—who was late for classes or forgot to polish his boots or his buttons, who talked out of turn or failed in proper respect to instructors or to upper-classmen, or ventured off grounds in search for food or for forbidden entertainment. Colonel Thayer, the Superintendent who had really made the Academy, was a strict disciplinarian, and failure to observe the rules was punished with demerits. Too many of these, and out you went!

The academic requirements, too, were stiff. Colonel Thayer had already established the rule, still an Academy tradition, that every cadet recite in every subject every day. There was no such thing as falling behind in your work, and then boning up for examinations: if you fell behind, you fell out. The course of study was a narrow one. The first year was devoted to mathematics and French. Gradually other subjects were added —drawing, surveying, engineering, a bit of physics and chemistry, a smattering of history, geography, and "moral philosophy." There was also something called "the science of war"—a subject which Lee certainly mastered, whether at the Academy or elsewhere.

This was all theoretical, and you couldn't make a soldier by theory alone. Colonel Thayer knew that well enough: he was an engineer himself. So on top of all the book-study, there was constant drill, and practical training. The cadets learned how to handle artillery, how to build forts, how to lay out roads and build bridges, how to survey and make maps. They were trained in tactics, and in the command of small groups of soldiers. All this was fun for the cadets: it took them out in the open, gave them a chance to ride horses, to use surveying instruments, to fire off guns, gave them a feeling that they were learning things of practical use.

Many a promising career was wrecked on the shoals of rules or grades. Of Lee's class of eighty-seven, almost half failed to graduate. But Lee had no difficulties either with the regulations or with his marks. From the beginning he was up among the first two or three in his class, and he held this position through the four years he was at the Academy. In his second year Lee was named staff sergeant, and asked to teach mathematics to the Plebes; thereafter he was both instructor and student. In his last year he won the most prized of all Academy distinctions—the position of Adjutant of the Corps. When he graduated he was number two in his class, and what is more, he had come through four years without a single demerit! As a "distinguished cadet" he could choose his own branch of service, and, like so many others, he chose the engineers.

To his classmates Lee was known as the "Marble Model." He may have been a model, but he was far from marble, far from cold and aloof, and there was nothing about him of the prig. Joseph E. Johnston—his classmate and later his ablest general—describes him at this time:

We had the same intimate associates who thought as I did that no other youth or man so united the qualities that win warm friendship and command high respect. For he was full of sympathy and kindness, genial and fond of gay conversation, and even of fun, while his correctness of demeanor and attention to all duties, personal and official, and a dignity as much a part of himself as the elegance of his person, gave him a superiority that every one acknowledged in his heart.

Here we have the Lee of the future!

HELEN KELLER

Out of Darkness

BY HELEN KELLER

Helen Keller (B. 1880), whose sight and hearing were destroyed by illness before she was two years old, was left deaf, dumb, and blind. With the help of her teacher and companion, Anne Sullivan, she learned to "see" and to "read" with her hands. Without hearing a sound, she learned to speak. In 1904, Miss Keller was graduated with honors from Radcliffe College. After graduation, she worked actively to improve the conditions of the blind, giving lectures, and writing books and articles.

I DO not remember when I first realized that I was different from other people; but I knew it before my teacher came to me. I had noticed that my mother and my friends did not use signs as I did when they wanted anything done, but talked with their mouths. Sometimes I stood between two persons who were conversing and touched their lips. I could not understand, and was vexed. I moved my lips and gesticulated frantically without result. This made me so angry at times that I kicked and screamed until I was exhausted.

I think I knew when I was naughty, for I knew that it hurt Ella, my nurse, to kick her, and when my fit of temper was over I had a feeling akin to regret. But I cannot remember any instance in which this feeling prevented me from repeating the naughtiness when I failed to get what I wanted.

In those days a little coloured girl, Martha Washington, the child of our cook, and Belle, an old setter, and a great hunter in her day, were my constant companions. Martha Washington understood my signs, and I seldom had any difficulty in making her do just as I wished. It pleased me to domineer over her, and she generally submitted to my tyranny rather than risk a hand-to-hand encounter. I was strong, active, indifferent to consequences. I knew my own mind well enough and always had my own way, even if I had to fight tooth and nail for it. We spent a great deal of time in the kitchen, kneading dough balls, helping make ice-cream, grinding coffee, quarreling over the cake-bowl, and feeding the hens and turkeys that swarmed about the kitchen steps. Many of them were so tame that they would eat from my hand and let me feel them. One big gobbler snatched a tomato from me one day and ran away with it. Inspired, perhaps, by Master Gobbler's success, we carried off to the woodpile a cake which the cook had just frosted, and ate every bit of it. I was quite ill afterward, and I wonder if retribution also overtook the turkey.

The guinea-fowl likes to hide her nest in out-of-the-way places, and it was one of my greatest delights to hunt for the eggs in the long grass. I could not tell Martha Washington when I wanted to go egg-hunting, but I would double my hands and put them on the ground, which meant something round in the grass, and Martha always understood. When we were fortunate enough to find a nest I never allowed her to carry the eggs home, making her understand by emphatic signs that she might fall and break them.

The sheds where the corn was stored, the stable where the horses were kept, and the yard where the cows were milked morning and evening were unfailing sources of interest to Martha and me. The milkers would let me keep my hands on the cows while they milked, and I often got well switched by the cow for my curiosity.

The making ready for Christmas was always a delight to me. Of course I did not know what it was all about, but I enjoyed the pleasant odours that filled the house and the tidbits that were given to Martha Washington and me to keep us quiet. We were sadly in the way, but that did not interfere with our pleasure in the least. They allowed us to grind the spices, pick over the raisins and lick the stirring spoons. I hung my stocking because the others did; I cannot remember, however, that the ceremony interested me especially, nor did my curiosity cause me to wake before daylight to look for my gifts.

Martha Washington had as great a love of mischief as I. Two little children were seated on the veranda steps one hot July afternoon. One was black as ebony, with little bunches of fuzzy hair tied with shoestrings sticking out all over her head like corkscrews. The other was white, with long golden curls. One child was six years old, the other two or three years older. The younger child was blind—that was I—and the other was Martha Washington. We were busy cutting out paper dolls; but we soon wearied of this amusement, and after cutting up our shoestrings and clipping all the leaves off the honeysuckle that were within reach, I turned my attention to Martha's corkscrews. She objected at first, but finally submitted. Thinking that turn and turn about is fair play, she seized the scissors and cut off one of my curls, and would have cut them all off but for my mother's timely interference.

Belle, our dog, my other companion, was old and lazy and liked to sleep by the open fire rather than to romp with me. I tried hard to teach her my sign language, but she was dull and inattentive. She sometimes started and quivered with excitement, then she became perfectly rigid, as dogs do when they point a bird. I did not then know why Belle acted in this way; but I knew she was not doing as I wished. This vexed me and the lesson always ended in a one-sided boxing match. Belle would get up, stretch herself lazily, give one or two contemptuous sniffs, go to the opposite side of the hearth and lie down again, and I, wearied and disappointed, went off in search of Martha.

Many incidents of those early years are fixed in my memory, isolated, but clear and distinct, making the sense of that silent, aimless, dayless life all the more intense.

One day I happened to spill water on my apron, and I spread it out to dry before the fire which was flickering on the sitting-room hearth. The apron did not dry quickly enough to suit me, so I drew nearer and threw it right over the hot ashes. The fire leaped into life; the flames encircled me so that in a moment my clothes were blazing. I made a terrified noise that brought Viny, my old nurse, to the rescue. Throwing a blanket over me, she almost suffocated me, but she put out the fire. Except for my hands and hair I was not badly burned.

About this time I found out the use of a key. One morning I locked my mother up in the pantry, where she was obliged to remain three hours, as the servants were in a detached part of the house. She kept pounding on the door, while I sat outside on the porch steps and laughed with glee as I felt the jar of the pounding. This most naughty prank of mine convinced my parents that I must be taught as soon as possible. After my teacher, Miss Sullivan, came to me, I sought an early opportunity to lock her in her room. I went upstairs with something which my mother made me understand I was to give to Miss Sullivan; but no sooner had I given it to her than I slammed the door to, locked it, and hid the key under the wardrobe in the hall. I could not be induced to tell where the key was. My father was obliged to get a ladder and take Miss Sullivan out through the window—much to my delight. Months after I produced the key.

When I was about five years old we moved from the little vine-covered house to a large new one. The family consisted of my father and mother, two older half-brothers, and, afterward, a little sister, Mildred. My earliest distinct recollection of my father is making my way through great drifts of newspapers to his side and finding him alone, holding a sheet of paper before his face. I was greatly puzzled to know what he was doing. I imitated this action, even wearing his spectacles, thinking they might help solve the mystery. But I did not find out the secret for several years. Then I learned what those papers were, and that my father edited one of them.

My father was most loving and indulgent, devoted to his home, seldom leaving us, except in the hunting season. He was a great hunter, I have been told, and a celebrated shot. Next to his family he loved his dogs and gun. His hospitality was great, almost to a fault, and he seldom came home without bringing a guest. His special pride was the big garden where, it was said, he raised the finest watermelons and strawberries in the county; and to me he brought the first ripe grapes and the choicest berries. I remember his caressing touch as he led me from tree to tree, from vine to vine, and his eager delight in whatever pleased me.

He was a famous story-teller; after I had acquired language he used to spell clumsily into my hand his cleverest anecdotes, and nothing pleased him more than to have me repeat them at an opportune moment.

I was in the North, enjoying the last beautiful days of the summer of 1896, when I heard the news of my father's death. He had had a short illness, there had been a brief time of acute suffering, then all was over. This was my first great sorrow—my first personal experience with death.

How shall I write of my mother? She is so near to me that it almost seems indelicate to speak of her.

For a long time I regarded my little sister as an intruder. I knew that I had ceased to be my mother's only darling, and the thought filled me with jealousy. She sat in my mother's lap constantly, where I used to sit, and seemed to take up all her care and time. One day something happened which seemed to me to be adding insult to injury.

At that time I had a much-petted, much-abused doll, which I afterward named Nancy. She was, alas, the helpless victim of my outbursts of temper and of affection, so that she became much the worse for wear. I had dolls which talked, and cried, and opened and shut their eyes; yet I never loved one of them as I loved poor Nancy. She had a cradle, and I often spent an hour or more rocking her. I guarded both doll and cradle with the most jealous care; but once I discovered my little sister sleeping peacefully in the cradle. At this presumption on the part of one to whom as yet no tie of love bound me I grew angry. I rushed upon the cradle and overturned it, and the baby might have been killed had my mother not caught her as she fell. Thus it is that when we walk in the valley of twofold solitude we know little of the tender affections that grow out of endearing words and actions and companionship. But afterward, when I was restored to my human heritage, Mildred and I grew into each other's hearts, so that we were content to go hand-in-hand wherever caprice led us, although she could not understand my finger language, nor I her childish prattle.

UNITED PRESS INTERNATIONAL

Helen Keller at the age of seven

Meanwhile the desire to express myself grew. The few signs I used became less and less adequate, and my failures to make myself understood were invariably followed by outbursts of passion. I felt as if invisible hands were holding me, and I made frantic efforts to free myself. I struggled—not that struggling helped matters, but the spirit of resistance was strong within me; I generally broke down in tears and physical exhaustion. If my mother happened to be near I crept into her arms, too miserable even to remember the cause of the tempest. After awhile the need of some means of communication became so urgent that these outbursts occurred daily, sometimes hourly.

My parents were deeply grieved and perplexed. We lived a long way from any school for the blind or the deaf, and it seemed unlikely that any one would come to such an out-of-the-way place as Tuscumbia to teach a child who was both deaf and blind. Indeed, my friends and relatives sometimes doubted whether I could be taught. My mother's only ray of hope came from Dickens's "American Notes." She had read his account of Laura Bridgman, and remembered vaguely that she was deaf and blind, yet had been educated. But she also remembered with a hopeless pang that Dr. Howe, who had discovered the way to teach the deaf and blind, had been dead many years. His methods had probably died with him; and if they had not, how was a little girl in a far-off town in Alabama to receive the benefit of them?

When I was about six years old, my father heard of an eminent oculist in Baltimore, who had been successful in many cases that had seemed hopeless. My parents at once determined to take me to Baltimore to see if anything could be done for my eyes.

The journey, which I remember well, was very pleasant. I made friends with many people on the train. One lady gave me a box of shells. My father made holes in these so that I could string them, and for a long time they kept me happy and contented. The conductor, too, was kind. Often when he went his rounds I clung to his coat tails while he collected and punched the tickets. His punch, with which he let me play, was a delightful toy. Curled up in a corner of the seat I amused myself for hours making funny little holes in bits of cardboard.

My aunt made me a big doll out of towels. It was the most comical, shapeless thing, this improvised doll, with no nose, mouth, ears or eyes—nothing that even the imagination of a child could convert into a face. Curiously enough, the absence of eyes struck me more than all the other defects put together. I pointed this out to everybody with provoking persistency, but no one seemed equal to the task of providing the doll with eyes.

A bright idea, however, shot into my mind, and the problem was solved. I tumbled off the seat and searched under it until I found my aunt's cape, which was trimmed with large beads. I pulled two beads off and indicated to her that I wanted her to sew them on my doll. She raised my hand to her eyes in a questioning way, and I nodded energetically. The beads were sewed in the right place and I could not contain myself for joy; but immediately I lost all interest in the doll. During the whole trip I did not have one fit of temper, there were so many things to keep my mind and fingers busy.

When we arrived in Baltimore, Dr. Chisholm received us kindly: but he could do nothing. He said, however, that I could be educated, and advised my father to consult Dr. Alexander Graham Bell, of Washington, who would be able to give him information about schools and teachers of deaf or blind children. Acting on the doctor's advice, we went immediately to Washington to see Dr. Bell, my father with a sad heart and many misgivings, I wholly unconscious of his anguish, finding pleasure in the excitement of moving from place to place. Child as I was, I at once felt the tenderness and sympathy which endeared Dr. Bell to so many hearts, as his wonderful achievements enlist their admiration. He held me on his knee while I examined his watch, and he made it strike for me. He understood my signs, and I knew it and loved him at once. But I did not dream that that interview would be the door through which I should pass from darkness into light, from isolation to friendship, companionship, knowledge, love.

Dr. Bell advised my father to write to Mr. Anagnos, director of the Perkins Institution in Boston, the scene of Dr. Howe's great labours for the blind, and ask him if he had a teacher competent to begin my education. This my father did at once, and in a few weeks there came a kind letter from Mr. Anagnos with the comforting assurance that a teacher had been found. This was in the summer of 1886. But Miss Sullivan did not arrive until the following March.

Thus I came up out of Egypt and stood before Sinai, and a power divine touched my spirit and gave it sight, so that I beheld many wonders. And from the sacred mountain I heard a voice which said, "Knowledge is love and light and vision."

LADIES' HOME JOURNAL

Anne Sullivan at the time she became
Helen Keller's teacher

The most important day I remember in all my life is the one on which my teacher, Anne Mansfield Sullivan, came to me. I am filled with wonder when I consider the immeasurable contrasts between the two lives which it connects. It was the third of March, 1887, three months before I was seven years old.

On the afternoon of that eventful day, I stood on the porch, dumb, expectant. I guessed vaguely from my mother's signs and from the hurrying to and fro in the house that something unusual was about to happen, so I went to the door and waited on the steps. The afternoon sun penetrated the mass of honeysuckle that covered the porch, and fell on my upturned face. My fingers lingered almost unconsciously on the familiar leaves and blossoms which had just come forth to greet the sweet southern spring. I did not know what the future held of marvel or surprise for me. Anger and bitterness had preyed upon me continually for weeks and a deep languor had succeeded this passionate struggle.

Have you ever been at sea in a dense fog, when it seemed as

if a tangible white darkness shut you in, and the great ship, tense and anxious, groped her way toward the shore with plummet and sounding-line, and you waited with beating heart for something to happen? I was like that ship before my education began, only I was without compass or sounding-line, and had no way of knowing how near the harbour was. "Light! give me light!" was the wordless cry of my soul, and the light of love shone on me in that very hour.

I felt approaching footsteps. I stretched out my hand, as I supposed, to my mother. Some one took it, and I was caught up and held close in the arms of her who had come to reveal all things to me, and, more than all things else, to love me.

The morning after my teacher came she led me into her room and gave me a doll. The little blind children at the Perkins Institution had sent it and Laura Bridgman had dressed it; but I did not know this until afterward. When I had played with it a little while, Miss Sullivan slowly spelled into my hand the word "d-o-l-l." I was at once interested in this finger play and tried to imitate it. When I finally succeeded in making the letters correctly I was flushed with childish pleasure and pride. Running downstairs to my mother I held up my hand and made the letters for doll. I did not know that I was spelling a word or even that words existed; I was simply making my fingers go in monkey-like imitation. In the days that followed I learned to spell in this uncomprehending way a great many words, among them *pin, hat, cup* and a few verbs like *sit, stand* and *walk*. But my teacher had been with me several weeks before I understood that everything has a name.

One day, while I was playing with my new doll, Miss Sullivan put my big rag doll into my lap also, spelled "d-o-l-l" and tried to make me understand that "d-o-l-l" applied to both. Earlier in the day we had had a tussle over the words "m-u-g" and "w-a-t-e-r." Miss Sullivan had tried to impress it upon me that "m-u-g" is *mug* and that "w-a-t-e-r" is *water,* but I persisted in confounding the two. In despair she had dropped the subject for the time, only to renew it at the first opportunity. I became impatient at her repeated attempts and, seizing the new doll, I dashed it upon the floor. I was keenly delighted when I felt the fragments of the broken doll at my feet. Neither

LADIES' HOME JOURNAL

The pump at which Helen Keller learned the meaning of "w-a-t-e-r"

sorrow nor regret followed my passionate outburst. I had not loved the doll. In the still, dark world in which I lived there was no strong sentiment or tenderness. I felt my teacher sweep the fragments to one side of the hearth, and I had a sense of satisfaction that the cause of my discomfort was removed. She brought me my hat, and I knew I was going out into the warm sunshine. This thought, if a wordless sensation may be called a thought, made me hop and skip with pleasure.

We walked down the path to the well-house, attracted by the fragrance of the honeysuckle with which it was covered. Some one was drawing water and my teacher placed my hand under the spout. As the cool stream gushed over one hand she spelled into the other the word *water*, first slowly, then rapidly. I stood still, my whole attention fixed upon the motions of her fingers. Suddenly I felt a misty consciousness as of something forgotten—a thrill of returning thought; and somehow the mystery of language was revealed to me. I knew then that "w-a-t-e-r" meant the wonderful cool something that was flowing over my hand. That living word awakened my soul, gave it light, hope, joy, set it free! There were barriers still, it is true, but barriers that could in time be swept away.

I left the well-house eager to learn. Everything had a name, and each name gave birth to a new thought. As we returned to the house every object which I touched seemed to quiver with life. That was because I saw everything with the strange, new sight that had come to me. On entering the door I remembered the doll I had broken. I felt my way to the hearth and picked up the pieces. I tried vainly to put them together. Then my eyes filled with tears; for I realized what I had done, and for the first time I felt repentance and sorrow.

I learned a great many new words that day. I do not remember what they all were; but I do know that *mother, father, sister, teacher* were among them—words that were to make the world blossom for me, "like Aaron's rod, with flowers." It would have been difficult to find a happier child than I was as I lay in my crib at the close of that eventful day and lived over the joys it had brought me, and for the first time longed for a new day to come.

I recall many incidents of the summer of 1887 that followed my soul's sudden awakening. I did nothing but explore with my hands and learn the name of every object that I touched; and the more I handled things and learned their names and uses, the more joyous and confident grew my sense of kinship with the rest of the world.

When the time of daisies and buttercups came Miss Sullivan took me by the hand across the fields, where men were preparing the earth for the seed, to the banks of the Tennessee River, and there, sitting on the warm grass, I had my first lessons in the beneficence of nature. I learned how the sun and the rain make to grow out of the ground every tree that is pleasant to the sight and good for food, how birds build their nests and live and thrive from land to land, how the squirrel, the deer, the lion and every other creature finds food and shelter. As my knowledge of things grew I felt more and more the delight of the world I was in. Long before I learned to do a sum in arithmetic or describe the shape of the earth, Miss Sullivan had taught me to find beauty in the fragrant woods, in every blade of grass, and in the curves and dimples of my baby sister's hand. She linked my earliest thoughts with nature, and made me feel that "birds and flowers and I were happy peers."

But about this time I had an experience which taught me that nature is not always kind. One day my teacher and I were returning from a long ramble. The morning had been fine, but it was growing warm and sultry when at last we turned our faces homeward. Two or three times we stopped to rest under a tree by the wayside. Our last halt was under a wild cherry tree a short distance from the house. The shade was grateful, and the tree was so easy to climb that with my teacher's assistance I was able to scramble to a seat in the branches. It was so cool up in the tree that Miss Sullivan proposed that we have our luncheon there. I promised to keep still while she went to the house to fetch it.

Suddenly a change passed over the tree. All the sun's warmth left the air. I knew the sky was black, because all the heat, which meant light to me, had died out of the atmosphere. A strange odour came up from the earth. I knew it, it was the odour that always precedes a thunderstorm, and a nameless fear clutched at my heart. I felt absolutely alone, cut off from my friends and the firm earth. The immense, the unknown, enfolded me. I remained still and expectant; a chilling terror crept over me. I longed for my teacher's return; but above all things I wanted to get down from that tree.

There was a moment of sinister silence, then a multitudinous stirring of the leaves. A shiver ran through the tree, and the wind sent forth a blast that would have knocked me off had I not clung to the branch with might and main. The tree swayed and strained. The small twigs snapped and fell about me in showers. A wild impulse to jump seized me, but terror held me fast. I crouched down in the fork of the tree. The branches lashed about me. I felt the intermittent jarring that came now and then, as if something heavy had fallen and the shock had traveled up till it reached the limb I sat on. It worked my suspense up to the highest point, and just as I was thinking the tree and I should fall together, my teacher seized my hand and helped me down. I clung to her, trembling with joy to feel the earth under my feet once more. I had learned a new lesson —that nature "wages open war against her children, and under softest touch hides treacherous claws."

After this experience it was a long time before I climbed another tree. The mere thought filled me with terror. It was the sweet allurement of the mimosa tree in full bloom that finally overcame my fears. One beautiful spring morning when I was alone in the summer-house, reading, I became aware of a wonderful subtle fragrance in the air. I started up and instinctively stretched out my hands. It seemed as if the spirit of spring had passed through the summer-house. "What is it?" I asked, and the next minute I recognized the odour of the mimosa blossoms. I felt my way to the end of the garden, knowing that the mimosa tree was near the fence, at the turn of the path. Yes, there it was, all quivering in the warm sunshine, its blossom-laden branches almost touching the long grass. Was there ever anything so exquisitely beautiful in the world before! Its delicate blossoms shrank from the slightest earthly touch; it seemed as if a tree of paradise had been transplanted to earth. I made my way through a shower of petals to the great trunk and for one minute stood irresolute; then, putting my foot in the broad space between the forked branches, I pulled myself up into the tree. I had some difficulty in holding on, for the branches were very large and the bark hurt my hands. But I had a delicious sense that I was doing something unusual and wonderful, so I kept on climbing higher and higher, until I reached a little seat which somebody had built there so long ago that it had grown part of the tree itself. I sat there for a long, long time, feeling like a fairy on a rosy cloud. After that I spent many happy hours in my tree of paradise, thinking fair thoughts and dreaming bright dreams.

I had now the key to all language, and I was eager to learn to use it. Children who hear acquire language without any particular effort; the words that fall from others' lips they catch on the wing, as it were, delightedly, while the little deaf child must trap them by a slow and often painful process. But whatever the process, the result is wonderful. Gradually from naming an object we advance step by step until we have traversed the vast distance between our first stammered syllable and the sweep of thought in a line of Shakespeare.

At first, when my teacher told me about a new thing I asked very few questions. My ideas were vague, and my vocabulary was inadequate; but as my knowledge of things grew, and I learned more and more words, my field of inquiry broadened, and I would return again and again to the same subject, eager for further information. Sometimes a new word revived an image that some earlier experience had engraved on my brain.

I remember the morning that I first asked the meaning of the word, "love." This was before I knew many words. I had found a few early violets in the garden and brought them to my teacher. She tried to kiss me: but at that time I did not like to have any one kiss me except my mother. Miss Sullivan put her arm gently round me and spelled into my hand, "I love Helen."

"What is love?" I asked.

She drew me closer to her and said, "It is here," pointing to my heart, whose beats I was conscious of for the first time. Her words puzzled me very much because I did not then understand anything unless I touched it.

I smelt the violets in her hand and asked, half in words, half in signs, a question which meant, "Is love the sweetness of flowers?"

"No," said my teacher.

Again I thought. The warm sun was shining on us.

"Is this not love?" I asked, pointing in the direction from which the heat came. "Is this not love?"

It seemed to me that there could be nothing more beautiful than the sun, whose warmth makes all things grow. But Miss Sullivan shook her head, and I was greatly puzzled and disappointed. I thought it strange that my teacher could not show me love.

A day or two afterward I was stringing beads of different sizes in symmetrical groups—two large beads, three small ones, and so on. I had made many mistakes, and Miss Sullivan had pointed them out again and again with gentle patience. Finally I noticed a very obvious error in the sequence and for an instant I concentrated my attention on the lesson and tried to think how I should have arranged the beads. Miss Sullivan touched my forehead and spelled with decided emphasis, "Think."

In a flash I knew that the word was the name of the process that was going on in my head. This was my first conscious perception of an abstract idea.

For a long time I was still—I was not thinking of the beads in my lap, but trying to find a meaning for "love" in the light of this new idea. The sun had been under a cloud all day, and there had been brief showers; but suddenly the sun broke forth in all its southern splendour.

Again I asked my teacher, "Is this not love?"

"Love is something like the clouds that were in the sky before the sun came out," she replied. Then in simpler words than these, which at that time I could not have understood, she explained: "You cannot touch the clouds, you know; but you feel the rain and know how glad the flowers and the thirsty earth are to have it after a hot day. You cannot touch love either; but you feel the sweetness that it pours into everything. Without love you would not be happy or want to play."

The beautiful truth burst upon my mind—I felt that there were invisible lines stretched between my spirit and the spirits of others.

From the beginning of my education Miss Sullivan made it a practice to speak to me as she would speak to any hearing child; the only difference was that she spelled the sentences into my hand instead of speaking them. If I did not know the words and idioms necessary to express my thoughts she supplied them, even suggesting conversation when I was unable to keep up my end of the dialogue.

This process was continued for several years; for the deaf child does not learn in a month, or even in two or three years, the numberless idioms and expressions used in the simplest daily intercourse. The little hearing child learns these from constant repetition and imitation. The conversation he hears in his home stimulates his mind and suggests topics and calls forth the spontaneous expression of his own thoughts. This natural exchange of ideas is denied to the deaf child. My teacher, realizing this, determined to supply the kinds of stimulus I lacked. This she did by repeating to me as far as possible, verbatim, what she heard, and by showing me how I could take

UNITED PRESS INTERNATIONAL

Twelve-year-old Helen Keller studying with her teacher

part in the conversation. But it was a long time before I ventured to take the initiative, and still longer before I could find something appropriate to say at the right time.

The deaf and the blind find it very difficult to acquire the amenities of conversation. How much more this difficulty must be augmented in the case of those who are both deaf and blind! They cannot distinguish the tone of the voice or, without assistance, go up and down the gamut of tones that give significance to words; nor can they watch the expression of the speaker's face, and a look is often the very soul of what one says.

The next important step in my education was learning to read.

As soon as I could spell a few words my teacher gave me slips of cardboard on which were printed words in raised letters. I quickly learned that each printed word stood for an object, an act, or a quality. I had a frame in which I could arrange the words in little sentences; but before I ever put sentences in the frame I used to make them in objects. I found the slips of paper which represented, for example, "doll," "is," "on," "bed" and placed each name on its object; then I put my doll on the bed with the words *is, on, bed* arranged beside the doll, thus making a sentence of the words, and at the same time carrying out the idea of the sentence with the things themselves.

One day, Miss Sullivan tells me, I pinned the word *girl* on my pinafore and stood in the wardrobe. On the shelf I arranged the words, *is, in, wardrobe.* Nothing delighted me so much as this game. My teacher and I played it for hours at a time. Often everything in the room was arranged in object sentences.

From the printed slip it was but a step to the printed book. I took my "Reader for Beginners" and hunted for the words I knew; when I found them my joy was like that of a game of hide-and-seek. Thus I began to read. Of the time when I began to read connected stories I shall speak later.

For a long time I had no regular lessons. Even when I studied most earnestly it seemed more like play than work. Everything Miss Sullivan taught me she illustrated by a beautiful story or a poem. Whenever anything delighted or interested me she talked it over with me just as if she were a little girl herself. What many children think of with dread, as a painful plodding through grammar, hard sums and harder definitions, is to-day one of my most precious memories.

I cannot explain the peculiar sympathy Miss Sullivan had with my pleasures and desires. Perhaps it was the result of long association with the blind. Added to this she had a wonderful faculty for description. She went quickly over uninteresting details, and never nagged me with questions to see if I remembered the day-before-yesterday's lesson. She introduced dry technicalities of science little by little, making every subject so real that I could not help remembering what she taught.

We read and studied out of doors, preferring the sunlit woods to the house. All my early lessons have in them the breath of the woods—the fine, resinous odour of pine needles, blended with the perfume of wild grapes. Seated in the gracious shade of a wild tulip tree, I learned to think that everything has a lesson and a suggestion. "The loveliness of things taught me all their use." Indeed, everything that could hum, or buzz, or sing, or bloom, had a part in my education—noisy-throated frogs, katydids and crickets held in my hand until, forgetting their embarrassment, they trilled their reedy note, little downy chickens and wildflowers, the dogwood blossoms, meadow-violets and budding fruit trees. I felt the bursting cotton-bolls and fingered their soft fiber and fuzzy seeds; I felt the low soughing of the wind through the cornstalks, the silky rustling of the long leaves, and the indignant snort of my pony, as we caught him in the pasture and put the bit in his mouth—ah me! how well I remember the spicy, clovery smell of his breath!

Sometimes I rose at dawn and stole into the garden while the heavy dew lay on the grass and flowers. Few know what joy it is to feel the roses pressing softly into the hand, or the beautiful motion of the lilies as they sway in the morning breeze. Sometimes I caught an insect in the flower I was plucking, and I felt the faint noise of a pair of wings rubbed together in a sudden terror, as the little creature became aware of a pressure from without.

Another favourite haunt of mine was the orchard, where the fruit ripened early in July. The large, downy peaches would reach themselves into my hand, and as the joyous breezes flew about the trees the apples tumbled at my feet. Oh, the delight with which I gathered up the fruit in my pinafore, pressed my face against the smooth cheeks of the apples, still warm from the sun, and skipped back to the house!

Our favourite walk was to Keller's Landing, an old tumble-down lumber-wharf on the Tennessee River, used during the Civil War to land soldiers. There we spent many happy hours and played at learning geography. I built dams of pebbles, made islands and lakes, and dug river-beds, all for fun, and

BETTMANN ARCHIVE

Helen Keller at her desk as a young girl

never dreamed that I was learning a lesson. I listened with increasing wonder to Miss Sullivan's descriptions of the great round world with its burning mountains, buried cities, moving rivers of ice, and many other things as strange. She made raised maps in clay, so that I could feel the mountain ridges and valleys, and follow with my fingers the devious course of rivers. I liked this, too; but the division of the earth into zones and poles confused and teased my mind. The illustrative strings and the orange stick representing the poles seemed so real that even to this day the mere mention of temperate zone suggests a series of twine circles; and I believe that if any one should set about it he could convince me that white bears actually climb the North Pole.

Arithmetic seems to have been the only study I did not like. From the first I was not interested in the science of numbers. Miss Sullivan tried to teach me to count by stringing beads in groups, and by arranging kindergarten straws I learned to add and subtract. I never had patience to arrange more than five or six groups at a time. When I had accomplished this my conscience was at rest for the day, and I went out quickly to find my playmates.

In this same leisurely manner I studied zoölogy and botany.

Once a gentleman, whose name I have forgotten, sent me a collection of fossils—tiny mollusk shells beautifully marked, and bits of sandstone with the print of birds' claws, and a lovely fern in bas-relief. These were the keys which unlocked the treasures of the antediluvian world for me. With trembling fingers I listened to Miss Sullivan's descriptions of the terrible beasts, with uncouth, unpronounceable names, which once went tramping through the primeval forests, tearing down the branches of gigantic trees for food, and died in the dismal swamps of an unknown age. For a long time these strange creatures haunted my dreams, and this gloomy period formed a somber background to the joyous Now, filled with sunshine and roses and echoing with the gentle beat of my pony's hoof.

Another time a beautiful shell was given me, and with a child's surprise and delight I learned how a tiny mollusk had built the lustrous coil for his dwelling place, and how on still nights, when there is no breeze stirring the waves, the Nautilus sails on the blue waters of the Indian Ocean in his "ship of pearl." After I had learned a great many interesting things about the life and habits of the children of the sea—how in the midst of dashing waves the little polyps build the beautiful coral isles of the Pacific, and the foraminifera have made the chalk-hills of many a land—my teacher read me "The Chambered Nautilus," and showed me that the shell-building process of the mollusks is symbolical of the development of the mind.

Just as the wonder-working mantle of the Nautilus changes the material it absorbs from the water and makes it a part of itself, so the bits of knowledge one gathers undergo a similar change and become pearls of thought.

Again, it was the growth of a plant that furnished the text for a lesson. We bought a lily and set it in a sunny window. Very soon the green, pointed buds showed signs of opening. The slender, fingerlike leaves on the outside opened slowly, reluctant, I thought, to reveal the loveliness they hid; once having made a start, however, the opening process went on rapidly, but in order and systematically. There was always one bud larger and more beautiful than the rest, which pushed her outer covering back with more pomp, as if the beauty in soft, silky robes knew that she was the lily-queen by right divine, while her more timid sisters doffed their green hoods shyly, until the whole plant was one nodding bough of loveliness and fragrance.

Once there were eleven tadpoles in a glass globe set in a window full of plants. I remember the eagerness with which I made discoveries about them. It was great fun to plunge my hand into the bowl and feel the tadpoles frisk about, and to let them slip and slide between my fingers. One day a more ambitious fellow leaped beyond the edge of the bowl and fell on the floor, where I found him to all appearance more dead than alive. The only sign of life was a slight wriggling of his tail. But no sooner had he returned to his element than he darted to the bottom, swimming round and round in joyous activity. He had made his leap, he had seen the great world, and was content to stay in his pretty glass house under the big fuchsia tree until he attained the dignity of froghood. Then he went to live in the leafy pool at the end of the garden, where he made the summer nights musical with his quaint love-song.

Thus I learned from life itself. At the beginning I was only a little mass of possibilities. It was my teacher who unfolded and developed them. When she came, everything about me breathed of love and joy and was full of meaning. She has never since let pass an opportunity to point out the beauty that is in everything, nor has she ceased trying in thought and action and example to make my life sweet and useful.

It was my teacher's genius, her quick sympathy, her loving

tact which made the first years of my education so beautiful. It was because she seized the right moment to impart knowledge that made it so pleasant and acceptable to me. She realized that a child's mind is like a shallow brook which ripples and dances merrily over the stony course of its education and reflects here a flower, there a bush, yonder a fleecy cloud; and she attempted to guide my mind on its way, knowing that like a brook it should be fed by mountain streams and hidden springs, until it broadened out into a deep river, capable of reflecting in its placid surface, billowy hills, the luminous shadows of trees and the blue heavens, as well as the sweet face of a little flower.

Any teacher can take a child to the classroom, but not every teacher can make him learn. He will not work joyously unless he feels that liberty is his, whether he is busy or at rest; he must feel the flush of victory and the heart-sinking of disappointment before he takes with a will the tasks distasteful to him and resolves to dance his way bravely through a dull routine of textbooks.

My teacher is so near to me that I scarcely think of myself apart from her. How much of my delight in all beautiful things is innate, and how much is due to her influence, I can never tell. I feel that her being is inseparable from my own, and that the footsteps of my life are in hers. All the best of me belongs to her—there is not a talent, or an aspiration or a joy in me that has not been awakened by her loving touch.

MOHANDAS GANDHI

Fighter Without a Sword

BY JEANETTE EATON

Illustrations by Ralph Ray

Gandhi (1869-1948) accomplished more towards winning independence for India through fasting and Satyagraha (non-violent resistance) than had ever been achieved by fighting. From Brahmins to Untouchables, Indians came to Gandhi and his wife Kasturbai at Ashram to prove that they could live in brotherhood, united for the sake of their country. They called Gandhi "Mahatma"—The Great-Souled One.

ONE April morning in 1917, in a small town within sight of the glittering Himalaya Mountains a tense drama was taking place. The rising sun lighted up a huge crowd massed in front of the brick courthouse. Milling about, chattering together, shouting out threats, waving sticks and hoes, hundreds of ragged peasants faced a handful of policemen who stood on the courthouse steps. The indigo workers had come to protest the arrest of Mohandas Gandhi.

For more than a week he had been traveling from village to village in the northern section of Bihar. A number of small farm owners who were unselfishly interested in the peasants had made this possible. Joined by several lawyers and a professor from a near-by school, the group had guided him, sometimes by car and sometimes on elephant back, through the plain framed by mighty mountains. Several independent farmers went with them as guides and interpreters.

In a first interview with Gandhi the local farmers said, "We have to tell you we are afraid of the big landowners. They beat and abuse us if we complain about raising indigo for them. The government always sides with the planters whatever they do. All the same we shall help all we can."

Fear! That was the atmosphere in which the majority of people lived in Bihar. Each time Gandhi walked down the single dusty street of a village he breathed it like a smell. At sight of strangers, children sprang up out of the dirt and ran to hide; women closed doors and shutters; men coming from the fields stopped in their tracks to stare in terror of they knew not what.

Nevertheless, this fog of fright blew away almost at once. None of the peasants had heard of Mahatma Gandhi. Since they could not read, they never saw a newspaper, and their tiny villages of thatched mud huts were isolated from the rest of the world. What they realized at a close glance was that a friend had come to help them. As soon as they looked into Gandhi's eyes and heard him say, "Don't be afraid," they trusted him. Strained faces brightened with the joyous astonishment of people coming out of a black dungeon into the sunlight. Like a ray of such light, news that a powerful friend was listening to what the farm workers had to say spread swiftly through the region.

Those who ruled in Bihar were equally well informed. According to his principles of fair play, Gandhi went to see both the British commissioner and the secretary of the Planters Association. He told first one and then the other that he meant to find out how much of their rented land farmers were forced to cultivate in indigo for the benefit of the landowners. Courteously he asked each man to explain the justice of demanding this work without pay. The two interviews ended in the same way. Gandhi was angrily told that he was an outsider without authority and must leave the district at once.

Frankly he warned his group of helpers. "This investigation of the unjust system carried on by Bihar planters may land us all in prison."

"This is a new idea," the men replied gravely, "but we shall not desert you."

Some days later the local magistrate, urged on by the planters, sent Gandhi an official order to leave Bihar by the next train. He sent back word that he could not and would not

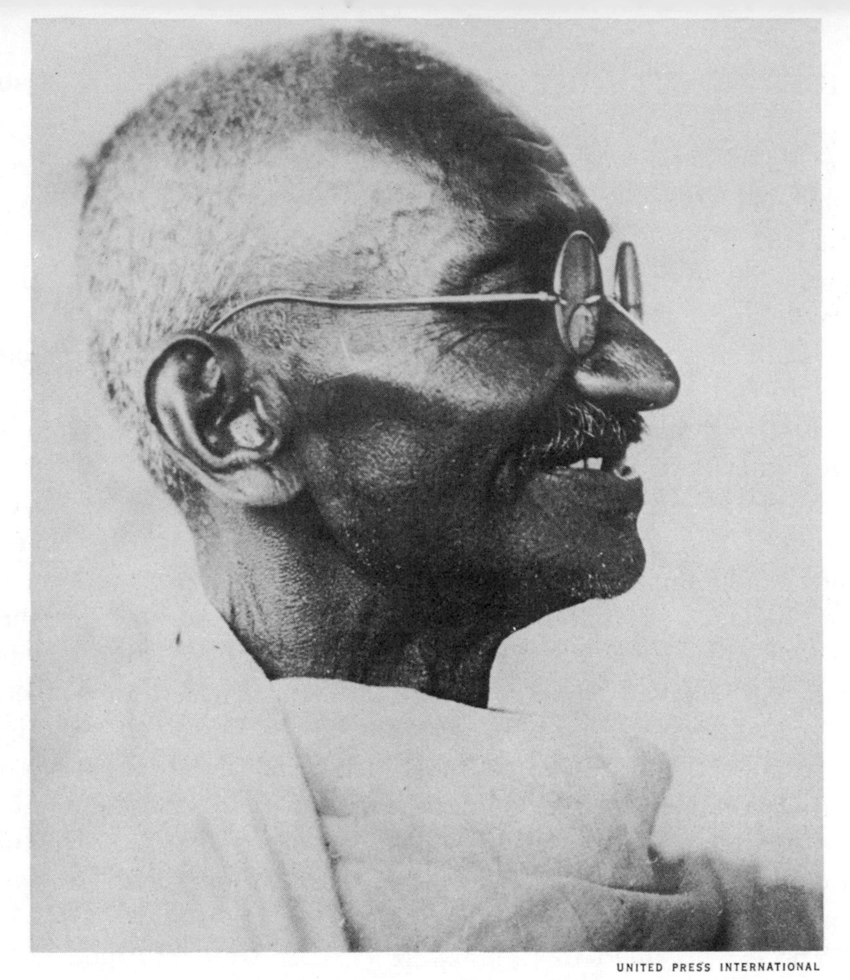

UNITED PRESS INTERNATIONAL

Mohandas Gandhi in 1934

give up the inquiry he had been asked by the peasants to make. That very day he received a summons to appear at the courthouse for trial next morning.

All night Gandhi sat writing messages. To the viceroy he sent a telegram reporting his arrest and its cause. He wrote letters to the Ashram and to such leaders as he knew best. Early next morning he set out with several of his party for his trial.

The instant he stepped into the road, he found himself heading a procession. Men, women, and children were there as if conjured up by magic from wheat patches and mango groves. Shouting his name, the ragged mob escorted him to the courthouse and there joined the hundreds who had come from miles around and had been waiting since the evening before.

In astonishment Gandhi asked one of his helpers, "What has become of their fear?"

Now it was the policemen who were afraid. They well knew that if the mob chose to storm the courthouse they could not be kept back. Gandhi glanced at a policeman's hand nervously fingering the pistol at his belt. "I'll help you calm these people," he said. "Let me speak to them."

From the top of the steps he called out to the crowd and they stood still to listen. "Friends," he said slowly and clearly, "you must show your faith in me and in our work by being patient and quiet. The policemen are only doing their duty. The magistrate had a perfect right to arrest me. I disobeyed his ruling that I leave Bihar. If I am sent to prison, you must accept my sentence as just. We must work together peacefully. Any violent act will hurt our good cause."

Nodding at the policeman who stared at him in astonished gratitude, Gandhi went into the building. In the courtroom were many officials and a number of planters. As the trial began, a nervous government lawyer rose to ask the magistrate to postpone the case. But Gandhi protested. He pleaded guilty and read a statement explaining why he had disobeyed the order to leave the district.

"As a law-abiding citizen I should rather have obeyed. But so great was my sense of duty to the peasants who have asked me to inquire peaceably into their troubles that I could not help choosing this course. I preferred to let the government take the responsibility of removing me from the midst of these helpless people. So proceed, gentlemen."

The officials had never faced anything like this before. The calm, friendly man in the prisoner's dock had suddenly become the judge and made his accusers feel guilty. The case was postponed. Sentence was never passed. In a few days Gandhi received two remarkable letters. The first was from the magistrate, who reported that the lieutenant governor of Bihar had ordered the case withdrawn. The second letter came from the tax collector. He said Gandhi was free to gather all the facts about the demands imposed by the planters on the peasants. Moreover, he promised that officials would help him do so.

Reporters from newspapers in nearby towns rushed to the house where Gandhi was staying. After interviewing him, they hurried away to publish the amazing story of his victory. It was wired to English and Indian journals all over the country. Gandhi had given India its first lesson in civil disobedience.

To the peasants he had given courage and hope. Not for nothing had they seen operating a force more powerful than the government. When Gandhi started his inquiry into their working conditions, they came from every corner of the indigo district to tell him their pitiful stories. Not even the presence of government secret service men at the interviews disturbed them. Each account proved that no Bihar farmer could make even a bare living if he had to raise indigo without pay.

Busy as he was taking down evidence and teaching his helpers to accept only proved facts, Gandhi started reforms in six villages. Adults were taught sanitation and how to use simple home remedies. Neglected children were gathered into primary classes held in rude shelters.

For this work Mohandas sent to the Ashram for Kasturbai and his son Manilal. He also sent to newspapers a public appeal for volunteers. It brought to Bihar half a dozen trained and exceptional people eager to carry out his ideas. Among them was Mahadev Desai, a university man who was a scholar, teacher, and writer.

When he and his wife arrived at the town where Gandhi had his headquarters, they stared about in amazement. With money given by a special friend, the group had rented a house and set up tents in the open space around it. Almost a hundred peasants were seated on the ground waiting to be interviewed. In the house at half a dozen low tables men were writing busily, as indigo workers seated on the floor before them told their stories. Gandhi was walking about, listening, correcting statements, seeing that everyone, including the secret service men, had water to drink.

Warmly welcoming the newcomers, Mohandas took them to a quiet corner and told them his plans. Later he escorted them to one of the forlorn and dirty villages near by. The volunteers saw with what adoration Gandhi was greeted and how careful he was not to show his impatience of such homage.

What he wanted was to get latrines dug and schoolrooms opened.

Before a week was over, Mahadev Desai came to the leader and said, "Gandhiji, my wife and I wish to devote our lives to your work. Will you take us into your Ashram?"

Gandhi was delighted to have such a pair join his colony. He saw that no one was happier than Desai over the action of Bihar's lieutenant governor. He had appointed a committee to study the evidence collected from the indigo workers and present an opinion on it. When the report was made, the fair-minded official accepted it promptly. The planters were then obliged to refund payments to the peasants for their labor in cultivating indigo, and the unjust system of unpaid work was ended for good and all.

Gandhi said to his rejoicing helpers, "It is you who have brought this happy result to pass. Because owners of small farms and people of education have joined with the peasants to right a great wrong, the stain of indigo has been washed away!"

Mohandas was delighted on their return to the Ashram to see the warm welcome given Kasturbai. Women and children rushed to embrace her, crying, "It is good to see you, Ba!" Ba is the intimate word for mother in India and everyone felt Kasturbai's motherliness. Yet despite this joy over the returned travelers a cloud hung over the colony. Cholera had broken out in a near-by village and many of the mothers and fathers begged Gandhi to find a more healthful site for the Ashram.

This he proceeded to do. With a friend from Ahmedabad he searched the district and found a good site on the beautiful Sabarmati River just across from the town. True, in the rough field the prospectors found a number of serpents. But Mohandas said, "Somehow, I think they will not trouble us."

He had found awaiting him two important calls for help. One was from a group of peasants in a town not far from Bombay. They wanted Gandhi to persuade the government to cancel their taxes until rain came to end the long drought afflicting the region. The earth was baked and dry. No crops would grow and the farmers were starving and penniless. The other request was from the mill workers in Ahmedabad. They had asked for higher wages and, because the mill owners would not even discuss the matter, they had decided to go on strike. But they needed Gandhi's advice.

This request he answered first. He could meet the strikers and still supervise the moving of the Ashram. Tents were set up on the new site along the Sabarmati River until huts could be built. There were now some forty people in the group and all set to work with a will.

In Ahmedabad Gandhi first talked to labor leaders and then interviewed the owners of the textile mills. A number of them were his friends and supporters of the colony. By this time most of the contributors to its support had accepted the fact that Untouchables had to belong to the Ashram. When Mohandas approached them on the matter of increased wages, however, they refused to discuss the matter.

Calling the labor leaders together, Gandhi said, "I think your cause is just. If you will accept four conditions, I will support your strike."

He demanded nonviolence during the struggle, no interference with those who would not join the strike, self-support at odd jobs instead of depending on charity during the strike, and firmness of purpose no matter how long the strike might last.

Without hesitation the leaders accepted the conditions. Then at a general meeting the strikers accepted them. Almost every day the citizens of Ahmedabad were treated to a parade of strikers proudly carrying banners which read, "Keep the pledge." Thousands of them gathered each afternoon at the new Ashram. Seated on the grass near the river, they listened to Gandhi's talks on the evils of violence and hate. "These wrong deeds and feelings," said he, "hold back progress. We must obey only the law of love."

Two weeks passed. By this time a number of strikers were growing impatient and discouraged. Their discontent brought on quarrels with strikebreakers. It was when many of them began to drift back to work that Gandhi met the situation head on. Calling together a great meeting of the men, he announced his decision on a course of action. Because he had advised the strike and had stood back of it, he had to take upon himself its failure. "I am to blame for your broken pledge," said he, "and I shall do penance for it. I shall go on a fast until the strike is settled."

For a long moment the crowd was shocked into silence. Then one of the leaders sprang up. "No! No!" he shouted, and tears began to stream down his cheeks. "You must not take the blame. It is for us to fast for wrongdoing, not you."

Groans were heard from the crowd. Shouts of "Forgive us!" and "We will take the pledge again!" filled the air. But Gandhi gently repeated his vow and the repentant workers walked soberly from the meeting.

Next day one of the mill owners who was still a warm friend of Gandhi's drove out in his car to the Ashram. He found Mohandas, with trowel in hand, helping to lay the foundation for the new weaving shed. Weaving was to be one of the main sources of income for the colony.

"Gandhiji!" called the visitor. "Are you really able to do this work? My wife and I have been very anxious about your undertaking a fast."

Dropping his trowel and folding his hands in the Indian greeting, Gandhi came forward, smiling. "Come to my tent and talk to me, my friend," said he. "I am in excellent health, as you see."

As soon as he had seated himself on Gandhi's low couch,

the mill owner announced that now a compromise with the strikers was on the way. At Gandhi's expression of surprise, he burst out laughing and reported a remark made by an American manufacturer who had been visiting Ahmedabad. The American had watched the parades of strikers and heard the general lamentation over the Mahatma's fast. "Indians are amazing," he said. "I cannot imagine that in our country either strikers or employers would give a fig who fasted or why. We don't reverence leaders."

Gandhi's fast lasted just three days. The strike was settled on fair terms for the workers, and the mill owners celebrated by giving them a big party.

As soon as this happy event took place, Mohandas set off to meet the group of starving peasants who had asked for help. In their village he found a bitter struggle on. District officials had absolutely refused to delay collecting taxes. They were confiscating cattle and any odd stores of grain as substitute for cash payment. No persuasion of Gandhi's softened their hearts.

His arrival in the village, however, had made a stir in the big city of Bombay. Merchants, lawyers, and teachers came forward with offers of money to finance a campaign of protest. Reporters from English and Indian newspapers published daily accounts of the situation. All this hullabaloo displeased Mohandas. He wanted to keep the issue clear and the battle peaceful.

"None of these people understand the principle of *satyagraha,*" he lamented to Mahadev Desai. "Too much hatred of the British government fills their hearts."

Nevertheless, the case was won for the peasants. Rich farmers were persuaded to fight for their cause. They announced that they would not pay a cent of taxes unless the peasants were relieved of all obligation to pay until the drought was over and crops were good again. This threat forced the government to yield. Confiscated cattle were restored to the owners and peace was made.

Not only did this victory impress all the educated people in India; the fact that it was won by cooperative effort excited them. Rich and poor, powerful and helpless had united in a single effort. As for British administrators, they learned from

UNITED PRESS INTERNATIONAL

Mohandas Gandhi as a young lawyer

this affair that Gandhi was a leader to be reckoned with. To get cooperation from their subjects in a project, they had first to win over the small, quiet man called the Mahatma.

The important project facing the viceroy at the moment was to secure Indian help in the war. Although the United States had joined the Allies against Germany, no American troops had yet reached the battle front. In the spring of 1917, Germany had inflicted crushing defeats on both British and French troops in France. Turkey had held out against the English attack at Gallipoli. Russia's war effort had collapsed and the revolutionists were threatening its government. It was a black hour.

For two years Indian factories had turned out quantities of munitions. However, her vast population had taken no part in the world struggle. Now, faced with the need of fresh troops, the English looked wistfully toward their Indian subjects. It was with the idea of getting Indian volunteers that the viceroy summoned leaders to New Delhi, and Gandhi was among those invited.

During his first interview with the viceroy, Gandhi had had a favorable impression of the man. In spite of Gokhale's disillusionment, Mohandas held fast to his faith in British honor. For this reason he joined the group meeting at the capital. There he was convinced, just as he had been in the Boer War and the Zulu rebellion, that it was the duty of his fellow countrymen to fight in England's battle.

But could he persuade them? Certainly the Mohammedans created a stumbling block. For Turkey, the chief Mohammedan country, was one of England's enemies. Indeed, because of their publicly expressed sympathy with Turkey some of India's most vigorous Mohammedan patriots had been imprisoned by the government. If he supported this recruiting measure, might not Gandhi alienate those Mohammedan friends whom he so passionately longed to unite with the Hindus in every effort for progress?

Yet he had to speak the truth as he saw it. Rising to face the viceroy and his fellow Indians from the congress, Gandhi turned to the former with a smile. "May I speak in Hindustani?" And when the Englishman nodded, he said solemnly, "With a full sense of responsibility I beg to support the resolution to recruit volunteers."

Only one sentence! Yet because at an official conference it was not spoken in English but in Hindustani, the sentence made a deep impression. For the first time a man had dared to shun the language of the conquerors.

Before Gandhi started recruiting volunteers for the British army, he wrote the viceroy a long statement. Without trying to make a bargain in return for his freely offered service, he said he did expect that after the war ended England would begin to organize home rule for India. He assured the viceroy that not only educated citizens but also simple farmers and peasants now wanted political freedom. Religious differences were being submerged in patriotic fervor. The Moslem League had made an alliance with the Indian Congress to demand self-government. England, concluded Gandhi, could count on a peaceful and happy people only if she granted them self-rule. The letter was published in all important newspapers.

His recruiting efforts nearly ruined Gandhi's health. He often walked twenty miles a day from village to village to make speeches and interview young men. Suddenly his strength gave out and he became extremely ill. For a time he thought he might die and his family and friends had the same fear.

Kasturbai never left his side. One morning she stood with the doctor beside her husband's bed. Both were anxious and bewildered. Kasturbai laid a finger on her husband's thin arm and said, "The doctor wants you to drink milk. I know you have vowed never to drink cow's milk, but you took no vow not to touch the milk of goats. Why not try that if you wish to get well? Isn't your work worth this sacrifice?"

Feebly Mohandas smiled up at the two worried faces. "Poor souls, you have a crank to nurse! Very well, although it goes against my conscience to break my vow, I'll drink goat's milk."

Very slowly he gained strength. One day he sat propped up on his bed reading the newspapers. It was plain in this early summer of 1918 that the Allies were going to win the war. Turning from reports of their gains on the battlefield, he noticed an announcement of a new bill just presented to the Indian government. It was a measure to prevent possible uprisings. The government was to be given power to imprison without trial and to try in secret without jury any person suspected of disloyal activity.

Gandhi fell back as if he had received a blow. At that moment Mahadev Desai, who was now acting as Gandhi's secretary, entered the room with a pile of letters. Mohandas pointed out the item in the journal and gasped out, "Look! Just look at this!"

Desai's face grew pale as he read. "I can't believe it!" he exclaimed. "It's terrorism! Do Englishmen mean to overthrow in India all the principles they believe in? Think how they fought and worked for centuries in their own country to defend the rights of the individual!"

Gandhi's dark eyes were smoldering. "All India must protest this bill. No people with a shred of self-respect could submit to such an attack on their liberties."

That very day several of the leaders from Ahmedabad came out for consultation. They helped Gandhi in the next weeks to organize a protest. First of all, a league was formed to spread the doctrine of *satyagraha.* From his bed Gandhi wrote articles for Indian papers, to explain how nonviolent opposition to tyranny could be made in a loving spirit of self-sacrifice. He cited the new bill as an act of tyranny. As soon as possible, he dragged himself up to make speeches in several cities. To the viceroy he addressed private letters and public appeals begging him to take a stand against the bill.

In the midst of these activities came news that Germany had surrendered. The terrible war was over. In this land as in every land flags were flying, bells were ringing, and people rejoiced together.

Yet there was no peace in India. As 1918 ended and 1919 began, storm clouds gathered ever more thickly. From the battle front thousands of soldiers, deeply affected by contact with Westerners, were coming back to all parts of the country. As workers in munition factories were laid off, cities filled with the unemployed.

In the political field the prospect was gloomy. Loyal support in the "war for democracy" had won nothing for the Indians. No move was made toward giving the people a constitution. A few unimportant measures were introduced to allow the minority a little more responsibility. But at the same time the government passed the bill granting itself illegal powers of arrest and punishment of suspected persons.

Although the quiet routine of the Sabarmati Ashram was unbroken, although the bell for morning prayers rang at four in the morning and Gandhi took his brisk walk before breakfast, kept an eye on all activities, and held his prayer meeting at sunset, everyone was aware of intense undercurrents. Day by day men of importance from many parts of India drove from the Ahmedabad station to Gandhi's thatched cottage. Conferences on his veranda were held each day. Enormous heaps of letters came and went.

"Now we must act," Gandhi kept saying. "Since all our protests have been in vain, we must work out a means of refusing to accept this new tyranny."

On February 28th he sent to the press a pledge for all brave men to sign. They were to promise to be ready to undertake nonviolent disobedience. With the pledge was printed a manifesto announcing that a general *satyagraha* would soon be called. Then with Mahadev Desai he started on a round of speeches at various cities.

When they reached Allahabad, a small city not far from Benares, a message was waiting for Gandhi. He read it with surprise. It was from Motilal Nehru, the wealthy Brahmin lawyer whom he had met at the Indian Congress almost three years before. In spite of the fact that this conservative man was not in sympathy with *satyagraha,* he had invited Gandhi to his house.

A handsome motor car was sent to bring Mohandas to that interview. As he got out, he looked about curiously. The driveway, curving at one side of the superb garden, was lined with hibiscus plants set between palm and pomegranate trees. On the enormous space fronting the mansion was a tennis court and a summerhouse covered with flowering vines. Behind it the visitor caught a glimpse of a fruit orchard stretching back to the walled compound facing the servants' quarters.

Gandhi was warmly greeted by his host and taken into a study lined with books and furnished in Western style. Without wasting an instant, the lawyer began to talk with vigorous frankness, and Gandhi found himself even more strongly drawn to him than he had been at their first meeting. Here, he thought, is a person of force and sterling character. He may not be ready yet, but some day he will help guide us through our battle for freedom.

"It is my son Jawaharlal of whom I wish to speak," said Nehru. "He has been deeply moved by your discussion of *satyagraha.* Jawaharlal has been so disgusted with the do-nothing policy of congress and of most businessmen that he wants to join your party of action. But neither he nor I realized at first that you really want people to court arrest and imprisonment. I see no sense, Gandhiji, in clever, much-needed men going to jail. My

son and I have argued by the hour. I am opposed to his embarking on such a course."

"That I understand," replied Gandhi gently. He smiled at the man in his well-tailored English clothes. "The sacrifice is heavy. No one should undertake *satyagraha* who is not fully ready for the perils involved. Nevertheless, this is the most effective protest against a tyrannical government that any people can make."

Over the whole household that evening Mohandas shed his affectionate interest. Motilal's sensitive wife, his handsome elder daughter, and Jawaharlal's beautiful young bride, all three wearing on their foreheads the small red circle with which high-caste Brahmin women adorn themselves, Jawaharlal and his father—this tightly knit family seemed to the visitor an almost perfect group of its kind. He could find it in his heart to wish that nothing might threaten its security and joy.

At dinner they sat on cushions on the veranda enclosed in colonnades. A fine tablecloth was spread upon the tiled floor and servants swiftly served curries, wheat cakes, rice, pepper water, sweets, and fruits. It was a merry party.

"Please forgive me," Gandhi said, "for refusing so many of these exquisite dishes. I am a most unsatisfactory guest."

Motilal gave a hearty boom of laughter. "Ah, tonight we are serving in the Indian style in your honor. There is a dining room on the other side of the hall with a banquet table and on it we serve roast beef, potatoes, and puddings in the English fashion."

Before he left, Gandhi had a long talk with the youthful Jawaharlal. He strongly advised him to bide his time and not plunge into action at once. "You can safely leave things to India's unfolding destiny. Your father is too noble a man and too great a patriot to stand aside or to ask you to do so when the need for personal sacrifice becomes clear."

Gandhi's next sojourn was at Madras on the southeast coast. He had addressed meetings there before and was welcomed by an enthusiastic audience. His host was a lawyer deeply interested in political problems. He and several other leaders tried to thrash out with Mohandas a plan of action. Something more than merely holding public meetings had to be done. But what?

One early morning Mohandas came into the garden where the group was already gathered. The fragrance of jasmine flowers, the shine of marigolds, the fresh sunlit air gave the scene a joyousness which was reflected on Gandhi's face.

"My friends," he cried, "I have been given an inspiration in a dream. Let us announce to all the millions of our people that they should set aside a day of prayer and mourning as a public protest against this insulting new law. Let no work be done except what is essential for the public good. All can join in such a peaceful expression of reproach."

"A day of prayer, a *hartal!*" exclaimed the lawyer excitedly. "A *hartal* in which rich and poor, people of all religions can unite. That is it! We must choose a day at once and announce it in the press."

Since there was need of haste, April 6th, 1919, was chosen. "Of course," said Gandhi, "we have little time to organize the demonstration. All we can do is to spread word of it to all the provinces. We could hardly expect a complete response throughout the country."

By April 4th Gandhi reached Bombay. He was in time to start the ceremonies there with an enormous parade. But Bombay was only one small part of the extraordinary spectacle that met the eyes of the British on April 6th. For then the clock stopped in India. Not a wheel turned in a factory. Every shop was closed. No farmer went out with his plow. In cities, towns, and tiny villages from the Himalayas to the tip of the peninsula, the *hartal* was celebrated. Mohammedans, Hindus, Parsis, Buddhists, people of every faith, joined together in fasting, prayer, and peaceful processions. The striken face of India was turned to its rulers in eloquent appeal.

Too eloquent! Such unity of protest frightened the governors of almost four hundred million people. Fear drove the British to acts which changed the whole temper of the country and stamped a new pattern on the life of Mohandas Gandhi.

SAMUEL LANGHORNE CLEMENS (MARK TWAIN)

The First Tom Sawyer

BY MARK TWAIN

Edited by Charles Neider

Sam Clemens (1835-1910), like his boys Tom and Huck, explored caves and sailed rafts during his youth in Missouri. He piloted steamboats on the restless Mississippi, then became restless himself. For fifty years Sam crossed the country and toured the world under the name of Mark Twain, filling books with his wry comments on human nature.

IN 1849, when I was fourteen years old, we were still living in Hannibal, on the banks of the Mississippi, in the new "frame" house built by my father five years before. That is, some of us lived in the new part, the rest in the old part back of it and attached to it. In the autumn my sister gave a party and invited all the marriageable young people of the village. I was too young for this society and was too bashful to mingle with young ladies, anyway, therefore I was not invited—at least not for the whole evening. Ten minutes of it was to be my whole share. I was to do the part of a bear in a small fairy play. I was to be disguised all over in a close-fitting brown hairy stuff proper for a bear. About half past ten I was told to go to my room and put on this disguise and be ready in half an hour. I started but changed my mind, for I wanted to practice a little and that room was very small. I crossed over to the large unoccupied house on the corner of Main Street, unaware that a dozen of the young people were also going there to dress for their parts. I took the little black boy, Sandy, with me and we selected a roomy and empty chamber on the second floor. We entered it talking and this gave a couple of half-dressed young ladies an opportunity to take refuge behind a screen undiscovered. Their gowns and things were hanging on hooks behind the door but I did not see them; it was Sandy that shut the door but all his heart was in the theatricals and he was as unlikely to notice them as I was myself.

That was a rickety screen with many holes in it but as I did not know there were girls behind it I was not disturbed by that detail. If I had known, I could not have undressed in the flood of cruel moonlight that was pouring in at the curtainless windows; I should have died of shame. Untroubled by apprehensions, I stripped to the skin and began my practice. I was full of ambition, I was determined to make a hit, I was burning to establish a reputation as a bear and get further engagements; so I threw myself into my work with an abandon that promised great things. I capered back and forth from one end of the room to the other on all fours, Sandy applauding with enthusiasm; I walked upright and growled and snapped and snarled, I stood on my head, I flung handsprings, I danced a lubberly dance with my paws bent and my imaginary snout sniffing from side to side, I did everything a bear could do and many things which no bear could ever do and no bear with any dignity would want to do, anyway; and of course I never suspected that I was making a spectacle of myself to anyone but Sandy. At last, standing on my head, I paused in that attitude to take a minute's rest. There was a moment's silence, then Sandy spoke up with excited interest and said:

"Mars Sam, has you ever seed a dried herring?"

"No. What is that?"

"It's a fish."

"Well, what of it? Anything peculiar about it?"

"Yes, suh, you bet you dey is. *Dey* eats 'em innards and all!"

There was a smothered burst of feminine snickers from behind the screen! All the strength went out of me and I toppled forward like an undermined tower and brought the screen down with my weight, burying the young ladies under it. In their fright they discharged a couple of piercing screams—and possibly others—but I did not wait to count. I snatched my clothes and fled to the dark hall below, Sandy following. I was dressed in half a minute and out the back way. I swore Sandy

THE MARK TWAIN ESTATE

Samuel Clemens on "Lover's Leap"

to eternal silence, then we went away and hid until the party was over. The ambition was all out of me. I could not have faced that giddy company after my adventure, for there would be two performers there who knew my secret and would be privately laughing at me all the time. I was searched for but not found, and the bear had to be played by a young gentleman in his civilized clothes. The house was still and everybody asleep when I finally ventured home. I was very heavy-hearted and full of a bitter sense of disgrace. Pinned to my pillow I found a slip of paper which bore a line which did not lighten my heart but only made my face burn. It was written in a laboriously disguised hand and these were its mocking terms:

You probably couldn't have played bear but you played bare very well—oh, very *very* well!

We think boys are rude, unsensitive animals but it is not so in all cases. Each boy has one or two sensitive spots and if you can find out where they are located you have only to touch them and you can scorch him as with fire. I suffered miserably over that episode. I expected that the facts would be all over the village in the morning but it was not so. The secret remained confined to the two girls and Sandy and me. That was some appeasement of my pain but it was far from sufficient—the main trouble remained: I was under four mocking eyes and it might as well have been a thousand, for I suspected all girls' eyes of being the ones I so dreaded. During several weeks I could not look any young lady in the face; I dropped my eyes in confusion when any one of them smiled upon me and gave me greeting; I said to myself, "That is one of them," and got quickly away. Of course I was meeting the right girls everywhere but if they ever let slip any betraying sign I was not bright enough to catch it. When I left Hannibal four years later the secret was still a secret; I had never guessed those girls out and was no longer hoping or expecting to do it.

One of the dearest and prettiest girls in the village at the time of my mishap was one whom I will call Mary Wilson, because that was not her name. She was twenty years old; she was dainty and sweet, peach-blooming and exquisite, gracious and lovely in character. I stood in awe of her, for she seemed to me to be made out of angel clay and rightfully unapproachable by just any unholy ordinary kind of boy like me. I probably never suspected *her*. But—

The scene changes to Calcutta—forty-seven years later. It was in 1896. I arrived there on a lecturing trip. As I entered the hotel a vision passed out of it, clothed in the glory of the

Indian sunshine—the Mary Wilson of my long-vanished boyhood! It was a startling thing. Before I could recover from the pleasant shock and speak to her she was gone. I thought maybe I had seen an apparition but it was not so, she was flesh. She was the granddaughter of the other Mary. The other Mary, now a widow, was upstairs and presently sent for me. She was old and gray-haired but she looked young and was very handsome. We sat down and talked. We steeped our thirsty souls in the reviving wine of the past, the pathetic past, the beautiful past, the dear and lamented past; we uttered the names that had been silent upon our lips for fifty years and it was as if they were made of music; with reverent hands we unburied our dead, the mates of our youth, and caressed them with our speech; we searched the dusty chambers of our memories and dragged forth incident after incident, episode after episode, folly after folly, and laughed such good laughs over them, with the tears running down; and finally Mary said, suddenly, and without any leading up:

"Tell me! What is the special peculiarity of dried herrings?"

It seemed a strange question at such a hallowed time as this. And so inconsequential, too. I was a little shocked. And yet I was aware of a stir of some kind away back in the deeps of my memory somewhere. It set me to musing—thinking—searching. Dried herrings? Dried herrings? The peculiarity of dri . . . I glanced up. Her face was grave, but there was a dim and shadowy twinkle in her eye which—All of a sudden I knew and far away down in the hoary past I heard a remembered voice murmur, "Dey eats 'em innards and all!"

"At—last! I've found one of you, anyway! Who was the other girl?"

But she drew the line there. She wouldn't tell me.

An exciting event in our village was the arrival of the mesmerizer. I think the year was 1850. As to that I am not sure but I know the month—it was May; that detail has survived the wear of fifty years. A pair of connected little incidents of that month have served to keep the memory of it green for me all this time; incidents of no consequence and not worth embalming, yet my memory has preserved them carefully and flung away things of real value to give them space and make them comfortable. The truth is, a person's memory has no more sense than his conscience and no appreciation whatever of values and proportions. However, never mind those trifling incidents; my subject is the mesmerizer now.

He advertised his show and promised marvels. Admission as usual: 25 cents, children and negroes half price. The village had heard of mesmerism in a general way but had not encountered it yet. Not many people attended the first night but next day they had so many wonders to tell that everybody's curiosity was fired and after that for a fortnight the magician had prosperous times. I was fourteen or fifteen years old, the age at which a boy is willing to endure all things, suffer all things short of death by fire, if thereby he may be conspicuous and show off before the public; and so, when I saw the "subjects" perform their foolish antics on the platform and make the people laugh and shout and admire I had a burning desire to be a subject myself.

Every night for three nights I sat in the row of candidates on the platform and held the magic disk in the palm of my hand and gazed at it and tried to get sleepy, but it was a failure; I remained wide awake and had to retire defeated, like the majority. Also, I had to sit there and be gnawed with envy of Hicks, our journeyman; I had to sit there and see him scamper and jump when Simmons the enchanter exclaimed, "See the snake! See the snake!" and hear him say, "My, how beautiful!" in response to the suggestion that he was observing a splendid sunset; and so on—the whole insane business. I couldn't laugh, I couldn't applaud; it filled me with bitterness to have others do it and to have people make a hero of Hicks and crowd around him when the show was over and ask him for more and more particulars of the wonders he had seen in his visions and manifest in many ways that they were proud to be acquainted with him. Hicks—the idea! I couldn't stand it; I was getting boiled to death in my own bile.

On the fourth night temptation came and I was not strong enough to resist. When I had gazed at the disk a while I pre-

BROWN BROTHERS

Samuel Clemens at eighteen

tended to be sleepy and began to nod. Straightway came the professor and made passes over my head and down my body and legs and arms, finishing each pass with a snap of his fingers in the air to discharge the surplus electricity; then he began to "draw" me with the disk, holding it in his fingers and telling me I could not take my eyes off it, try as I might; so I rose slowly, bent and gazing, and followed that disk all over the place, just as I had seen the others do. Then I was put through the other paces. Upon suggestion I fled from snakes, passed buckets at a fire, became excited over hot steamboat-races, made love to imaginary girls and kissed them, fished from the platform and landed mud cats that outweighed me—and so on, all the customary marvels. But not in the customary way. I was cautious at first and watchful, being afraid the professor would discover that I was an imposter and drive me from the platform in disgrace; but as soon as I realized that I was not in danger, I set myself the task of terminating Hicks's usefulness as a subject and of usurping his place.

It was a sufficiently easy task. Hicks was born honest, I without that incumbrance—so some people said. Hicks saw what he saw and reported accordingly, I saw more than was visible and added to it such details as could help. Hicks had no imagination; I had a double supply. He was born calm, I was born excited. No vision could start a rapture in him and he was constipated as to language, anyway; but if I saw a vision I emptied the dictionary onto it and lost the remnant of my mind into the bargain.

At the end of my first half-hour Hicks was a thing of the past, a fallen hero, a broken idol, and I knew it and was glad and said in my heart, "Success to crime!" Hicks could never have been mesmerized to the point where he could kiss an imaginary girl in public or a real one either, but I was competent. Whatever Hicks had failed in, I made it a point to succeed in, let the cost be what it might, physically or morally. He had shown several bad defects and I had made a note of them. For instance, if the magician asked, "What do you see?" and left him to invent a vision for himself, Hicks was dumb and blind, he couldn't see a thing nor say a word, whereas the magician soon found out that when it came to seeing visions of a stunning and marketable sort I could get along better without his help than with it.

Then there was another thing: Hicks wasn't worth a tallow dip on mute mental suggestion. Whenever Simmons stood behind him and gazed at the back of his skull and tried to drive a mental suggestion into it, Hicks sat with vacant face and never suspected. If he had been noticing he could have seen by the rapt faces of the audience that something was going on behind his back that required a response. Inasmuch as I was an imposter I dreaded to have this test put upon me, for I knew the professor would be "willing" me to do something, and as I couldn't know what it was, I should be exposed and denounced. However, when my time came, I took my chance. I perceived by the tense and expectant faces of the people that Simmons was behind me willing me with all his might. I tried my best to imagine what he wanted but nothing suggested itself. I felt ashamed and miserable then. I believed that the hour of my disgrace was come and that in another moment I should go out of that place disgraced. I ought to be ashamed to confess it but my next thought was not how I could win the compassion of kindly hearts by going out humbly and in sorrow for my misdoings, but how I could go out most sensationally and spectacularly.

There was a rusty and empty old revolver lying on the table among the "properties" employed in the performances. On May Day two or three weeks before there had been a celebration by the schools and I had had a quarrel with a big boy who was the school bully and I had not come out of it with credit. That boy was now seated in the middle of the house, halfway down the main aisle. I crept stealthily and impressively toward the table, with a dark and murderous scowl on my face, copied from a popular romance, seized the revolver suddenly, flourished it, shouted the bully's name, jumped off the platform and made a rush for him and chased him out of the house before the paralyzed people could interfere to save him. There was a storm of applause, and the magician, addressing the house, said, most impressively—

"That you may know how really remarkable this is and how wonderfully developed a subject we have in this boy, I assure you that without a single spoken word to guide him he has carried out what I mentally commanded him to do, to the minutest detail. I could have stopped him at a moment in his vengeful career by a mere exertion of my will, therefore the poor fellow who has escaped was at no time in danger."

So I was not in disgrace. I returned to the platform a hero and happier than I have ever been in this world since. As regards mental suggestion, my fears of it were gone. I judged that in case I failed to guess what the professor might be will-

MISSOURI RESOURCES COMMISSION

Mark Twain's boyhood home in Hannibal, Missouri

ing me to do, I could count on putting up something that would answer just as well. I was right, and exhibitions of unspoken suggestion became a favorite with the public. Whenever I perceived that I was being willed to do something I got up and did something—anything that occurred to me—and the magician, not being a fool, always ratified it. When people asked me, "How *can* you tell what he is willing you to do?" I said, "It's just as easy," and they always said admiringly, "Well, it beats *me* how you can do it."

Hicks was weak in another detail. When the professor made passes over him and said "his whole body is without sensation now—come forward and test him, ladies and gentlemen," the ladies and gentlemen always complied eagerly and stuck pins into Hicks, and if they went deep Hicks was sure to wince, then that poor professor would have to explain that Hicks "wasn't sufficiently under the influence." But I didn't wince; I only suffered and shed tears on the inside. The miseries that a conceited boy will endure to keep up his "reputation"! And so will a conceited man; I know it in my own person and have seen it in a hundred thousand others. That professor ought to have protected me and I often hoped he would, when the tests were unusually severe, but he didn't. It may be that he was deceived as well as the others, though I did not believe it nor think it possible. Those were dear good people but they must have carried simplicity and credulity to the limit. They would stick a pin in my arm and bear on it until they drove it a third of its length in, and then be lost in wonder that by a mere exercise of will power the professor could turn my arm to iron and make it insensible to pain. Whereas it was not insensible at all; I was suffering agonies of pain.

After that fourth night, that proud night, that triumphant night, I was the only subject. Simmons invited no more candidates to the platform. I performed alone every night the rest of the fortnight. Up to that time a dozen wise old heads, the intellectual aristocracy of the town, had held out as implacable unbelievers. I was as hurt by this as if I were engaged in some honest occupation. There is nothing surprising about this. Human beings feel dishonor the most, sometimes, when they most deserve it. That handful of overwise old gentlemen kept on shaking their heads all the first week and saying they had seen no marvels there that could not have been produced by collusion; and they were pretty vain of their unbelief too and liked to show it and air it and be superior to the ignorant and the gullible. Particularly old Dr. Peake, who was the ringleader of the irreconcilables and very formidable; for he was an F.F.V., he was learned, white-haired and venerable, nobly and richly clad in the fashions of an earlier and a courtlier day, he was large and stately, and he not only seemed wise but was what he seemed in that regard. He had great influence and his opinion upon any matter was worth much more than that of any other person in the community. When I conquered him at last, I knew I was undisputed master of the field; and now after more than fifty years I acknowledge with a few dry old tears that I rejoiced without shame.

In 1847 we were living in a large white house on the corner of Hill and Main Streets—a house that still stands but isn't large now although it hasn't lost a plank; I saw it a year ago and noticed that shrinkage. My father died in it in March of the year mentioned but our family did not move out of it until some months afterward. Ours was not the only family in the house; there was another, Dr. Grant's. One day Dr. Grant and Dr. Reyburn argued a matter on the street with sword canes and Grant was brought home multifariously punctured. Old Dr. Peake calked the leaks and came every day for a while to look after him.

The Grants were Virginians, like Peake, and one day when Grant was getting well enough to be on his feet and sit around in the parlor and talk, the conversation fell upon Virginia and old times. I was present but the group were probably unconscious of me, I being only a lad and a negligible quantity. Two of the group—Dr. Peake and Mrs. Crawford, Mrs. Grant's mother—had been of the audience when the Richmond theater burned down thirty-six years before, and they talked over the frightful details of that memorable tragedy. These were eyewitnesses, and with their eyes I saw it all with an intolerable vividness: I saw the black smoke rolling and tumbling toward the sky, I saw the flames burst through it and turn red, I heard the shrieks of the despairing, I glimpsed their faces at the windows, caught fitfully through the veiling smoke, I saw them jump to their death or to mutilation worse than death. The picture is before me yet and can never fade.

In due course they talked of the colonial mansion of the Peakes, with its stately columns and its spacious grounds, and by odds and ends I picked up a clearly defined idea of the place. I was strongly interested, for I had not before heard of such palatial things from the lips of people who had seen them with their own eyes. One detail, casually dropped, hit my imagination hard. In the wall by the great front door there was a round hole as big as a saucer—a British cannon ball had made it in the war of the Revolution. It was breathtaking; it made history real; history had never been real to me before.

Very well, three or four years later, as already mentioned, I was king bee and sole "subject" in the mesmeric show; it was the beginning of the second week; the performance was half over; just then the majestic Dr. Peake with his ruffled bosom and wrist-bands and his gold-headed cane entered, and a deferential citizen vacated his seat beside the Grants and made the great chief take it. This happened while I was trying to invent something fresh in the way of vision, in response to the professor's remark—

"Concentrate your powers. Look—look attentively. There—don't you see something? Concentrate—concentrate! Now then—describe it."

Without suspecting it, Dr. Peake, by entering the place, had reminded me of the talk of three years before. He had also furnished me capital and was become my confederate, an accomplice in my frauds. I began on a vision, a vague and dim one (that was part of the game at the beginning of a vision; it isn't best to see it too clearly at first, it might look as if you had come loaded with it). The vision developed by degrees and gathered swing, momentum, energy. It was the Richmond fire. Dr. Peake was cold at first and his fine face had a trace of polite scorn in it; but when he began to recognize that fire, that expression changed and his eyes began to light up. As soon as I saw that, I threw the valves wide open and turned on all the steam and gave those people a supper of fire and horrors that was calculated to last them one while! They couldn't gasp when I got through—they were petrified. Dr. Peake had risen and was standing—and breathing hard. He said, in a great voice:

"My doubts are ended. No collusion could produce that miracle. It was totally impossible for him to know those details, yet he has described them with the clarity of an eyewitness—and with what unassailable truthfulness God knows I know!"

I saved the colonial mansion for the last night and solidified and perpetuated Dr. Peake's conversion with the cannon-ball hole. He explained to the house that I could never have heard of that small detail, which differentiated this mansion from all other Virginian mansions and perfectly identified it, therefore the fact stood proven that I had *seen* it in my vision. Lawks!

It is curious. When the magician's engagement closed there

was but one person in the village who did not believe in mesmerism and I was the one. All the others were converted but I was to remain an implacable and unpersuadable disbeliever in mesmerism and hypnotism for close upon fifty years. This was because I never would examine them, in after life. I couldn't. The subject revolted me. Perhaps it brought back to me a passage in my life which for pride's sake I wished to forget; though I thought, or persuaded myself I thought, I should never come across a "proof" which wasn't thin and cheap and probably had a fraud like me behind it.

The truth is I did not have to wait long to get tired of my triumphs. Not thirty days, I think. The glory which is built upon a lie soon becomes a most unpleasant incumbrance. No doubt for a while I enjoyed having my exploits told and retold and told again in my presence and wondered over and exclaimed about, but I quite distinctly remember that there presently came a time when the subject was wearisome and odious to me and I could not endure the disgusting discomfort of it. I am well aware that the world-glorified doer of a deed of great and real splendor has just my experience; I know that he deliciously enjoys hearing about it for three or four weeks and that pretty soon after that he begins to dread the mention of it and by and by wishes he had been with the damned before he ever thought of doing that deed. I remember how General Sherman used to rage and swear over "While we were marching through Georgia," which was played at him and sung at him everywhere he went; still, I think I suffered a shade more than the legitimate hero does, he being privileged to soften his misery with the reflection that his glory was at any rate golden and reproachless in its origin, whereas I had no such privilege, there being no possible way to make mine respectable.

How easy it is to make people believe a lie and how hard it is to undo that work again! Thirty-five years after those evil exploits of mine I visited my old mother, whom I had not seen for ten years; and being moved by what seemed to me a rather noble and perhaps heroic impulse, I thought I would humble myself and confess my ancient fault. It cost me a great effort

WIDE WORLD

Mark Twain, late in his career as author-lecturer

to make up my mind; I dreaded the sorrow that would rise in her face and the shame that would look out of her eyes; but after long and troubled reflection, the sacrifice seemed due and right and I gathered my resolution together and made the confession.

To my astonishment there were no sentimentalities, no dramatics, no George Washington effects; she was not moved in the least degree; she simply did not believe me and said so! I was not merely disappointed, I was nettled to have my costly truthfulness flung out of the market in this placid and confident way when I was expecting to get a profit out of it. I asserted and reasserted, with rising heat, my statement that every single thing I had done on those long-vanished nights was a lie and a swindle; and when she shook her head tranquilly and said she knew better, I put up my hand and *swore* to it—adding a triumphant, "*Now* what do you say?"

It did not affect her at all; it did not budge her the fraction of an inch from her position. If this was hard for me to endure, it did not begin with the blister she put upon the raw when she began to put my sworn oath out of court with *arguments* to prove that I was under a delusion and did not know what I was talking about. Arguments! Arguments to show that a person on a man's outside can know better what is on his inside than he does himself. I had cherished some contempt for arguments before, I have not enlarged my respect for them since. She refused to believe that I had invented my visions myself; she said it was folly: that I was only a child at the time and could not have done it. She cited the Richmond fire and the colonial mansion and said they were quite beyond my capacities. Then I saw my chance! I said she was right—I didn't invent those, I got them from Dr. Peake. Even this great shot did not damage. She said Dr. Peake's evidence was better than mine, and he had said in plain words that it was impossible for me to have heard about those things. Dear, dear, what a grotesque and unthinkable situation: a confessed swindler convicted of honesty and condemned to acquittal by circumstantial evidence furnished by the swindled!

I realized with shame and with impotent vexation that I was

defeated all along the line. I had but one card left but it was a formidable one. I played it and stood from under. It seemed ignoble to demolish her fortress after she had defended it so valiantly but the defeated know not mercy. I played that master card. It was the pin-sticking. I said solemnly—

"I give you my honor, a pin was never stuck into me without causing me cruel pain."

She only said—

"It is thirty-five years. I believe you do think that now but I was there and I know better. You never winced."

She was so calm! and I was so far from it, so nearly frantic. "Oh, my goodness!" I said, "let me *show* you that I am speaking the truth. Here is my arm; drive a pin into it—drive it to the head—I shall not wince."

She only shook her gray head and said with simplicity and conviction—

"You are a man now and could dissemble the hurt; but you were only a child then and could not have done it."

And so the lie which I played upon her in my youth remained with her as an unchallengeable truth to the day of her death. Carlyle said "a lie cannot live." It shows that he did not know how to tell them. If I had taken out a life policy on this one the premiums would have bankrupted me ages ago.

MARY McLEOD BETHUNE

Greek and a Toothbrush

BY EMMA GELDERS STERNE

Illustrations by Raymond Lufkin

Mary McLeod Bethune (1875–1955) was the fifteenth child of a poor Negro family in South Carolina. She knew from experience the meaning of poverty and ignorance and was driven by this knowledge to help her people. Mrs. Bethune became the founder of Bethune-Cookman College, an adviser to statesmen, and a symbol of freedom and equality for all.

ON a back street in Denver, Colorado, Mary Crissman, a Quaker seamstress, pedaled away at her sewing machine. In the spring and fall, she went out to sew, spending a few days at a time in the homes of her neighbors, making up bolts of gingham or calico into dresses and shirts, or woolens or silks into Sunday clothes. In between times, she did plain sewing that was brought to her at home in her rented room. Sometimes she was called on to make a wedding dress of ivory brocade ordered from San Francisco or from the East. Or a hand-stitched christening dress for the newborn child of one of the wealthier mine-owners or merchants in town.

She had never married, but she loved little children. And as she worked she often thought of the Negro children in the South, not yet brought to that full freedom that allows human beings to develop themselves in the fullness of the promise of God who made the world. Her father had gone into the South with the Army during the war. Being a Quaker, he wouldn't fight, not even for freedom of God's most forsaken children. But the Anti-Slavery Association had sent him down, even before the Freedman's Bureau was established, to teach the slaves to read and write, to care for their bodies and their souls. He had gone away on his mission the day after Abraham Lincoln's Emancipation Proclamation was signed. That was all he was waiting for. Mary Crissman had been ten years old at the time. She still had the letters he wrote home.

Miss Crissman was pious. She took great comfort in her beliefs and practiced her Christianity as best she could. She went to the little stone meeting-house on Sundays. She "tithed," setting aside ten cents of every dollar she earned to give to the poor, the oppressed, and the heathen. For years she had given her tithe money to many good causes, a little at a time.

In August of the year 1889, when her customers were beginning to ask how soon she could come to them to outfit their children for another school year, Mary Crissman thought of a new plan of giving. There is no record of how the idea came to her. The inspiration might have come from a human-interest paragraph in *Godey's Lady's Book*—a story about the struggle of the Negroes to continue the education started under Lincoln's armies and under Reconstruction governments. Surprising bits of information often appeared in the fashion magazine, sandwiched between patterns of bustled skirts and shirtwaists with leg-o'-mutton sleeves. Or it may be that, at the homes of her customers, the middle-aged seamstress read in the home missions columns of the *Presbyterian Review* of the need for education in the South. The reasons for Mary Crissman's decision are buried in obscurity. Yet what she did that midsummer afternoon in Colorado changed the lives of many people over the continent and continued in its influence long after she was dead.

She sat down and wrote a letter to a small Presbyterian boarding-school for daughters of freedmen, offering to send her tithe money to provide a year's schooling for some Negro girl—"one you are sure will make good." The letter was addressed to the principal of Scotia Seminary at Concord, North Carolina.

Since Scotia was supported almost entirely by contributions from individuals or church groups outside the South, Miss Crissman's letter was one of several in the mailbox at the Concord post office. Nevertheless, it excited the interest of Dr. Satterfield, the headmaster, and of the half-dozen former students staying at the school in vacation time. It was rare that one contributor was willing to take full responsibility for a scholar. And the seamstress from Colorado had left the choice of the new student to the school.

A week later, Miss Emma Wilson, who had, as usual, been spending her free time at her old school, boarded the railroad train for Mayesville, South Carolina. She had Mary Crissman's letter in her skirt pocket and, folded carefully inside the envelope, enough money to pay for a ticket from Mayesville back to Concord.

No one met Miss Wilson at the depot because she wasn't expected back so soon. It was cotton-picking time, and the school term would not begin until the cotton was ginned and baled. She asked the baggageman to keep her valise because she had a four-mile walk ahead of her.

As it turned out, however, the young schoolteacher got a ride for most of the way in a mule cart, so she arrived at the McLeod farm before sundown. The whole family was out in the field, bent over the rows of heavy-headed cotton. All the family, that is, who were still left at home. Sally had married and gone. And the older boys had gone, too. There wasn't much on a five-acre farm to hold them.

Mary saw Miss Wilson coming across the dusty field, stepping carefully between the cotton rows. Coming, maybe, to say the new term was beginning? But it wasn't any use. Mary prayed every night to ask God to help her find a way to finish her studies so she could go to teach His Word to her kin in Africa. But how could she? They didn't have a mule yet, any more than they had in the spring.

As her teacher's trim figure came closer, Mary's mind darted down a dozen trails of thought. Maybe Miss Wilson wasn't coming for her after all, but for one of the little children. Maybe, when the cotton was baled and sold, there'd be enough money to buy a mule. But then there was the debt to the white man at the bank, for her father, in spite of all his determination, had had to borrow. And Granny wasn't getting any younger. Mama would need help with the ironing if Granny's health failed. . . . It just wasn't any use for Miss Wilson to be coming around.

"Short of a miracle," Mary said to herself, with unaccustomed bitterness, "my schooling is done with."

Patsy McLeod got up off her knees and went toward the visitor; but Mary kept on picking cotton. She didn't look up from the row until she heard her mother calling her name in a voice like a jubilee.

"Mary! Your teacher chose you! The school chose my girl to get the scholarship. Come here, every last one of you, while Miss Wilson reads the letter again. Mary's going to Scotia!"

There were Miss Wilson and Mama hugging each other and laughing and crying over the news in the letter fluttering in the breeze. And her father and Granny and the girls crowding around, and the little ones hanging onto Miss Wilson's skirt with their grimy hands.

But Mary just stayed on her knees where she was in the cotton row and prayed to God in thankfulness.

Many times in the years to come, in her writings and on the lecture platform and in conversation with friends, Mary McLeod Bethune spoke about that moment in her life. To her it was proof of victory through prayer. And the faith that her teacher had that she was "one who would make good" was a talisman, a treasure, a foundation rock to be added to her family's faith in her. On this was built the faith in herself which many people believe to be the key to her character.

"I believe, first of all, in God, and next of all, in Mary McLeod Bethune," she said years later. Some thought her vain with pride, because she believed so confidently, so joyously, first in her God, then in herself. Yet her faith in herself was built upon the belief *that she was one chosen to advance the welfare of her people,* to bring nearer reality the American dream. And, as Rollins Winslow put it, "operating under this very credo, she launched and won many frontier battles in human relations."

There was no more cotton picked at the McLeods' that day. Miss Wilson stayed to supper. Granny killed one of the frying-size chickens and cooked it, crisp and golden. Patsy made up a pan of biscuits while Mary churned a fresh batch of butter.

BETTMANN ARCHIVE

A home similar to the one in which
Mary McLeod Bethune was raised

Then she went to the spring across the road for a bucket of cool water.

The short walk in the dusk alone under the still branches of the liveoaks gave Mary time to think about the change that had come in her life. She was concerned about her family. How would they manage without her? Winter time wouldn't be so bad. With her gone, there'd be one less to feed. But plowing time would come again. Maybe she oughtn't to go at all. But that was unthinkable. Her mother wouldn't let her give up the scholarship. Neither would her father, though he didn't drive for knowledge the way Mary and her mother did. Freedom was her father's driving force—the freedom that lets a human being take from life what his spirit needs. He knew that Mary wanted learning the same as he wanted to make his land yield a crop. As long as her father had his two hands, he'd plant seed and make a harvest—whether anybody was there to help or not.

Walking back with the water sloshing in the wooden pail, the girl considered her home almost with the eyes of a stranger. Or with Miss Wilson's eyes. The schoolteacher was kind and good, but she was not from this part of the country. She'd never known what it was to be poor-slave poor. She, likely, was wondering how they all managed in such a little place. Twenty souls there used to be, counting Granny, when all the McLeods were living at home.

Yet they hadn't felt very crowded. It was easy, if you didn't have many possessions. Pallets to sleep on weren't like having a lot of beds. Pallets could be rolled up in a corner of the back room in the daytime. If everybody had just two garments apiece—one on his back and one in the washtub—you didn't need wardrobe room. There wasn't room for enough chairs or benches around the table where they ate. But that was all right because they didn't have dishes enough for all the family to eat at the same time anyway. Granny had her rocker by the fireplace, and the two cane-bottom chairs were good to sit on when they weren't being used to prop up the ironing-board. Outside of those, there were homemade benches and the floor. Anybody that didn't feel like sitting on the floor, could fetch a stump from the wood pile to sit on.

Looking at it piece by piece this way, Mary had to admit the McLeods didn't have much in the way of a house. But yet it was better than some the white farmers lived in. It had a floor. It was so clean that Reverend Bowen used to say Sister Sophia and Sister Patsy must have a soap factory hidden somewhere behind the cow shed.

Mary stopped to change the bucket to her other hand and noticed that the persimmon tree was loaded with a good crop this year. She'd have to remember to warn little Hattie again not to chunk the fruit down until after a frost. She'd pucker her mouth, for sure. Hattie took a lot of looking after and lately she'd turned to Mary more than to her mother. Hattie would miss her when she went away to Scotia and she'd miss Hattie. Hattie was bright. Maybe, someday, Miss Wilson would take her in the school. Mary had never given up hope that some of the family beside herself would get an education.

When she got back to the house, her father and Granny and Miss Wilson were sitting at the table eating supper, and Miss Wilson was telling what the school would be like. The rest of the family were clustered around in silence, all except Hattie and the baby, who were gnawing the chicken wings on the back step. The rest of them would eat later. There might not be much chicken left but there'd be plenty of biscuits and gravy and buttermilk.

After family prayers were over, Sam went over to a neighbor's house to ask for the loan of his mule and cart to drive Miss Wilson out to Reverend Bowen's home, near Sumter, where she always roomed during school term.

"I'll have to stop at the depot to get my valise," Miss Wilson said. "And before I forget, I'd like to give you Mary's railroad ticket to Concord. Though I'll see you again before she leaves."

Patsy took the ticket and laid it between two pages of the Bible up on the shelf. There it would be safe and come to no harm.

"When do you want she should go?" Patsy asked.

"A month from today," the schoolteacher said. "If you can get her ready by then."

Get Mary ready! Miss Wilson's words seemed to linger in the air long after the squeaking cart had gone down the road. Granny settled back in her rocking-chair and lit her corncob pipe. She sucked away at the stem without speaking. Patsy didn't say anything either. But, as she cleaned up the supper things, she rattled the tin pieplate dishes and her lips were pressed close together in a way she had when she was worried or anxious.

Finally, Mary spoke. "What did Miss Wilson mean 'get me ready'?"

Becky came in from milking the cow in time to hear the question. She set down the milk pail and the lantern she'd used to see by.

"You might be book smart, Mary McLeod," she said, "but you don't seem to have no common sense at all. There's more to going away to school than a railroad ticket and a letter. There's clothes to put on your back and something to carry them in. You saw all that extra ironing Mama did for little Miss Essie last week. Fluted ruffled drawers and starched petticoats and dressing-sacks with ribbons run through. Miss Essie going to Charleston to boarding-school, that's why. And when I carried the basket of clothes home there was a dressmaker from Sumter stitching on a sewing machine in the back room and Mrs.

Wilson scurrying around with dress goods on her arm, matching colors."

"That's white people's way," the grandmother interrupted sharply.

Patsy sat down wearily. "White people's way or not, Mary's got to have some good clothes to wear so far from home. It would shame me to let her go shabby. It comes at a bad time, too. A little later and the cotton would be sold. We'd have a little money for cloth and such, after paying the storekeeper and getting the flour and meal and sidemeat."

Mary shook her head emphatically. "Money from the cotton isn't going on my back," she said. "It's for a mule. I'm going to Scotia for learning. I can study my lessons without shoes and stockings. I can wash one dress while I've got on the other, same as always. Miss Wilson didn't choose me for pretty. She don't expect I should carry along any finery."

Stiffly, Sophia raised herself from her chair, and moved toward her little wooden chest where she kept her things. She had brought the chest along with her when she came, the day after Emancipation, to make her home with Patsy and Sam. That was more than twenty years ago and she had never let anybody see to the bottom of it. But whenever need got beyond a point, it seemed the old woman would open her chest and pull out something to help out. The blanket Mary was wrapped in when she was born had come from the treasure chest. So had the button string she had played with as a little child.

Hattie and little Maggie drew close, now, to watch the lid raised. Sophia pulled out a length of linsey-woolsey cloth, the kind the Wilson slaves always got for Christmas. She pulled out a spool of thread and four pearl buttons and handed them to Mary.

"I been saving this cloth too long as it is," she said. "It'll make a good dress and us has got plenty floursacking for underwear. The Lord means you shall have an education and He means you shall be dressed fitting for His work. You ain't pretty but you're a good girl to look at. You fix up the best you can and respect your body as you do your soul. And all of you quit fretting. Mary's going to that school in a manner that won't disgrace her. The Lord will provide."

As Mary McLeod told about it long afterward, the Lord did

provide, through the willing hands and good hearts of the neighbors. When the news got around the McLeod girl was going to North Carolina to get more schooling, neighbors knitted stockings. They sewed pretty aprons. They brought dresses they could spare—or said they could spare—for Patsy to make over. And Mr. Hawkins pulled a pair of brown high shoes with copper tips off his shelf. He'd had 'em, he said, since before the War, and they were too shopworn to sell. He wasn't like some folks. He liked to see colored people trying to better themselves. Sam was welcome to the shoes for his girl if she didn't have something better.

The end of September came and the day Mary was to take the train to Concord. Everybody in the neighborhood came down to the depot to see her off. In wagons, on mules, in oxcarts and afoot, they made a regular procession through the streets of Mayesville to see Mary get on the train.

Most of them had never been on a railroad train themselves but they hadn't come out of curiosity just to see the train go by. They had come because Mary McLeod already was becoming a symbol to her people. She was moving ahead on the path of freedom. Here at last was one of their own, going off to a big school to make something of herself. Maybe a teacher, maybe a missionary . . . Some predicted one thing, some another. But each of them shared in her victory over almost unsurmountable obstacles. Each had a share of the miracle. Each felt renewed hope in the promise of America while they waited at the depot for the northbound train to come in.

No doubt the stationmaster was a little dismayed to see all the country carts pouring in, taking up space at the hitching posts. Was Mayesville going to be subjected to one of those mass exoduses he'd been hearing about? There'd been rumors floating about that colored people were leaving the state in droves. They'd better stay where they were and not go running off to the North or to Kansas where they'd freeze to death. Had some agitator slipped into Mayesville stirring up trouble? He was scarcely less disturbed when he found out that all the hubbub was just because a black girl in a linsey-woolsey dress was going off to North Carolina to school. Education were sure to give the colored people the big head and make 'em feel as good as if they were white.

He stood in the depot door and scowled. But he didn't try to order the crowd away. There were too many of them together. Anyhow the train was due in five minutes. . . .

As the time grew close, the neighbors drew away, leaving the family to cluster around to say good-by. But Miss Wilson, who had come in from Summit, stayed a minute longer. She explained once more that a teacher from the school would meet the train in Concord. Mary was not to worry. She was just to take a seat in the cars, put her bundles on the floor and give her ticket to the conductor. The trip would take eight hours. She would be in Concord before dark.

Then Miss Wilson put a lovely plaid shawl around Mary's shoulders, because, she said, it got colder in Concord than down here. "You write a letter," she whispered. "I'll take it to your mother. And I'll write letters, too."

"Yes, ma'am," was all that Mary had time to answer. But the school teacher's promise lifted a load from her heart.

The inability of members of loving and close-knit families to communicate with each other when they were separated by distance was one of the tragic features of slavery. It was one of the saddest results of the Southern program of illiteracy in the period when Mary McLeod was growing up. It is still a problem today. Miss Wilson's thoughtfulness meant that the bond between Mary and her family need not be broken. There could be letters between them. She would know how the planting was going in the spring—how the mule her father was bargaining for worked out—whether Granny's new rheumatism medicine did any good. Above all, words could flow between herself and her mother. Someday, maybe, there'd be time for Miss Wilson to teach her mother to read!

"You heard what Miss Wilson said?" Mary held the thin, bony shoulders of her mother in her strong arms. The engine roared in with a rush of air. She had to raise her voice to be heard. "I'm going to write you all about Scotia. And about the train ride . . ."

The brakes screeched and groaned. The train hardly came to a stop before Mary's foot was on the car step. She remembered to wave good-by to the crowd of friends standing at a respectful distance. Sam handed up the bundle of clothes and the lunch Granny had put up and wrapped in an old newspaper. The whistle blew and the wheels began slowly to turn. The shouting, waving, loving people at the depot disappeared from Mary's sight. An era in the life of Mary McLeod had ended. But the love she had been surrounded with went with her always.

"I was shown goodness in my childhood," she wrote. "My parents believed in me. I learned to believe in other people. To be sure I saw trouble and the way was not easy; but I have thanked God and said Glory Hallelujah!"

Eight hours was not enough to savor all the wonders of that first train trip. To this child of a log cabin, the day-coach with its red-plush seats, its polished ceiling, and its spacious glass windows was unheard-of luxury. The only thing like it that she could think of was the picture of Queen Victoria's throne-room that Miss Wilson had pinned up on the schoolroom wall.

She sat primly on the cushioned seat and it seemed to her that the queen on her throne could not be more comfortable. She held onto her bundles with one hand and clutched her ticket in the other until the blue-coated conductor came to punch it. But after the first hour she felt at ease, as if traveling on the railroad cars was something the McLeods did every day.

When she saw an old lady across the aisle open a shoe box and take out a sandwich, she unwrapped her own lunch. Tears came to her eyes. Granny had put in a whole half of a chicken, breast and all. Mary ate every bit of it and licked her fingers. She saw a smile cross the old lady's face.

"First time I ever had enough chicken in my life," Mary said, leaning across the aisle.

She hadn't meant to talk to anybody, especially not to white folks, but before they had crossed the state line to North Carolina she knew the life stories of half a dozen passengers and was minding a year-old baby while the mother took a nap! That was

Mary's way. She cared about people and drew them to her always. She never held back her warmth and friendliness out of concern about the impression she was making. She always assumed that people liked her—and generally they did.

The thing that Mary remembered most about that train ride however, was neither the red-plush luxury nor the people. It was the sight of America skimming past her window. It was not the detail of the countryside that engaged her attention, for she knew every tree and bush and flowering weed at a glance. She knew the names and habits and seasons of the moss-hung live-oak, the slick green magnolia standing in front of a half-burned, abandoned mansion, the sweetgum, tawny-red now, storing sap that would make sweet twigs to chew next spring. And she could tell the number of bales of cotton a farmer must have raised, just from looking at a ragged, picked-over field. It was neither the farmhouses nor the little towns on both sides of the railroad tracks that excited her interest; nor the rivers they crossed on high wooden trestles, nor the distant mountains, the color of russet apples. None of these things made her heart jump, looked at by themselves.

It was the largeness, the sweep of her native land. And the Carolinas were only two states in the Union. There were thirty-seven more states, and the Territories, and Mexico and Canada. North America, South America, Asia, and Africa, Europe, and all the oceans—Mary could almost hear Miss Wilson's geography class reciting. She wanted suddenly to see the whole world—God's whole beautiful world. If people knew how beautiful the earth was and all the fullness thereof, how could they ever be mean to one another? It was so wonderfully big—and way off, beyond those everlasting hills in the setting sun, was Miss Mary Crissman, giving her this gift of learning and expecting her to make good. She wouldn't disappoint Miss Crissman. She would make good, all right. She felt it in her bones!

This quality of self-confidence stood Mary McLeod in good stead in her first days at boarding-school. The change in her surroundings was so great that a less outgoing person might have been overawed and confused. But Mary loved every bit of it, from the moment when Miss Rebecca Cantcy, Miss Wilson's friend, met her at the station.

"How did you know it was me?" Mary asked as she walked along beside the teacher, unconscious that she looked in any way different.

Rebecca Cantcy forbore to correct the grammar. That would come later. But she was glad Emma Wilson had suggested that the scholarship pupil from Mayesville come a few days early to get used to the environment of Scotia. Emma had warned the other teachers that Mary McLeod was a raw country girl. It had been a bit of a shock, nevertheless, to see the pigtails, the brass-tipped shoes, the paper-wrapped bundles. Miss Cantcy was glad that Dr. and Mrs. Satterfield were called away from Concord. She had a great admiration for the austere New England couple who had founded the school and were giving their lives to the work of educating the former slaves. But sometimes Dr. Satterfield didn't understand—how could he understand?

She smiled at the girl bouncing along beside her with the awkward energy of an untamed colt. They rounded a corner and Miss Cantcy pointed to a red-brick two-story house set back from the road.

"There it is," she said. "There's Scotia."

The only brick building in Mayesville was the Episcopal Church—for whites only. Mary had never been inside a brick building. She had never walked up a staircase.

Rebecca Cantcy opened the door with a key and led the new pupil upstairs to a bedroom so she could wash up before meeting the others.

It was a small room with two narrow beds. The bedspreads were snowy white. So were the curtains at the window. There were two chairs, a chest of drawers, and a table with a washbowl and pitcher decorated with pink roses. Two toothbrushes stood in a tumbler and two towels were neatly folded over a rod at the side. A small mirror hung above the dressing table and beside it, a colored print of the infant Jesus in the manger. On the other side was a picture of turrets and towers and yellow clouds: Jerusalem the Golden.

"You'll have a roommate, Mary, but Abby Greeley hasn't come yet," Miss Cantcy said.

"A whole room, just for two people!" Mary sat down on the

edge of her bed and bounced up and down to feel the softness. She changed her vision of Heaven, then and there. "I used to think Heaven was towers of gold and wings of angels," she confided. "But maybe it's a room like this for every one of God's children!"

When Mary had washed and smoothed her braids, the teacher led the way down to the dining-room. The school term would not begin for several days. Only a few teachers were at the school—the ones who had been there all summer studying and getting the house ready. Miss Cantcy introduced Mary and showed her where to sit.

The table was set with a white cloth like the one Mary's mother washed and ironed every week for the Wilsons. Mary had never eaten at a table like this one, with a place set for each and every person and platters of cold meat and fried mush and little dishes of applesauce—and in the middle, flowers in a vase. Black-eyed Susans. They were pesky weeds in the cotton rows but Mary had always had a liking for their perky faces.

She bent her head while Miss Cantcy, sitting at the head of the table, said the blessing. A knife and spoon lay on one side of her plate, and on the other—a fork. Mary's self-confidence suddenly left her. She didn't hear "for what we are about to receive . . ." She forgot to say Amen. The McLeods didn't have any forks. A spoon or a knife if you needed one, but never any forks. She had heard about forks from Sally, who was always grumbling about having to shine the silver at her cook job. Maybe, if she watched carefully, she could see how to hold it and the teachers wouldn't know her ignorance.

But Mary McLeod's innate honesty and frankness would not permit even such a small deception. It wasn't any sin to be fourteen years old and not know how to hold a fork.

She threw back her head and laughed at her own moment of panic. "You'll have to show me, ma'am," she said to the young teacher at her right. "Forks are just for white folks in Mayesville!"

It was like that all the first few days. Everything was different. The iron cookstove in the kitchen that burned coal instead of wood. The lamps in every room with chimneys that had to be polished every morning. The water pumped from a deep well right by the house. And that beautiful room she slept in!

By the time the other girls began to come, though, Mary felt at ease. One or two of the new girls were from homes almost as poor as her own. Mary took them in hand and spared them the awkward shyness which usually made the beginning of a new term at a school like Scotia rather difficult. She had them practicing how to hold a fork, and made the dinner table rock with merriment.

The night before Dr. and Mrs. Satterfield were to return, something happened, however, that jolted Mary McLeod. The last two teachers came from their homes in the North. The new girls were introduced to them: Miss Chapman and Miss Bowers. Mary put out her hand, then drew it back quickly. The two young women were white!

Miss Chapman, the tall, willowy one, took the girl's rough, work-worn hand in hers. "I'm glad you've come to Scotia, Mary," she said. "Emma Wilson has told us a great deal about you. I think Miss Crissman will be proud of her scholarship pupil."

Next morning, Dr. Satterfield was at the head of the table to lead morning prayers. At the other end of the table was his wife. Somehow, it no longer came as a surprise to Mary to find that they, too, were white.

Classes began that morning. Mary's first class was with Miss Bowers.

"I am from Boston," the teacher began. "I'd like to tell you a story about something that happened to my ancestors a long time ago. It was a quiet night in December, 1773. A British merchant ship loaded with tea rode at anchor in Boston Harbor. Suddenly, some rowboats moved out from the shore. In them were my great-great-great grandfather and his neighbors, determined to have no more tea if it was taxed without their consent as citizens. They opened the boxes and dumped the king's tea into the ocean. They cried: 'Taxation without representation is tyranny!' That was a beginning of the American Revolution, a beginning of the struggle for government by consent of the governed. Americans struck out against injustice and tyranny and oppression, just as they have struck out again and again. They said that 'all men are created equal, that they are endowed by their Creator with certain Unalienable Rights.'"

Miss Bowers's people were white; yet they had had to fight for their freedom too. They were oppressed and they struck out. And claimed *Unalienable Rights* . . . Mary didn't know exactly what the word meant. She repeated it to herself several times so she would remember it and find out. *Unalienable* . . . Whatever it meant, it was a beautiful word on the tongue. And not all white people were the oppressors. Some, like Miss Bowers, remembered even when they had won their unalienable rights that other people still had their rights to win!

Never again would Mary lump all white people together. Those who wanted above all else to "keep the Negro in his place" had done their best to create a wall of hatred and distrust in Mary McLeod. But two young white women who taught at Scotia crumbled that barrier. A half-century later she still remembered.

"Through Miss Chapman and Miss Bowers," she wrote, "I came to understand that there were decent white people who cared about what I was as a person. For that, I have always been grateful."

When Mary entered Scotia College it had been in existence six years. It offered the courses that were everywhere considered proper to a school of higher learning at that time. Colleges for men had always taught "the classics" and "moral philosophy." Colleges offering higher education for women made sure to include all the same subjects. There were still people who sincerely believed that serious study of anything beyond music and penmanship and a smattering of polite literature would bring on brain fever in the female sex. The colleges had to prove this wasn't true. And in spite of the fact that dozens of free

Mary McLeod Bethune

Negroes had won degrees from universities in the United States and abroad, the majority of people, north and south, still doubted that the former slaves were capable of any intellectual achievement.

It was natural that schools like Scotia, founded to give the benefits of higher education to Negro girls, should cling to the traditional course of study. It was natural, too, that the students, taught all their lives that they were inferior beings, wanted—and needed—to prove that book learning was not beyond them.

So, at Scotia, the traditional college subjects were taught. And girls like Mary McLeod, only three years removed from illiteracy, doggedly recited Latin verbs and puzzled over algebra problems. In some ways, the classroom and life were far apart. Companionship with the students and teachers, the time to read, the time to think, and even the hours spent in household duties in a well-equipped home were valuable parts of Mary McLeod's education in the years she spent at Scotia. She was never a great scholar, but she learned to use the library to satisfy her unending curiosity. The men and women, the events that were part of her own history, and had up to now been only half understood, passed in review before her. From the first day, when her desire to understand the word "unalienable" led her to the Declaration of Independence, she made the great ideas and language of American democracy her own, as much a part of her as the Bible had been. From the Declaration, her reading led her to the speeches of Lincoln, to Thoreau's letter on the death of John Brown, to Thomas Paine's writings. She thrilled to the stories of one of the older teachers who had been a nurse with the Union forces and knew Harriet Tubman.

In informal talks like this, Mary learned the history of the long struggle against slavery and the history of other countries too. Lecturers came to the school and told what was going on over the whole South—bad things and good. She came to understand, from the lists of men who lost their lives in other parts of the South, why her mother sat tight-lipped but proud when her father went off to the polls to vote on election days and why so many of their neighbors in Mayesville had gone off to Kansas that time when she was just a baby.

Other lecturers came—missionaries going off to save the souls of their brothers and sisters in Africa. Mary sat on the edge of her bench and listened to the frock-coated, eloquent preachers. And she got the "somedays" again, more fiercely than ever. She was awed by these men who were going across the ocean to carry the words of Jesus to the heathen. One thing troubled her, though. They spoke as if all the Africans were savages, as if Africa had no history. As if the judges, the cities, the songs and legends Granny knew about had never existed.

On her first trip home, Mary asked her grandmother why it was the missionaries didn't seem to know more about the way Africa used to be. The old woman had grown very feeble, but her mind was as clear as ever and her tongue as sharp.

"When I was a little thing, size of Sally's girl-baby, I remember a big rock in a creek, down by the slave-quarters. Must have been near Charleston—I disremember the place. But I remember that rock. My mama used to set me on top of it—it were that big, like an island. But the creek waters kept beatin' against it, crunchin' off a piece here, a piece there. Before I got sold away from there, the drops of water had cut that big rock down to size, the everlasting tiny drops of water. Last time I saw it, that rock wasn't bigger than a pebble. Likely it's gone now altogether."

Sophia, descendant of an African chief, leaned back in her rocker and sighed.

"That's what the white people done to the remembrance our people brought from Africa. They dribbled it away until it were no more than a pebble or a grain of sand. Bless you, child, they *had* to. Even the whites—the most of 'em—have got a conscience. Didn't they receive the word of God straight from the Bible? They know the Bible say all men are brothers. But they want hands to till the fields and dig the ditches and cook their victuals and wash their clothes so they can wear the clothes and eat good and read the Book. They come fetch black hands from the kingdoms of Africa. Conscience say that wouldn't be a brotherly act if the black hands belonged to *men*. The devil whisper: 'Make them blacks leave behind all that makes men and women. Make 'em forget all that makes 'em proud.' And they done it, bit by bit, like the water crumble that rock. White people never did know about Africa neither, same as water didn't know about the rock it crumble away. But the glory of our people, it were real."

Coming home that summer had a curious effect on Mary. She was like two people—one part of her was bubbling over with eagerness to pour out all she had learned about better ways of living. Another side was suddenly shy.

She saw Granny grown suddenly very old. She saw her parents working year after year without any material change in their lives. Her mother was smaller and thinner than she had remembered, her father more silent. And there'd been trouble and disappointments they hadn't let Miss Wilson write to her about. Last year had been a good cotton year and cotton sold for twenty-five cents a pound. But the bank had called in the loan of any Negro who went to the polls to vote. Her father still had a little owing on the new mule he'd bought. He had cast his vote, as always. Then, paying off the little debt had taken all the money from the cotton. So they had gone hungry.

And the white-sheeted Klan was marching again and burning crosses. People were leaving the county almost like the Kansas exodus twelve years ago. Benches in the church were empty. Even if families stayed behind, the young people were leaving. Sammy had gone. So had Sally and her husband.

Mary saw the burdens the people at home were bearing. She didn't want to add to them by new ways that might seem like criticism. She had managed to earn a little spending money, one way or another, and had bought a pocket handkerchief for Maggie, a doll for Hattie, and a string of yellow beads for Granny. Those presents didn't worry her. But she had a pair of house slippers for her father to cover his bare feet when he pulled off his work shoes; and for her mother, a dozen tin forks. And she'd brought toothbrushes for everybody.

Suppose they thought she was belittling those she loved best because they went barefoot and sopped up pot liquor with pieces of cornbread and ate crisp fried pork with their fingers? Suppose they thought she was setting herself apart? For three days, the slippers and forks stayed wrapped up in her bundle.

Mary was wrong. Her parents were delighted. Not only her own family, but all the little community looked to her to bring new ways from the outside world. A perfect rash of fork-buying broke out until Mr. Hawkins, down at the store, couldn't make out what was happening. And everybody who could get one took to carrying a clean white handkerchief to church.

Before the summer was out the girls and women from a mile around took to dropping by to ask "that McLeod girl" advice about everything from whether boiling drinking water really made you safe from the fever to how to trim a hat or fix their hair in a pompadour as she did. The yard sometimes had so many people sitting around that it looked as if Mary were holding class. That gave her an idea. She began to have a class one night a week for anybody who wanted to come—a class in literature and singing. She read aloud, sometimes Bible stories, more often scraps of poetry or things she had cut from newspapers. And she led singing of hymns and spirituals, in harmony, just as Miss Bowers did. Outdoors like that, with no light but the fireflies, it sounded beautiful.

Of course all the visiting stopped when the cotton was ready to be picked. Mary worked, then, from daybreak to dark, in the fields. For the first time, she outpicked her father. After the cotton was ginned, she persuaded her father to dig a well, so they'd have drinking water without depending on the open spring.

She was helping him, working with pick and shovel, when the barber from Sumter and his son came to call. They wanted to talk about colleges. The boy was hoping to go to Fisk University or to Howard.

"I want my son to have the best he can get," the old man said. "To partake of the feast of learning . . . but I heard you had to have some Latin and Greek before you could get in. Where can he get such a thing? I've been trying to teach him some this summer while Miss Wilson is away. But I never saw a book printed in Latin or Greek in my life."

Mary rubbed her hands clean on her skirt and went into the house. She took her Latin grammar out. She hadn't even opened it and the summer vacation was almost over! She had meant to study, to get ahead for next term. But if she lent it to the boy, maybe he'd manage to teach himself enough to enter the doors of a college.

She stood by the door with the book in her hand. *To partake of the feast of learning* . . . Yes. We have the right to sit at the table with the rest of God's children. The things of the spirit and mind—that's what her mother and Miss Wilson and Miss Crissman wanted to give her . . . what she longed for herself. But decent ways of living, weren't they important, too?

Mary McLeod had not consciously thought out her ideas of

BETHUNE-COOKMAN COLLEGE

Mary McLeod Bethune, in 1904, with her first class in the school she founded and developed into Bethune-Cookman College

education. She had heard the arguments at the dinner table at school over which was best for the Negro race. Howard and Fisk universities on one side—on the other, Hampton Industrial Institute and Mr. Booker T. Washington down at Tuskegee in Alabama. Mr. Washington's school, it was said, taught hardly more than reading and writing, but it did teach work skills and better ways of living. Mary herself had not entered the discussions. The talk about the kind of education her people needed was for people like Abby, her roommate, who cared for nothing but being a teacher. Mary's own mind was set on going to Africa as a missionary.

The summer at home had made a difference. It had given her a set of values—something to go by that lasted her her whole lifetime and in later years influenced many thousands, perhaps hundreds of thousands of people.

"Education," she said to herself, "it's Greek *and* a toothbrush. Learning for the sake of learning but learning for life's sake, too."

THOMAS ALVA EDISON

The Traveling Newspaper Office

BY WILLIAM H. MEADOWCROFT

"Al" Edison (1847-1931) grew up in a small Canadian town, roughhousing and tumbling into the canal like all the other boys. But when he was twelve, young Edison found his laboratory in the basement more exciting than games or sports. By the time he was fourteen the keenness of his scientific mind was matched only by his sense of humor and his business ability.

THOMAS asked so many questions that he fairly tired out his father, although the older man had no small ability. It has been reported that other members of the family regarded the boy as being mentally unbalanced and likely to be a lifelong care to his parents.

Even while he was quite a young child his mechanical tendencies showed themselves in his fondness for building little plank roads from the pieces of wood thrown out by the shipbuilding yards and the sawmills. One day he was found in the village square laboriously copying the signs of the stores.

To this day Mr. Edison is not inclined to accept a statement unless he can prove it for himself by experiment. Once, when he was about six years old, he watched a goose sitting on her eggs and saw them hatch. Soon after he was missing. By and by, after an anxious search, his father found him sitting in a nest he had made in the barn filled with goose and hen eggs he had collected, trying to hatch them out.

His remarkable memory was noticeable even when he was a child, for before he was five years old he had learned all the songs of the lumber gangs and of the canal men. Even now his recollection goes back to 1850, when, as a child three or four years old, he saw camped in front of his home six covered wagons, "prairie schooners," and witnessed their departure for California, where gold had just been discovered.

Another of his recollections of childhood is of a sadder nature. He went off one day with another boy to bathe in the creek. Soon after they entered the water the other boy disappeared. Young Edison waited around for about half an hour, and then, as it was growing dark, went home, puzzled and lonely, but said nothing about the matter. About two hours afterward, when the missing boy was being searched for, a man came to the Edison home to make anxious inquiry of the companion with whom he had last been seen. Edison told all the circumstances with a painful sense of being in some way guilty. The creek was at once dragged, and then the body was recovered.

Edison himself had more than one narrow escape. Of course, he fell into the canal and was nearly drowned—few boys in Milan worth their salt omitted that performance. On another occasion he fell into a pile of wheat in a grain elevator and was almost smothered. Holding the end of a skate-strap, that another lad might cut it with an ax, he lost the top of a finger. Fire also had its peril. He built a fire in a barn, but the flames spread so rapidly that, although he escaped himself, the barn was wholly destroyed. He was publicly whipped in the village square as a warning to other youths. Equally well remembered is a dangerous encounter with a ram which attacked him while he was busily engaged digging out a bumblebee's nest near an orchard fence, and was about to butt him again when he managed to drop over on the safe side and escape. He was badly hurt and bruised, and no small quantity of arnica was needed for his wounds.

It was when he was about seven years old that Edison's parents moved to Port Huron, Michigan, and it was there, a few years later, that he became a newsboy on a train.

Edison's train left Port Huron at seven o'clock in the morning and arrived at Detroit in about three hours. It did not leave

THOMAS ALVA EDISON FOUNDATION

Thomas Edison at the age of fourteen

Detroit again until quite late in the afternoon, arriving at Port Huron about nine-thirty at night. This made a long day for the boy, but it gave him an opportunity to do just what he wanted, which was to read, to buy chemicals and apparatus, and to indulge in his favorite occupation—chemical experimentation.

The train was made up of three coaches—baggage, smoking, and ordinary passenger. The baggage-car was divided into three compartments—one for trunks and packages, one for the mail, and one for smoking.

As there was no ventilation in this smoking-compartment, no use was made of it. It was therefore turned over to young Edison, who not only kept his papers there and his stock of goods as a "candy butcher," but he also transferred to it the contents of the precious laboratory from his mother's cellar. He found plenty of leisure on the two daily runs of the train to follow up his study of chemistry.

His earnings on the train were excellent, for he often took in eight or ten dollars a day. One dollar a day always went to his mother, and, as he was thus supporting himself, he felt entitled to spend any other profit left over on chemicals and apparatus. Detroit being a large city, he could obtain a greater variety there than in his own small town. He spent a great deal of time in reading up on his favorite subject at the public library, where he could find plenty of technical books. Thus he gave up most of his time and all his money to chemistry.

He did not confine himself entirely to chemistry in his reading at the Detroit public library, but sought to gain knowledge on other subjects. It is a matter of record that in the beginning of his reading he started in with a certain section of the library and tried to read it through, shelf by shelf, regardless of subject.

Edison went along in this manner for quite a long time. When the Civil War broke out he noticed that there was a much greater demand for newspapers. He became ambitious to publish a local journal of his own. So his little laboratory in the smoking-compartment received some additions which made it also a newspaper office.

He picked up a second-hand printing-press in Detroit and bought some type. With his mechanical ability, it was not a difficult matter to learn the rudiments of the printing art, and as some of the type was kept on the train he could set it up in moments of leisure. Thus he became the compositor, pressman, editor, proprietor, publisher, and newsdealer of the *Weekly Herald*. The price was three cents a copy, or eight cents a month for regular subscribers and the circulation ran up to over four hundred copies an issue. Only one or two copies of this journal are now to be found.

It was the first newspaper in the world printed on a train in motion. It received the patronage of the famous English engineer, Stephenson, and was also noted by the *London Times*. As the production of a boy of fourteen it was certainly a clever sheet, and many people were willing subscribers, for, by the aid of the railway telegraph, Edison was often able to print late news of local importance which could not be found in regular papers, like those of Detroit.

Edison's business grew so large that he employed a boy friend to help him. There was often plenty of work for both in the early days of the war, when the news of battle caused great excitement.

In order to increase the sales of newspapers, Edison would telegraph the news ahead to the agents of stations where the train stopped and get them to put up bulletins, so that, when the stations were reached, there would usually be plenty of purchasers waiting.

He recalls in particular the sensation caused by the great battle of Shiloh, or Pittsburg Landing, in April, 1862, in which both Grant and Sherman were engaged, in which the Confederate General Johnston was killed, and in which there was a great number of men killed and wounded.

The bulletin-boards of the Detroit newspapers were surrounded by dense crowds, which read that there were about sixty thousand killed and wounded, and that the result was uncertain. Edison, in relating his experience of that day, says:

"I knew if the same excitement was shown at the various small towns along the road, and especially at Port Huron, the sale of papers would be great. I then conceived the idea of telegraphing the news ahead, went to the operator in the depot, and, on my giving him *Harper's Weekly* and some other papers for three months, he agreed to telegraph to all the stations the matter on the bulletin-board. I hurriedly copied it, and he sent it, requesting the agents to display it on the blackboards used for stating the arrival and departure of trains. I decided that, instead of the usual one hundred papers, I could sell one thousand; but not having sufficient money to purchase that number, I determined in my desperation to see the editor himself and get credit. The great paper at that time was the *Detroit Free Press*. I walked into the office marked 'Editorial' and told a young man that I wanted to see the editor on important business—important to me, anyway.

"I was taken into an office where there were two men, and I stated what I had done about telegraphing, and that I wanted a thousand papers, but only had money for three hundred, and I wanted credit. One of the men refused it, but the other told the first spokesman to let me have them. This man, I afterward learned, was Wilbur F. Storey, who subsequently founded the *Chicago Times* and became celebrated in the newspaper world. With the aid of another boy I lugged the papers to the train and started folding them. The first station, called Utica, was a small one, where I generally sold two papers. I saw a crowd ahead on the platform, and thought it was some excursion, but the moment I landed there was a rush for me; then I realized that the telegraph was a great invention. I sold thirty-five papers there. The next station was Mount Clemens, now a watering-place, but then a town of about one thousand population. I usually sold six to eight papers there. I decided that if I found a corresponding crowd there the only thing to do to correct my lack of judgment in not getting more papers was to raise the price from five cents to ten. The crowd was there, and I raised the price. At the various towns there were corresponding crowds. It had been my practice at Port Huron to jump from the train at a point about one-fourth of a mile from the station, where the train generally slackened speed. I had drawn several loads of sand to this point to jump on, and had become quite expert. The little Dutch boy with the horse met me at this point. When the wagon approached the outskirts of the town I was met by a large crowd. I then yelled: 'Twenty-five cents apiece, gentlemen! I haven't enough to go around!' I sold out, and made what to me then was an immense sum of money."

But this and similar gains of money did not increase Edison's savings, for all his spare cash was spent for new chemicals and apparatus. He had bought a copy of Fresenius's *Qualitative Analysis,* and, with his ceaseless testing and study of its advanced problems, his little laboratory on the train was now becoming crowded with additional equipment, especially as he now added electricity to his studies.

"While a newsboy on the railroad," says Edison, "I got very much interested in electricity, probably from visiting telegraph offices with a chum who had tastes similar to mine."

We have already seen that he was shrewd enough to use the telegraph to get news items for his own little journal and also to bulletin his special news of the Civil War along the line. To such a ceaseless experimenter as he was, it was only natural that electricity should come in for a share of his attention. With his knowledge of chemistry, he had no trouble in "setting up" batteries, but his difficulty lay in obtaining instruments and material for circuits.

To-day any youth who desires to experiment with telegraphy or telephony can find plenty of stores where apparatus can be bought ready made, or he can make many things himself by following the instructions in *Harper's Electricity Book for Boys.* But in Edison's boyish days it was quite different. Telegraph supplies were hard to obtain, and amateurs were usually obliged to make their own apparatus.

However, he and his chum had a line between their homes, built of common stove-pipe wire. The insulators were bottles set on nails driven into trees and short poles. The magnet wire was wound with rags for insulation, and pieces of spring brass were used for telegraph keys.

With the idea of securing current cheaply, Edison applied the little he knew about static electricity, and actually experimented with cats. He treated them vigorously as frictional machines until the animals fled in dismay, leaving their marks to remind the young inventor of his first great lesson in the relative value of sources of electrical energy. Resorting to batteries, however, the line was made to work, and the two boys exchanged messages.

Edison wanted lots of practice, and secured it in an ingenious manner. If he could have had his way he would have sat up until the small hours of the morning, but his father insisted on eleven-thirty as the proper bed-time, which left but a short interval after a long day on the train.

Now, each evening, when the boy went home with newspapers that had not been sold, his father would sit up to read them. So Edison on some excuse had his friend take the papers, but suggested to his father that he could get the news from the chum

CULVER SERVICE

Thomas Edison in his laboratory

by telegraph bit by bit. The scheme interested the father, and was put into effect, the messages over the wire being written down by Edison and handed to the old gentleman to read.

This gave good practice every night until twelve or one o'clock, and was kept up for some time, until the father became willing that his son should sit up for a reasonable time. The papers were then brought home again, and the boys practised to their hearts' content, until the line was pulled down by a stray cow wandering through the orchard.

Now we come to the incident which may be regarded as turning Edison's thoughts more definitely to electricity. One August morning, in 1862, the mixed train on which he worked as newsboy was doing some shunting at Mount Clemens station. A laden box-car had been pushed out of a siding, when Edison, who was loitering about the platform, saw the little son of the station agent, Mr. J. U. Mackenzie, playing with the gravel on the main track, along which the car, without a brakeman, was rapidly approaching.

Edison dropped his papers and his cap and made a dash for the child, whom he picked up and lifted to safety without a second to spare, as the wheel struck his heel. Both were cut about the face and hands by the gravel ballast on which they fell.

The two boys were picked up by the train-hands and carried to the platform, and the grateful father, who knew and liked the rescuer, offered to teach him the art of train telegraphy and to make an operator of him. It is needless to say that the proposal was most eagerly accepted.

Edison found time for his new studies by letting one of his friends look after the newsboy work on the train for part of the trip, keeping for himself the run between Port Huron and Mount Clemens. We have already seen that he was qualified as a beginner, and, besides, he was able to take to the station a neat little set of instruments he had just finished at a gun shop in Detroit.

What with his business as newsboy, his publication of the *Weekly Herald*, his reading and chemical and electrical experiments, Edison was leading a busy life and making rapid progress, but unexpectedly there came disaster, which brought about a sudden change. One day, as the train was running swiftly over a piece of poorly laid track, there was a sudden lurch, and a stick of phosphorus was jarred from its shelf, fell to the floor and burst into flame.

The car took fire, and Edison was trying in vain to put out the blaze when the conductor rushed in with water and saved the car. On arriving at the next station the enraged conductor put the boy off with his entire outfit, including his laboratory and printing-plant.

The origin of Edison's deafness may be told in his own words: "My train was standing by the platform at Smith's Creek station. I was trying to climb into the freight car with both arms full of papers when the conductor took me by the ears and lifted me.

BROWN BROTHERS

Thomas Edison with his first phonograph

I felt something snap inside my head, and my deafness started from that time and has ever since progressed.

"This deafness has been a great advantage to me in various ways. When in a telegraph office I could hear only the instrument directly on the table at which I sat, and, unlike the other operators, I was not bothered by the other instruments. Again, in experimenting on the telephone, I had to improve the transmitter so that I could hear it. This made the telephone commercial, as the magneto telephone receiver of Bell was too weak to be used as a transmitter commercially. It was the same with the phonograph. The great defect of that instrument was the rendering of the overtones in music and the hissing consonants in speech. I worked over one year, twenty hours a day, Sundays and all, to get the word "specie" perfectly recorded and reproduced on the phonograph. When this was done I knew that everything else could be done—which was a fact. Again, my nerves have been preserved intact. Broadway is as quiet to me as a country village is to a person with normal hearing."

But we left young Edison on the station platform, sorrowful and indignant, as the train moved off, deserting him in the midst of his beloved possessions. He was saddened, but not altogether discouraged, and after some trouble succeeded in making his way home, where he again set up his laboratory and also his printing-office. There was some objection on the part of the family, as they feared that they might also suffer from fire, but he promised not to bring in anything of a dangerous nature.

He continued to publish the *Weekly Herald,* but after a while was persuaded by a chum to change its character and publish it under the name of *Paul Pry,* making it a journal of town gossip about local people and their affairs and peculiarities.

No copies of *Paul Pry* can now be found, but it is known that its style was distinctly personal, and the weaknesses of the townspeople were discussed in it very freely and frankly by the two boys. It caused no small offense, and in one instance Edison was pitched into the St. Clair River by one of the victims whose affairs had been given such unsought publicity.

Possibly this was one of the reasons that caused Edison to give up the paper not very long afterward. He had a great liking for newspaper work, and might have continued in that field had it not been for strong influences in other directions. There is no question, however, that he was the youngest publisher and editor of his time.

ANNA PAVLOVA

Dancing Star

BY GLADYS MALVERN

Anna Pavlova (1881–1931) was one of the greatest dancers who ever lived. She was trained at the Imperial Ballet School in Moscow, which for 150 years has turned out dancers and choreographers of the highest caliber. Anna brought to this training the spirit, talent, and will of a champion.

NOT now was Anna awakened in the morning by the soft voice of her mother. No longer could she suit her own whims as to when and how many hours she would practice.

Girls who were first-year students wore plain brown cashmere dresses. Anna, pale and dark, knew that the color was unbecoming, but it didn't matter—nothing mattered but just to learn to dance. Even if your hair was curly, you were not permitted to wear it that way. It had to be brushed back, straight and tight from your forehead, braided in a single braid, and tied at the end with a black ribbon.

Promptly at eight there reverberated through the long corridors and spacious dormitories the tolling of a great bell. Anna's dormitory held fifty beds, and scarcely had the echoes of the bell died away before fifty girls, eyes still heavy with sleep, rushed down the corridor to the washroom. After washing in cold water they formed a neat line and marched to the governesses, who were ready and waiting with combs and brushes. When their hair was combed, they returned to the dormitory and put on their dancing dresses, then they made their beds. When all beds were made, they fell into a single line and marched toward the door.

At the door sat another blue-robed governess, sober-faced,

From *Dancing Star: The Story of Anna Pavlova,* by Gladys Malvern, copyright 1942 by Gladys Malvern. Published by Julian Messner, Inc.

hawk-eyed. As they reached her, each girl stopped and curtsied.

Then, without being told, the girl turned all the way around. The governess looked the student over. If all was neat and tidy, she motioned the girl forward and turned her gaze to the next in line. If a governess was not liked, Anna soon learned that secretly she was called a "toad."

In winter, over the dancing dress, the girls wore a wide, dark woolen shawl with a long fringe. During the second year, the student received another dress, this time of blue serge with a tight waist and gathered skirt. There was a fichu of stiff white lawn which was worn crossed in front, a black apron, white cotton stockings, black slippers. The only change that was made was on Sundays, when a white apron was worn.

Every girl was given one new dress each year. The new one was worn on Sundays, the old one on weekdays.

Once inspection was over, the line formed again, this time two by two. Religious training was considered highly important. The school had its own chapel, and into it now every pupil marched, girls and boys, juniors and seniors. The boys sat on one side, the girls on the other. After chapel, there was the line to be formed again—boys two by two, girls two by two—this time the march led to a great, wide hall where long tables were set and breakfast was served.

Here, also, boys and girls were separated. The girls had their own tables, the boys had theirs. Each table was presided over by a governess who kept a strict, all-seeing eye over table manners.

After breakfast, the inevitable line had to be formed, and the boys went to a large, airy room on the third floor, while the girls went to one like it on the second floor. This was a vast, sunny room with tall windows. It was furnished simply with a grand piano, numerous small sofas against the walls, floor-length mirrors. On its walls were paintings of Russian rulers.

That first day, Anna was nervous. Her thin hands were trembling and clammy. Already she had learned a few of the rules—that you were not supposed to talk to boys, and if you were caught at it, you would be punished; and that the younger girls must show great respect for the seniors. But now she was going to dance. This was the greatest moment of her life. Suppose she did so badly that they sent her away? Most of the girls had been there longer than she. They were confident and laughing. She was strange, alone, wildly afraid. There was a terrible moment when she wanted to run away, back to Mamasha, back to the security of the familiar, shabby little flat.

Gazing frantically about, her eyes panic-stricken, her heart making a tumult, she chanced to look up at a portrait on the wall. It was a large painting of the Empress Catherine II, who had reigned from 1762 to 1792. The eyes of the portrait were looking straight at little, quivering, frightened Anna Pavlova; the eyes were kindly, smiling, encouraging; they seemed to be saying, "Don't be afraid. Don't be afraid, little girl." Anna relaxed now. She felt that the good Empress was helping her, somehow.

Always the first class consisted of younger children. They lined up before the teacher and he gave them the five positions. "Now then," he spoke sternly, "we begin. So. In line, please.

"You! In line there! In line! What's your name?"

"M-my—name?"

"Yes, what is it?"

"It's Anna, sir. Anna Pavlova."

"Oh. So. Anna Pavlova. Well, when I say a line, I mean a straight line. Ah. *Now*. Watch me, all of you. This is the first position . . . this is the second position . . . You see? It's very easy. *Very* easy. *Now!* First position!"

Over and over it they went. Was *this* dancing? Heels together like this, toes straight out at the sides? What had this to do with dancing? Catching sight of herself in one of the long mirrors, Anna thought she looked funny.

"So. Now. Rest, young ladies! Second class!"

How easily these others took the positions! But this—this wasn't *dancing!* Oh, why had she ever left Mamasha?

"So. Rest, young ladies. First class again. In line, please! Yes. Now then. First position! No! No! Heels together. Feet straight. Shoulders straight. Hold up your back! Head up! Yes—now then! See, watch me! See? When the heels are together, the feet must form a perfectly straight line. You—what's the matter with you? What did you say your name was?"

"Anna Pavlova. It *hurts!*"

"Of course it does! You wanted to be a dancer, didn't you? Then you must learn not to be afraid of pain! You must teach your body to obey you. *You* will learn to govern your body—every muscle, every nerve, every cell! The dancer's body never governs the dancer! The dancer learns to be *master* of the body! We teach our bodies not to talk back to us! So . . . again! First position!"

For weeks after that first day, Anna continued to be nervous whenever she entered the dancing room, but always her frightened eyes would seek for the eyes of the Empress, and always the Empress sustained her.

At last came the day when the lesson did not end with the five positions.

"Now then! In line, please! So. So. *Sur les pointes!* On your toes! No, try again! One, two—up! *Sur les pointes!* Ah, it's so easy! See, like this! Again, now! *Sur les pointes!*"

Watching the master, Anna's eyes were bright and eager. At first she could not stand even for a second on her toes. But when her own class had an interval of rest and the older girls took their places, Anna's eyes focused upon the instructor. It seemed the most wonderful thing in the world just to balance oneself on the toes. Though she had tried very hard to accomplish this at home, she had never been able to do it. After watching the master with absorbed and breathless interest, she ran to one corner and worked by herself until the maestro called her again.

"In line, please! Up! *Sur les pointes!*" over and over again. At long last she learned to balance herself, and finally she was able to take a few steps on her toes.

At noon, with the sharp ringing of the midday bell, the dancing lessons ended. Again the children formed into line and returned to the dining room for lunch. After lunch, they were taken for a walk in care of the governess. Even now, however, they did not leave the school. In the courtyard was a small garden, and round and round they walked sedately for twenty minutes.

In winter the girls wore black coats lined with red fox, high boots, and bonnets of black silk. Returning from their walk, lessons began again. This time in fencing, languages, reading, writing, arithmetic, music and—what Anna loved best—make-up. The students entered the make-up room, which had lights around each mirror like a real dressing room in the theater, and little tables crowded with grease paint, rouge, brushes, powder.

At four o'clock another bell summoned them to dinner. After dinner they had a little interval of freedom, then more lessons. Sometimes some of the children were to appear in mob scenes at the theater, sometimes there were pupils' performances. These occasions were times of jubilee, for the nightly lessons ended, and rehearsals took their place. Supper was at eight, and by nine the younger ones were in bed.

In a surprisingly short time Anna began to feel completely at home in the school. Discipline was strict, but she thrived on it. Every spare moment when she could get by herself, she practiced. The place fairly buzzed with energy, ambition. Everyone had a single idea—not just to dance, but to dance *beautifully*. Few of the girls ever achieved the exalted position of ballerina, but it was something even to look forward to being a member of the *corps de ballet* and, after that, small parts.

When Anna had been there only a short time, she was allowed to act in a children's performance which was given for the Emperor and Empress. The performance passed smoothly. Their Majesties were delighted with all this budding talent.

When it was over, the children clustered about the Emperor, Alexander III. Anna dressed in her costume of a dryad, looked at him with awe. To her amazement, he caught up little Stanislava Belinskaya and kissed her. Anna, nervous, a bit hysterical with the excitement, began to cry.

Everyone tried to console her. "Don't cry, little girl!"

"What's the matter with that child?"

"Why is she crying?"

"Is she ill?"

"Speak up, Anna Pavlova! Tell us, why are you crying?"

"I—I want the Emperor to kiss *me!*" she sobbed.

The Grand Duke Vladimar took Anna in his arms. "There now, don't cry. I'll kiss you," he said laughingly.

"No! No! I want the *Emperor* to kiss me!"

The governess came and took her away. "Anna, aren't you ashamed? Behaving like that! The idea! Why, you're just a disgrace to the school!"

The child stopped crying instantly. A disgrace to the school! Would they send her away after this year was up? "O dear God," she prayed, "don't let them send me away!"

She would work harder, harder than ever. They must keep her! In the dormitory was an icon. She went up to it, knelt, crossed herself. "*Please* don't let them send me away!" she pleaded. "I'll be so *very* good. I'll work harder than ever! *Don't* let me be a disgrace to the school! And one day—maybe when I am *première danseuse*—Oh, let me make them *proud* of Anna Pavlova!"

There had been nights when Anna lay in her bed and sobbed very softly beneath the covers, sobbed with the ache of her legs, her body, but now her body was more yielding, more supple. Every day her steps on her toes grew firmer, more graceful.

Her feet were so built as to make toe dancing especially difficult; her toes were formed at a definite angle, the big toe unusually long, so that the entire weight of her body had to be supported by the muscles of that big toe alone. This meant that she had to work even harder than the others. She begrudged every minute that took her away from her practicing, begrudged the time, even, on Fridays when they were all taken to a Russian bath. They had only one bath a week. The bathhouse was on the grounds. It was always full of steam. There was a large stove in the middle, which bulged with red-hot coals. Attendants kept throwing water on the coals. When the pupils had sat in the steam for the required time, maids came with soap and water and scrubbed their bodies hard, so that their skin was red.

It was, as Mamasha had said, a new world. Names, heretofore unheard, were now spoken with reverence. The two principal ballerinas were Kschessinska and Preobrajensky. All the girls looked up to them, watched them, tried to imitate them. Then there were Legat, Guerdt, Rimski-Korsakov, Borodin, Drigo, Cecchetti, and Marius Petipa, who had been master of the Imperial Ballet School for over fifty years.

CULVER SERVICE

Anna Pavlova in 1913

Cecchetti taught a senior class of girls in dancing. Pavel Guerdt taught an advanced class in pantomime. He looked very young, little more than a boy, although it was said he was over forty. Everyone in the school adored these two men. As for the aged Petipa, he was universally feared. Petipa was French, and he had never learned to speak good Russian. His word was law. Then there was Christian Johannsen; he was very old, too, almost ninety, but he still taught dancing. He was blind in one eye, and his voice was sharp, rasping.

"Here! Here! Go over that again," he'd shout. "Don't think I can't see when you make mistakes! I can see very well indeed! I can see better with this one eye than you can see with two! Again, young ladies! Again! *Sur les pointes!*"

And now, another name was being heard—Diaghilev. Once

when the girls were returning from a rehearsal, being herded from the big bus into the building under the watchful eye of the blue-robed governess, Anna noticed a tall, fleshy, arrogant-looking young man with a trim little mustache and a monocle in his eye, swaggering into the executive offices on the first floor. One of the older girls nudged her excitedly. "That's Sergei Diaghilev! Oh, isn't he *handsome?*"

"Who's Sergei Diaghilev?" asked Anna.

"He's a rich man, comes from a very important and aristocratic family. He's enormously interested in the ballet and the opera, but mostly he's interested in painters, they say!"

"Oh," said Anna, suddenly losing interest, "then he isn't a dancer!"

The girls laughed. "Listen to her! Wouldn't you think dancers were the *only* important people in the world?"

On visiting days, of course, there was always Mamasha, and sometimes Grandmother would come with her. But the visits were not satisfactory. They had to meet in the big reception room, and as all the other pupils' families were there on the same day, the room was a confusion of many voices.

During vacations they still went to the little house in the country, and then, seated on the veranda, they could talk at ease. Anna, of course, could think of nothing but the school. She told her mother about the great wardrobe department where all the costumes were made, of the scenic department where men were painting new scenery all the time, of the visits of the Emperor and Empress. Emperor Alexander had died, but the pupils loved the new Emperor even more, if possible, than they had loved his father.

Madame Pavlova was thrilled to think that her daughter had sat at the same table with the Empress.

"My," she gasped, "what a great day that must be when Their Majesties come!"

"But there's no formality at all! The Emperor sits at the boys' table. Her Majesty sits at the head of our table, and she chats just as if she were one of us."

"You mean you talk to the Empress just as you'd talk to me?" asked Madame Pavlova incredulously.

"Oh yes. We call the Empress 'Mamasha' and we call the Emperor 'Papasha' (Little Father)."

"Well!" exclaimed the older woman, "never did I think to see the day when my daughter would be sitting at the same table with the Empress!"

"This year we're having the great Pierrina Legnani to teach us the Italian style dancing. For over ten years she has been *prima ballerina assoluta!*"

"Is she pretty?"

"No, not pretty. She's short. She's robust. Oh, I wish I could get fatter! I asked the doctor how I could get fatter, and he says I may take cod-liver oil and perhaps that will do it. Legnani can make thirty-two pirouettes on her toes! All the girls are trying to do thirty-two turns, but nobody has ever been able to."

Anna was scarcely ever ill any more, and though she was still thin and frail-looking, she had amazing strength. Sometimes when she outlined her day's activities at the school, her mother would exclaim, "I don't see how you do it! You're sure you feel quite well, Niura?"

"Oh yes!"

"And you're happy?"

"Happy!"

The first year, Anna had told her mother all about her teacher, Oblakov. Now she never mentioned him any more. The second year she had been promoted to the class of Ekayerina Vasem, who had been a former ballerina, and Christian Johannsen. And she could talk of nothing but her new teacher, Sokolava, who had once been one of the greatest dancers of all.

"Oh Mamasha, you'd love her! She's very fat and jolly, and her legs are all swollen—and she keeps telling us never to marry. This is the way she talks, Mamasha—" And Anna gave an imitation of the famous Eugenie Sokolava: "'Remember, Anna Pavlova, whenever you give a performance, wear light-colored stockings and lie all day with your feet up! Tch! Don't you know how to tie the knot of your dancing slipper yet? Tch! If you don't moisten the knot of your dancing slipper with spit, it will come undone! Yes, there's only one way to tie a shoe ribbon—moisten it with spit!'"

UNITED PRESS INTERNATIONAL

Anna Pavlova at rehearsal

Anna and her mother laughed at the clever imitation. Then Anna sobered. "Next year—oh, next year perhaps I shall be permitted to go into Guerdt's class—and Cecchetti's! Oh, I can hardly wait to study with Cecchetti!"

"And you say when your lessons are over, you girls go off praticing by yourselves? Goodness, do you never get tired of dancing, Niura?"

"I get tired dancing, but I think I shall never get tired *of* dancing, Mamasha. Yesterday they let us watch the rehearsal of the *corps de ballet*. The *corps de ballet* at the theater is two hundred dancers, Mamasha! When we finish our instruction, we become members of it. Then, after awhile, if we're good, we get small parts."

"I suppose you study the dancing of the stars?"

"Oh yes, as much as we can. We each choose one of the stars as a model and try to do as she does, but, Mamasha, this—lately it has occurred to me, this isn't *right!*"

"Not right? Why, of course, it's right!"

"No," said Anna seriously. "I used to watch Kschessinska all the time. She's so sweet to me, sometimes she stops and talks and asks me how I'm getting on; but it's not right for me to copy anyone else. I shan't do that, not I. If you copy someone else, you can only be like him, but one ought to be—like one's *self,* I think!"

Her mother looked at her daughter with new interest. Anna was fourteen now, and growing fast. There was an inner growth, too, quite apart from the body. Now her opinions were becoming more decided, she seemed so sure of herself. She was so certain of everything.

At the end of August, Anna must return to school. As one of the older girls, wearing the blue dress, the younger girls, brown-robed, paid her homage. Now, with other pupils of her own age, she was taken to the theater for Saturday matinees, given elocution lessons, permitted to attend the dress rehearsals of the operas. Although she did not suspect it, her progress was being watched. The graduation of promising pupils was much anticipated by the stars and directors. Girls of her age were impatient to finish, to leave the school behind, to wear other clothes. They talked of nothing but the parts they would play someday and how extravagantly they would live when they became ballerinas.

When Anna returned to the country with Mamasha again, she could talk only of two names—Pavel Guerdt and Taglioni. She had read all she could about Taglioni, who had died in 1884, when Anna was only two years old.

"Oh, if only I could have seen her!" she sighed. "You know about Taglioni, Mamasha, of course?"

"N-no—"

"Well, she was taught dancing by her father. She worked hard, I think perhaps even harder than I. Sometimes after her daily lesson she'd drop to the floor in a faint, and while she was still unconscious, they'd undress her and dress her in her street clothes!"

Mamasha gasped. "I had no idea being a dancer was such a hard life! It all seems so easy as one watches from the auditorium. I've seen how young men stand outside the stage door, sometimes even in the snow, for hours. And why? Why? Just to catch a glimpse of a dancer as she hurries to her carriage. And what do they see of the dancer? Nothing but a figure all bundled up in furs!"

At fifteen Anna could look back and smile at the time she had cried because she had not been kissed by the Emperor. She knew, these days, that she was not going to be a disgrace to the school.

When she walked among the fir trees, she counted the months until she would be graduated. Success, she thought, would bring complete happiness. Yes, she would ask nothing more of life than this—success.

If only she could study under Cecchetti! She was beginning to notice a slight difficulty with her back. She knew that it marred her technique. It worried her. Her teachers had not noticed this slight fault, but she, who even then insisted upon perfection, worked secretly to overcome what was not apparent to anyone else. This fault was so slight that there were times when even Anna was unaware of it. More and more her body served her will. There were times lately when she scarcely thought of her body at all as she danced, scarcely even thought of the steps, and could give herself up wholly to the rapture of expression.

She felt that she was getting so much from Guerdt, who taught pantomime. He was less strict than the other teachers. He had a shock of blond hair, and sometimes when his patience was exhausted he would run his hands through it until it stood up on end.

"Let others achieve the acrobatics, Anna Pavlova, these are not for you," he would say. "Your insteps are too delicate to stand the pressure. Don't try to make yourself like Legnani."

He gazed at her, this wisp of a girl with the sweet, oval face, her long hair brushed back from a beautifully modeled brow and falling in a braid down her back. His voice was kindly.

"You work harder than you need to. My poor child, how thin you are! You must eat more. You must get some flesh on those bones. Well, let us get started. Now, that scene we began yesterday. You must *feel* what you're doing! Look, here's how I'd play it. . . ." And later, "Yes, that's better. Your facial expression is fair, quite fair, but you aren't *feeling* it enough. See, you're in love, ardently in love. *Feel* it! Suffer . . . love . . . *Feel!* . . . No! Again . . . Yes, that's good. That's right. So. Yes. That was *splendid! Bravo, ma belle Anna!* Now then, we'll go right back over it from the beginning—and make it *better!*"

"You're graduating this year, Anna Pavlova?" asked little Tamara Karsavina timidly.

"Yes. I hope so."

"You must be very happy!"

"I am."

"Are you still taking cod-liver oil?"

"Yes. I can hardly bear the sight of it! And it isn't doing me a bit of good. I haven't gained a pound!"

It was the first week of Lent, and during this week all dancing lessons ceased. The girls went to Communion and fasted that week, attending church twice every day. In the evenings they had to sit around reading the lives of the saints. No other books were permitted them for these seven days. Anna was unable to concentrate on the lives of the saints. In such a little while now she would be graduated. She was living in anticipation. On leaving, each pupil was presented with a hundred rubles. With this she was supposed to buy clothes. How wonderful it would be when she and Mamasha went shopping together! So long she had worn the school uniform. Now, soon, there would be street dresses, evening dresses, smart hats. Shopkeepers would be eager to give credit. She and Mamasha would have a little apartment of their own.

How often she had watched other girls on the day of their graduation! She would get up very early, and braid her hair, and put on the blue school dress with its fichu. Then she and the other girls of the graduating class would go to church, where thanks would be offered.

After this, there would be a hasty lunch. Then they would go to the dancing room and there, in the presence of relatives and teachers, they would be given diplomas. The priest would make a long speech, and then it would be over. There remained only to say good-by to the directress, the governesses—yes, even the "toads." There would be tearful good-bys to the maids, the younger girls, good-by to the music room, a little prayer of thanksgiving before the icon in the dormitory—and she would be free!

How long ago it seemed when she had stood there under the picture of Catherine II and struggled to master the first position—heels together, toes turned outward to form a perfectly straight line. How long ago it seemed when she had regarded some older girl, some girl approaching graduation, with the exorbitant respect, the reverence, with which now the little Karsavina was watching *her.*

Nowadays, the new director of the Imperial theaters, Prince Serge Wolkonsky, a tall, thin, dignified figure, came often to watch her at her lessons. She had never seen the former director, Vsevolojsky. Scarcely any of the pupils had even laid an eye on him, but with Wolkonsky it was different. You felt his interest, and it was encouraging, it goaded her on to even greater efforts. He was often present, he seemed even to make a point of being there, during her lessons with Guerdt twice a week. He would watch as Guerdt acted a scene from a certain ballet, and sometimes he would smile a little as she tried to do as Guerdt did. Even the great and charming Kschessinska, rich and powerful, smiled at her with a new warmth, something close to camaraderie.

"You are doing well, Anna Pavlova," Kschessinska had said only yesterday. "I shall be present at your debut."

At last, at last, it was all actually happening just as it had happened in anticipation. She and Mamasha were permitted to go shopping, feeling enormously rich and important with a hundred rubles to spend on clothes. And finally, there was Anna Pavlova, looking even younger than her seventeen years, receiving her diploma, listening to the speech of the priest, sobbing a little as she pressed the hands of the maids, and actually kissing the "toads."

It was all over now. She had changed from the blue uniform and was going home to a new apartment Mamasha had all ready and waiting. Seven hard years of training were over. In a week or two she would be entering into service in the *corps de ballet.*

The maid, who helped her on with her new coat, spoke respectfully. "You are wanted in the office of the director."

"I?" asked Anna. "You are sure?"

"Yes. I was to tell you. You are to go there right away."

Wondering, Anna went toward the sanctum sanctorum. What did it mean? Had she done something wrong? This was unusual, unprecedented. As she entered the palatial office, Wolkonsky did not arise from behind the desk. He looked up from some papers, stroked his well-groomed beard. His eyes were kindly.

She made a little curtsy before him, but she was so filled with apprehension that she could not speak.

"You have done well, Anna Pavlova," he began in a low, cultured voice, "so well, indeed, that we have decided that on the first of June, here at the Marinsky, you are to make your debut in a small part of a ballet which will be chosen later. It may be that you will play Ines in *Les Saisons,* or Gulnare in *Le Corsaire,* or Sister Anne in *Barbe-bleu*–"

Anna stared at him breathlessly, her dark eyes aglow. "Y-you mean, I—I'm to—have a part? I'm not to enter the *corps de ballet?*"

"In your case, we have decided to make the exception!"

"Oh."

"That is all."

He returned to his papers. Confused, wordless, she curtsied again and left the office. Never in her life had Anna Pavlova been so happy. She was to have a part! She would be earning seven hundred and twenty rubles a year! Life was moving swiftly. Success lay ahead–waiting. She had come to another turning point. At last she was a dancer! Dancers in Russia were among the truly important people of the realm, pampered, catered to, fêted, toasted.

Would Wolkonsky, she wondered, succeed in his effort to modify the extremely short ballet skirt? Was it true that Sergei

Diaghilev was to have the production of the *Imperial Theater's Year Book*? Was it a fact that he and Wolkonsky were quarreling? And yet, how could that be when it was rumored that Wolkonsky had put into Diaghilev's hands the production of the ballet *Sylvia*? Yes, she was living in a world of change. Life had never been so wonderful, so exciting.

From now on, on ballet nights, an Imperial carriage with a coachman would call for her, deliver her at the theater, bring her home again afterward. This service was accorded all the dancers. How proud her mother and grandmother would be!

As she and Mamasha were leaving the school, Madame Kschessinska drove up in her carriage. She gave Anna a gay smile, walked over to her, patted her on the shoulder.

"I congratulate you, Anna Pavlova, upon receiving a small part instead of beginning service as one of the two hundred members of the *corps de ballet!*"

"You—you have heard about it, Madame?"

"Of course. It has been discussed for some time. Russia is hearing, these days, of new names in the ballet—Sedova, Trefilova, Fokine—and soon—ah, soon now it will be hearing another name, eh? Soon it will hear about—*Anna Pavlova!*"

The great ballerina laughed, drew her sable cape closer about her, and entered the building.

"Anna!" gasped Mamasha, "is it true? You are to have a part?"

"Yes, yes, it's true, Mamasha."

"But this—this is wonderful, unheard of! Are you—are you not—a—little frightened that it should happen so soon?"

"Frightened? No. Surprised—yes; but frightened, not at all. I shall be a success!"

"How can you be so *sure* of success? Ah, Niura, you must not set your hopes too high, my dove!"

"And why not?"

"Because—dreams are seldom realized. One should learn to be content, to be satisfied. That is wisdom."

"Is it?" asked Anna.

She had always thought her mother very wise, but now she could not believe that Mamasha was so wise, after all. No, surely—ah, surely, it was not wise to be satisfied! How, if one were satisfied, could one always go on, growing, achieving,

CULVER SERVICE

Anna Pavlova dancing *The Swan*

working toward the goal of perfection? And why should one make oneself be satisfied with anything *less* than perfection? Did anyone think, for instance, that she, Anna Pavlova, would be satisfied with merely playing small parts? Oh yes, there were those who were satisfied to spend their lives in the chorus—but not she! No, never. One day she would be even *greater* than Kschessinska, than Preobrajensky, than Legnani. One day, perhaps, she might even be as great—as great as—*Taglioni!*

She had dreamed greatness, and she would go on with her dreams. Seemingly, a voice, as old as the earth, spoke within her: Trust to your dreams, dream nobly. Hold fast to your dreams, dream *boldly.* Does it seem too good to be true, this dream of yours? It is God's promise. Trust to it and live for it and work toward it. *This* is wisdom! Work. Action. Action in the planet. Action in the atom. Send your dreams a-winging—up—up—up—until they partake of the glory of the sun! Keep your vision high. Keep your eye fixed upon beauty, upon brightness, upon achievement, upon perfection—for this is life—and this is God!

Older ones, she thought, like Grandmother and Mamasha, they had long since stopped dreaming, dreaming high and clear and true.

"I shall be a great dancer," she announced aloud.

"What? What did you say? I didn't hear you?"

"I said I shall be a great dancer."

"I know. I understand. That is your dream, your hope, your ideal. It's all very fine and very brave; but—there are things that may come up that will keep you from your goal. Once *I* was very sure, too. But things interfered. Things happened."

"I shall not *let* them happen!" declared Anna Pavlova.

No, spoke the voice within her—no, you must not, not ever. This desire for perfection has in it the glory of the Divine. The dream of greatness, the stimulating dream, the lofty aim, the shimmering ideal—it will keep you always as wondrously alive as you are this minute, for it is beautiful and it is real. *Laugh* at Mamasha, at all those who say it is foolish to dream. Laugh at them—or pity them.

Success. What was it? What was it, after all? Back in the years when she was very young—fifteen, sixteen—she used to walk among the fir trees and think how happy she would be when she was successful. But what *was* success? What was it, *really?*

All the way home she thought about it. Success, this thing called success—what was it, exactly? All people want it, she thought, and some want it achingly, desperately. Most people think it means money, acclaim, power. But does it? Does it mean only that?

Success. Why, it was only having people *love* the thing you do!

"Why are you so silent, Anna? What are you thinking of?" Mamasha interrupted Anna's thoughts.

"Success. I was thinking of success. I was thinking—"

"Yes?"

"That—that if people aren't *loving* the thing I do, then no matter how much money I have, or how much people bow down to me, I'm not a success—and, in my heart, I'll know it!"

LOU GEHRIG

The Boy at Wrigley Field

BY FRANK GRAHAM

Lou Gehrig (1903–1941) batted a baseball with a power that is rare even in the major leagues. And he lived with a kindness, warmth, and humility that is rare in people. Young Lou, playing ball for the New York High School of Commerce, never imagined that one day he would take his place in Baseball's Hall of Fame.

ON a June day in 1920, at Wrigley Field, Lane Technical High School of Chicago was playing the High School of Commerce from New York in a game for the inter-city baseball championship. Lane scored four runs in the first inning, but the Commerce boys hammered back, and by the time the teams reached the ninth inning the score was tied at 8-8. Commerce filled the bases, and a wide-shouldered, thick-limbed kid stepped to the plate and hit the first ball pitched to him over the right-field fence.

After the game the Commerce coach beamed at the newspapermen who had rushed down to the dressing room.

"That was nothing," he said. "He hit a ball further than that out of Dexter Park in Brooklyn last week."

But it was something. It was a tremendous feat for a schoolboy to hit a ball out of a major league park, and that night for the first time the name of Lou Gehrig went out over the wires that stretch across the country. One writer hailed him as the schoolboy Babe Ruth. And that was the first time Gehrig's name ever was coupled with that of the Babe.

The stories were read with interest by college baseball coaches, by major and minor league managers and scouts. From that day the boy's path was marked clearly. Three years later it was to lead him to the Yankee Stadium.

As the years unwound before him he followed that path to heights of which as a boy he could not have dreamed, and when death, in a swift race, overtook him on June 2, 1941, James M. Kahn was to write of him in the *New York Sun:*

"Lou Gehrig was the greatest ball player ever produced in New York. He was one of the greatest ball players ever produced anywhere. For years a teammate of Babe Ruth, he was many times nominated to become the Babe's successor. But he was nothing like Ruth. He did not have the Babe's booming Falstaffian personality, nor the Babe's capacity for capturing the imagination of the crowd and electrifying it.

"Gehrig was quiet, somewhat shy, and sincerely modest. He was conscientious, uncomplaining, and persevering. He was not a natural athlete and had to work laboriously to become a great ball player. So it was, too, with his popularity. He was not a natural crowd pleaser. But just as his consistently fine ball playing, day after day, wore down the opposition and steadily drove him upward to a place among the greatest players of all time, so did his fine qualities, his character and his courage in the face of adversity, earn him a place in the affections of the public. When he retired from baseball he did so with the esteem and the sympathy of the whole country."

Only thirty-eight years old when he died, Lou had had a crowded and exciting life. Millions had seen him smash out home runs or make dazzling plays at first base as he took part in the astounding total of 2,130 consecutive games. To other millions, although they never had seen him, he was a familiar figure because they had heard or read so much about him. His travels covered this country, Europe, and the Orient. His salary and his share of world-series gate receipts had yielded about $400,000. The by-products of his career—endorsements, syndicated articles under his signature, a motion picture in which he was starred, radio broadcasts—had netted him another $100,000.

Fame and wealth touched him lightly and could not mar his simplicity nor the virtues with which he was endowed. When death claimed him he had become a symbol of decency and kindliness and courage, and this surprised him because he had not meant to become a symbol and never could quite understand the regard in which he was held not only by baseball fans but also by those who would not go across the street to see a ball game.

The child of Henry and Christina Gehrig, natives of Germany —there had been one child in the family before him and two came after him, but they died in infancy and he had no recollection of them—he was born at 1994 Second Avenue, near 102nd Street, on June 19, 1903, and was christened Henry Louis. When he was a small boy his parents, after several preliminary moves, settled at 170th Street and Amsterdam Avenue, and there, within sight and sound of the park where the New York American League team, known then as the Highlanders, first played, he grew up, attended elementary school, and learned to play baseball, football, and soccer on corner lots.

The neighborhood has changed greatly in recent years. Where the Highlanders played, the tall buildings of the Medical Center stand. Apartment houses, row on row and block on block, have crowded out the sandlots. But in those days there was room for a boy to play, and Lou played tirelessly at his games. Baseball from the first spring thaw to the first turning of the leaves. Then football and soccer.

"The boy must grow big and strong," his father said.

"And he must have an education," his mother said.

"Yes, an education. He must work hard and study and learn to be . . . what, Lou? What would you like to be?"

"An engineer," the boy said.

"An engineer? What kind of engineer?"

"I don't know. . . . An engineer. I want to build bridges and things."

His father nodded.

"Yes," he said. "Yes, an engineer."

"Then you must study, Lou," his mother said. "You must go to high school and to college."

"But he must play, too," his father said. "He must be strong."

His father belonged to a *Turnverein*, and there he took Lou, and the boy was fascinated by the parallel bars, the horses, the rings, the pulleys, the weights, the wrestling mats. On winter afternoons he exercised there and soon became one of the best of the younger gymnasts. He had found something to do between the end of the football season and the coming of spring. His young body was being hardened and developed.

Meanwhile, things were going badly at home. His father, worn by years of toil as a wrought iron worker, had become virtually an invalid. He could not work for more than a few days at a time. There were weeks, even months, when he couldn't work at all. Lou wanted to leave school and go to work, but his mother wouldn't hear of it.

"No," she said. "You must have a college education."

And so she assumed the burden of support for the family. She cooked, sewed, cleaned, became caretaker of the house in which they lived. Lou helped her in the morning before going to school, helped her again in the evening before doing his lessons. She was frugal and wise and spent her small income carefully, so that if they had few luxuries, they always managed to have plenty of plain but nourishing food. One of the boy's favorite dishes was pickled eels—pickled by his mother. In later years when baseball writers asked him what was the source of his power as a hitter, he would laugh and say:

"Pickled eels!"

And once when the whole Yankee team was in a hitting slump, he arrived at the clubhouse with six jars of pickled eels from his mother's shelves. He was half in jest, half in earnest, as he insisted that all the players eat some of them just before the game. Pickled eels had become almost a superstition with him, and his faith in their efficacy was heightened when the Yankees emerged from their slump that afternoon and clouted an unhappy White Sox pitcher out of the box.

Clothing was no problem to him in the lean days of his youth. All he needed was underwear, socks, shirt, coat, a pair of pants, and stout shoes. In the summer he discarded the coat. He never wore a vest, an overcoat, or a hat. His mother, naturally concerned about his appearance, often wished aloud that she could afford more and better clothing for him, but he would laugh and say:

"What's the matter with me? I look all right, don't I?"

He asked for little, was content with what he had, and was worried only over his father's condition and the fact that his mother had to work to support him.

"Never mind," he used to say. "I'll get a job one of these days, and then you can quit work and we can have the best doctors in New York for Pop."

He had entered the High School of Commerce down on Sixty-fifth Street, just off Columbus Avenue, when his mother and father obtained employment in the Sigma Nu fraternity house at Columbia University, his mother as cook, his father as handy man.

The new job meant long hours for Lou and his mother and father. They would get up early in the morning and ride down to the house on the Amsterdam Avenue car. Lou would help to prepare breakfast and then go on down to school. In the evening, he would return to the house, wait on table, clear it when dinner was over, and then help to wash and dry the dishes. Then they would go home to bed. His studies were becoming increasingly difficult for him, since he was not a brilliant student but must work hard at them. He would do his homework at the fraternity house or on the street cars.

He was popular with the fraternity members. "The Little Dutch Boy," they called him. They discovered that he not only liked to play ball but played it very well. On spring evenings, when his mother could spare him, they invited him to play with them on South Field. A few years later he was to star on that field both as a baseball and a football player. One day he was to drive a ball out of the field and across 116th Street, where it struck on the steps of the library.

But that was ahead of him. Now he was a student at Commerce and, between and after classes, one of the school's outstanding athletes. He wasn't the best player on the baseball team—that distinction was had by Bunny Bonura, the short stop—but he was the most versatile, pitching, playing first base and the outfield, and he was the best and most powerful hitter on the team. He was the fullback on the football team, played on the soccer and basketball teams, and could outdo the other boys in the gymnasium.

On a fall day in 1920 he twice humbled Commercial High

School of Brooklyn on Commercial Field. In the morning he kicked the decisive goal in a soccer game, and in the afternoon he threw a 40-yard forward pass for the touchdown that won the game for Commerce, 9 to 6.

"He was the greatest athlete I ever coached," Harry Kane was to say years afterward. "He was almost as big then as he was when he was at the height of his career with the Yankees, and he had the same team spirit and eagerness to win. It was a pleasure to coach him, for he constantly wanted to learn and improve his play, and when a weakness cropped up in his play he worked at it until he had eradicated it.

"For instance, when I first saw him, which was in his junior year, and I had him in both baseball and football, his main weakness in baseball was his inability to hit left-handed curve ball pitching. We set to work together, and after a few weeks of practice, day in and day out, he completely overcame his fault."

The lot back of the school was too small for use as a practice field. The home grounds were at the Catholic Protectory, away up in the east Bronx, and the team practiced there or in Central Park. It was a long and tedious journey from the school to the Protectory, for in those days the transportation facilities were not as adequate as they are now. But the boys didn't complain. The trip complicated Gehrig's daily routine because, of course, he had to come all the way back to the Sigma Nu house when the practice or the game was over.

One day, when a game was dragging into extra innings, he obviously was fretful, and Kane said:

"Don't worry. We'll get them."

"I know we will," Lou said. "I'm not worried about that. I'm worried because I'll be late and won't be able to help my mother with the dinner."

"That was the only time I ever heard him complain," Kane said. "But he wasn't worried long. He broke up the game in the next inning."

The trip to Chicago for the game with Lane Tech was the greatest adventure the boys on the Commerce team ever had had. Few of them had been as much as a hundred miles from

UNITED PRESS INTERNATIONAL

Lou Gehrig on the High School of Commerce football team

New York. Lou, for one, never had been west of Newark or north of Poughkeepsie.

When the boys first heard they had been selected to play this game, they crowded about Kane, hammering him with questions, for Kane had seen a good deal of the world, on his own and as a soldier in France during the World War, and they assumed he knew all the answers. As a matter of fact, he knew most of them. But nobody could know the answers to all the questions that boys could ask in a spot like that.

Harry did his best. He told them what it was like to sleep in a Pullman and eat in a dining car. And how they must be careful to look after their luggage and what they should take with them. The last was no problem to most of the boys. Least of all was it a problem to Lou. But when the great day came, Mrs. Gehrig packed his little bag for him—toothbrush, comb and brush, underwear, socks, and shirts.

Several hundred boys were at the Grand Central to see the team off. And it was just a team. Nine kids, with their coach. The rooters were very enthusiastic.

"Knock 'em off!" they were yelling. "Hey, Lou, when you go to bat, show 'em where you live!"

"Good luck, Al!"

"Give 'em that old fast ball, Eli!"

"Show 'em how, Bunny! Show 'em how!"

At last, as the shouts died away behind them, the train moved slowly out of the station and the kids sat there in their car looking at each other, scarcely believing they actually were on their way to Chicago: Eli Jacobs, the pitcher; Al McLaughlin, the catcher; Gehrig, the first baseman; Al Rosamondo, the second baseman; Bunny Bonura, the short stop; Sewell Johnson, the third baseman; and the outfielders, Schacht (a brother of Al Schacht, former pitcher and now nationally famous as a baseball clown), Stark, and Sammy Strum.

The first phase of the great adventure, after the exciting departure and the feel of the wheels turning under the train, was dinner in the big dining car. That evening before they retired there were two more thrills. Word that the team was aboard had spread through the train, and the boys had two visitors, distinguished in two widely separated fields: William Howard Taft, former President of the United States and at the time Justice of the Supreme Court; and Joe Frisco, the stuttering comedian.

Justice Taft joked with the boys, told them numerous experiences he had had in and out of office and in his wide travels and, before bidding them good night, wished them luck in their game. And then Frisco came in and had them rolling in the aisles with his gags and comic soft-shoe dances.

Then came the final adventure of the day—going to bed in Pullman berths, and lying there in the dark as the train rushed through the night, its whistle screeching as it approached a grade crossing or a station.

Wonder if Lou, lying in his berth, unable to sleep at first because of the excitement that had been crowded into the last few hours, looked ahead and saw, somehow, the endless miles he was destined to travel in Pullman cars, up and down and across the country?

When they reached Chicago, there was the further excitement of going to a hotel and being conducted to their rooms—two boys to a room—and then a sightseeing tour of the great city on Lake Michigan. The boys looked upon the lake unbelieving. A lake, to them, had been a small body of water such as they had seen in Central Park or on some summer journey to Long Island or New Jersey or the Catskills. This—why this looked like the ocean.

And then the ball game.

"I never thought we'd win it, the way it began," Harry Kane has said. "We couldn't score in the first inning, and when they went to bat, I thought the game had broken wide open. Eli Jacobs, really a fine schoolboy pitcher, must have had stage fright and was wild, and then when he did manage to get the ball over the plate he didn't have his usual stuff on it and they hit it hard. To make matters worse, McLaughlin, running back for a foul fly, wrenched his left ankle badly. Lane got four runs and there we were—four runs behind in the first inning, our pitcher staggering all over the box and our catcher so lame he hardly could walk.

"I should have taken both Jacobs and McLaughlin out of the game, but I couldn't. We had only the nine players with us. So there was nothing to do but keep them in there. McLaughlin became so lame as the innings went on that I almost had to carry him up to the plate and back at the start of their half of an inning or when it was his turn to bat. But he was a dead game kid and hung in there and did the best he could and was valuable because he kept the whole team on its toes. Meanwhile, Jacobs had settled down and was pitching good ball, although Lane tagged him for four more runs—one at a time—between the first inning and the eighth. And then we started to hit, and by the end of the eighth we had them tied at 8-8, and now I knew we were going to win.

"You may not believe me, but I really knew in my heart what

was going to happen when we started to hit in the ninth—and got the bases filled—and Gehrig walked up to the plate. He had played a great game and made a couple of hits before that, and he always was a great kid in a pinch, and I would have bet my life he was going to slough one this time.

"'Go and hit one out of the park!' I said to him.

"It was almost an order, I felt so confident he could do it. When he did—and what a wallop that was—our kids went crazy—and I don't believe I was exactly sane at the moment.

"Of course, we still had to get them out in their half of the inning. But that was easy. They were licked and they knew it, and we were so high we could have got anybody out. One-two-three—bing! The ball game was over."

The reception the Commerce players received when they returned to New York surpassed anything a schoolboy team ever had experienced in the big town. Gehrig, of course, was the main hero, and the rooters at the station—practically the entire student body—carried him from the gate to the exit, where cabs awaited them. They were driven to the school, where classes had been suspended for the morning, and there was an uproarious demonstration in the auditorium.

It was Lou's first brush with fame that extended beyond the confines of the New York high school circuit. He had heard a crowd, even though it had come to cheer for the opposing team, roar for him in Chicago. His name had been flashed over the wires from one end of the country to the other and had appeared in countless newspapers, from the great metropolitan dailies to the papers in the smallest towns reached by the press associations' wires. His name had been linked, however lightly, with Babe Ruth, the new home run king who had come to New York from Boston that year and was thrilling crowds at the Polo Grounds and wherever the Yankees played.

The narrow circumstances to which he had been born and in which he had lived were beginning to break and fall about him. He was emerging from the obscurity which he had accepted as his fate.

He was excited, naturally. But the modesty and the firmness of character that had been bred into him and nurtured by his parents kept him on a level keel. So he could return, the next

UNITED PRESS INTERNATIONAL

Lou Gehrig working out with Columbia

day, to his studies and to the chores he did to help his mother and father to make a living for all of them and keep their little home together.

"I hope he has sufficient credits to enter the university," Bobby Watt had said the day he and Buck O'Neill discovered Lou as a football player.

He hadn't. However, within a few days after his graduation from Commerce he was admitted to the Department of Extension at Columbia, there to prepare himself for admission as a freshman in the fall. From the beginning he proved that he was an eager and serious student. His progress was rapid. There was no doubt that he would pass the extension course and the college board examinations.

As a student in the extension school, he was not eligible for participation in freshman athletics, but with the approach of the baseball season he asked Andy Coakley, the baseball coach, for permission to work out with the squad, volunteering to be of any help that he could, such as pitching in batting practice or shagging flies for the hitters. Coakley was not only willing but glad to grant the permission. He had heard about Lou as a high-school player. He liked the look of him and the size of him. He liked him even better when he saw him slamming the ball around South Field. Here, obviously, was varsity material in the making.

Lou was supremely happy that spring. He was at Columbia, he was progressing in his studies, and he was playing ball every day. He didn't like to withdraw from the field at the start of a game—Andy, after one good look at him, had told him to forget about the freshman and to work out with the varsity—but, after all, a fellow couldn't have everything right away. Things worth while were worth waiting for. His time would come. Meanwhile, it was great to be out there working with the varsity, hitting with the regulars in batting practice, working out at first base in the fielding practice after the regulars were through and just before the game started.

The course ended in June. The summer stretched ahead. It might seem long to him, but at the end of it he would be a regular freshman, eligible for the freshman football team. . . .

One day that summer Bobby Watt was in his office and Buck O'Neill called him on the telephone.

"Where's Gehrig?" he asked.

Bobby was surprised.

"Gehrig?" he said. "Why, I don't know. Home, I suppose. Working at some summer job. Why?"

O'Neill was silent for a moment. And then:

"You haven't heard anything?"

"Heard anything? What would I hear?"

"Well," Buck said, "I hear he is playing with the Hartford club of the Eastern League under the name of Lewis."

"What!"

"Take it easy," Buck said. "I don't know that it's true. But that's what I have heard. And, naturally, I am concerned because I want that young man to play football for me."

"So do I," Bobby said. "And I want him to play baseball for us, too. Who told you this?"

"A friend of mine."

"Have your friend call me," Bobby said. "I want to run this thing down as quickly as possible."

The friend called within an hour.

"Do you know this to be true?"

"I do."

"How do you know?"

"I saw him."

"When?"

"The other day."

"And you're sure you're not mistaken?"

"I talked to him."

"Thank you," Bobby said. "Thank you very much."

The next morning Bobby was on an early train for Hartford. He never had been to the Connecticut capital. Arriving there, he didn't know where to go to look for the boy until, of course, it was game time. He was strolling about and came to the park in front of the capitol. There was Lou, sitting on a bench, head down, looking very disconsolate.

Bobby sat down next to him but said nothing. After a few moments Lou looked up. His eyes widened.

"Bobby!" he said.

"What are you doing here?" Bobby asked.

Lou was very uncomfortable.

"Playing ball."

"With the Hartford club?"

"Yes."

"Under the name of Lewis?"

"Yes."

"Why? Don't you know that you probably have forfeited your amateur status and that you will not be able to play for Columbia?"

"No!" the boy cried. "No! They told me it would be all right!"

"Who told you that?"

"The—the—the baseball people. They said college players could play summer ball and it wouldn't affect their status as amateurs. They said all college players do it. And we need the money at home . . . and I believed them . . . and I thought it would be a good way to put in the summer. But I don't like it. I miss Mom and Pop. I . . . I guess I'm just homesick."

"How did all this come about, Lou? Who told you about this job in the first place?"

As they sat there on the bench, Lou told his side of the story.

He was leaving South Field after the last game of the season, he said, when a man approached him. A very pleasant chap. In his sixties, probably. White hair, close-cropped white mustache, ruddy-cheeked, smiling, immaculate.

"You're Lou Gehrig, aren't you?" he asked.

"Yes, sir."

"My name is Irwin," he said. "Arthur Irwin. I am a baseball scout. I've seen you working out here . . . I understand you're not eligible for the team . . . and I like your work very much."

"Thank you," Lou said. "That's very nice to hear."

"Think you'd like to play professional ball?"

Lou laughed.

"Well, someday, perhaps," he said. "But I guess that day is a long way off. I want to go through college first."

"Of course," Irwin said. "But there is no harm in getting around and having somebody look at you. It might help a lot when you get ready to play professionally. . . . How would you like to work out with the Giants for a few days?"

"The Giants! The New York Giants?"

Irwin smiled.

"Exactly," he said. "I'd like to have John McGraw see you. I have an idea he might be interested in you."

The thought was exciting. John McGraw! The Giants!

"Why," he said, "I hardly know . . ."

"Suppose," Irwin said, "you meet me at the Polo Grounds at one o'clock tomorrow."

Lou nodded.

"All right," he said. "I'll be there, Mr. Irwin."

For four days he worked out on the Polo Grounds. John McGraw scarcely looked at him. The Giants were going badly, and McGraw was rasping at his players and had no time for a nondescript kid that Arthur Irwin had dragged in from some college field. McGraw didn't know what college field and didn't care.

"How do you like him, Mac?" Irwin asked at the end of the fourth day.

"Who?" McGraw demanded.

"That college fellow."

"Get him out of here," McGraw said.

"You mean you don't like him?"

"I don't even know what he looks like," McGraw said. "Here I am trying to get this team of mine straightened out, and you come around bothering me with a college player. I've got enough incompetents in Giant uniforms cluttering up the field without you bringing in another one."

"There is nothing around here for you right now," Irwin told the boy. "McGraw hasn't had a chance to look at you. He's too busy with his team."

"That's all right with me," Lou said. "I've had a chance to look at him . . . and listen to him. I wouldn't want to play ball for him."

Irwin shook his head.

"You've got him wrong," he said. "McGraw is one of the grandest men I've ever known—and I've known him for years. We used to play ball together, and in one way or another I have been associated with him ever since. You just happened to catch him at a bad time. Ask any of his ball players about him. He may yell at them when things are going bad, but there isn't one of them who wouldn't do anything in the world for him because they know he is the best friend they have."

"That may be true," Lou said. "But I don't like him."

Irwin laughed.

"Scared you a little, did he?"

"Maybe."

If McGraw had been indifferent to Lou, Irwin had been increasingly impressed with him.

"Want to go to Hartford?" he asked.

"What for?"

"To play ball, of course. With the Hartford team of the Eastern League."

"Wouldn't that bar me from playing college ball?"

Irwin shrugged.

"If it would," he said, "I guess there wouldn't be any ball players left in the colleges. Most college players play summer ball to make a little money to pay for their tuition and books or to help out at home. . . . Could you use some money?"

"I should say I could."

"You're in," Irwin said. "Meet me at the Grand Central in the morning."

And so, with the assurance that everything was all right he had gone to Hartford and joined the ball club. But he didn't like it there, and he was homesick.

"There," he said. "That's the story."

"All right," Bobby said. "Now I'll tell you what you do. You tell them this afternoon that you're through. Then get your clothes together and come back to New York tonight with me."

"Am I through as a college player?" Lou asked anxiously.

"I don't know," Bobby said. "That isn't up to me. But you can bet I will go to bat for you and do everything I can to see that you're not ruled out."

On his return to New York, Watt took Lou's case up with the Columbia Athletic Council.

"At first glance," he said, "the boy's action may seem indefensible. He did go to Hartford and he did play with a professional team. However, I am convinced, having heard his story, that he believed this was quite the ordinary thing among college ball players. I also am convinced that if he had thought otherwise, he never would have taken the job.

"Ignorance of the law, they say, is no excuse. I don't believe that should be applied indiscriminately. I ask you to bear in mind that he never has taken part in athletics at Columbia and never has had occasion to familiarize himself with our rules."

He could see by the faces of the men around the board that he wasn't getting anywhere in particular.

"All right, then," he said. "Now, let me put it this way. It isn't sound technically or legally but here's what I think: I think that here is a fine, decent kid who has set his heart on playing baseball and football at Columbia. That for him to do so will enrich his life. And that for us to prevent him from doing so may embitter him. Good heavens, gentlemen, what did he do? He spent a couple of weeks in Hartford, he played a few games, he earned a few dollars that were badly needed at home. It isn't as though he were a regular professional ball player who was trying to put something over on us—or whom we were trying to use to put something over on our rivals. He has broken the college rules, granted that he is no better—and no worse—for having played those few games than he was when he walked off South Field in June. He's just a big, swell kid with his life before him and his way to make, and I don't think we would be serving a good end by making him pay for this mistake by forfeiting his entire college athletic career."

Now he could see he was on the right track. The members of the council began to discuss the case among themselves, to turn to him and ask him questions.

"Mind," he said, "it is my idea that we shouldn't deprive him of his entire career at Columbia. I do think we must take some action against him but that we must not be too severe. Here's what I propose: Let me write to all the colleges with whom we have baseball and football relations—and to any others with whom we might enter into negotiations during the next couple of years—tell them the truth, and ask them if they will permit us to play Gehrig against them provided we bar him from competition in his freshman year, which will start in September, and from baseball in his sophomore year. In other words, that his eligibility be suspended until the fall of 1922."

It seemed a reasonable solution. A compromise with the rules, of course. But a compromise prompted by the undeniably fine qualities of the boy involved. A vote of the council resulted in its unanimous adoption.

Watt communicated with Columbia's athletic rivals. The replies were prompt. Every one of them was to the effect that Columbia had handled a difficult situation sensibly and that Lou would be welcomed on the field of play in the fall of 1922—or before that, if Columbia wanted to lighten the sentence.

So, through his freshman year and the spring of his sophomore year Lou was permitted to work out in daily practice with the teams but had to remain on the sidelines when the games started. Naturally, there were times when it irked him to have to sit by when he felt it was his turn to hit or when there seemed to be a spot in which he should be carrying the ball. But he never complained.

He realized belatedly that he had made a sorry mistake

when, having been approached by Arthur Irwin—who (if he has been made to appear as the villain in the piece) was no villain at all but a hearty and pleasant old chap who merely did as any other scout would have done in the circumstances—he had not sought advice from Coakley or Watt. He realized with dismay how narrowly he had missed being banished from South Field so far as varsity competition was concerned, and he reflected that if he hadn't had a friend at court, he would not have had a chance at a university with a deserved reputation for strict adherence to the eligibility code.

So he never complained but practised faithfully—just as faithfully as he would have done had he been in the regular baseball and football line-ups. He had become a familiar figure on the campus among those who followed the athletic teams closely. They knew and liked this big, wavy-haired, smiling kid, who some day would reap honors on the baseball field and the gridiron for Columbia. And although he had first attracted attention there as a football player, it was as a baseball player that they knew him chiefly now. This was partly because they saw more of him in that role—secret practice screened most of his skill as a football player—and partly because he seemed to get more enjoyment from playing baseball than from football. But mostly it was a result of his daily practice on the diamond—he was the first out and the last in, and as the twilight gathered over the campus, he frequently could be found playing with groups of students who liked the game but were not sufficiently skilled in it to make the squad. He constantly was improving.

This was an accurate forecast of his competitive career at Columbia once it got under way. Contrary to a rather widely held opinion, which is that he was no great shakes as a football player, he was a very good one. Characteristically, he was willing to play anywhere, eager only to be of service to the team. Thus he played part of the time as a tackle and part as a halfback. As a lineman he hit hard on the offense and was stout and resourceful on defense. He preferred to play in the backfield, however—what kid, given his choice, wouldn't prefer to carry the ball or pass it or kick it to the grind of line play? Lou was a triple-threat man and in addition a fine blocker and a letter man on the 1922 team.

UNITED PRESS INTERNATIONAL

Lou Gehrig on the Columbia baseball team

Probably the thing he did best, however, was to punt. Just as he was a long hitter in baseball, he could get tremendous distances with his punts, and long after his football days were behind him and he was living in New Rochelle, he went, many an afternoon, to the high-school football field and spent an enjoyable hour kicking.

Bill McKenna, who has been football and baseball coach at New Rochelle High for many years and has developed numerous players who became famous in college competition, says of Lou:

"He was one of the best punters I ever saw. He never lost the knack of getting the ball away, he had a terrific leg drive and—which also figured in it—he never lost his enthusiasm. Our kids used to stand and gape at him as he would boot the ball down the field, and more than once I said to them:

" 'Don't get so lost in your admiration for him that you overlook how he is doing it. Take a good look at him. He's doing everything I have been trying to teach you fellows to do.'

"Which was so. He had perfect form and compared favorably with the best professionals I have seen—and I have seen all of them since the professional game became a major league sport."

But baseball—that was Lou's game. Harry Kane had discovered when he was in high school that Lou was weak against left-handed curve ball pitching and had worked hard with him and helped him to eradicate that weakness. On South Field, where he was looking at better pitching than he had seen in high school, right-handed curve ball pitchers bothered him at first. So Coakley had right-handed curve ball pitchers firing at him constantly in batting practice, and after a time he could straighten out any curve they threw at him.

When Lou began to play with the varsity in the spring of 1923, this had an amusing sequel. Coakley, just before a game one day, heard somebody tell the opposing coach to pitch curve balls to Lou because they were his weakness.

"When I heard that," Andy said, "I knew everything was going to be all right."

Sure enough, the opposing pitcher gave Lou a curve ball the first time he went to bat, and Lou flattened it for three bases. The coach must have thought that was an accident because the next time Lou went up he signed for another curve ball. Lou hit that one for a whistling single that drove two runs over the plate. By that time the coach must have concluded a mistake had been made somewhere, for he had his pitcher pitch fast balls to Lou, but, of course, that didn't do any good because Lou always could hit a fast ball. He wound up with four hits in four times at bat—but the hits he had made off the curve balls were the ones that really ruined the enemy.

Lou pitched, played first base and outfield for Columbia. This was no sign that Coakley didn't know where to play him or that he showed any weakness at first base. It simply was a sign that he was the most valuable man on the team and that Coakley shunted him around where, in a given game, he thought he would do the most good.

"Judged by college baseball standards," Andy said, "he was a fair outfielder and a good pitcher. In the outfield, he covered a lot of ground, got most of the drives hit his way, and had a strong arm and got the ball away fast. As a pitcher he didn't have much stuff, but he did have a better fast ball than most college pitchers and against certain teams he could just rear back and fire that fast ball all afternoon and win going away. There were days, too, when he seemed to have even more speed than usual. On such days no college team could beat him.

"However, in our more important games I used him at first base. That was where he really belonged because—again according to college standards—he was a good first baseman. It is true that when he made the big jump from Columbia to the Yankees, they discovered there was a lot he had to learn about first base play. These were the things he never could have learned in college baseball and the things that nobody could teach him because the only place to learn them is in the major leagues. But he was a very good first baseman for us, and you could see, every step of the way, that he was going to get better as he went along and that some day, with proper training and experience, he might become a great one—which, of course, was what happened."

In the spring of 1923, at the training camp of the Yankees in New Orleans, a short, broad-shouldered, powerfully built man warmed up the pitchers before they took their turns in the box in batting practice or in one of the games between the regulars and the rookies. The chances are that Lou Gehrig never had heard of him.

This training camp bull-pen catcher was Paul Krichell, chief of the Yankees' scouting force until his death in 1957. Years before, he had caught for the St. Louis Browns and for numerous minor league clubs. Now he worked out with the Yankees every spring to keep himself fit for his job of stalking baseball talent in the raw through the minor leagues and the college

UNITED PRESS INTERNATION

Lou Gehrig in 1923

towns. He had discovered some of the rookies in the camp this year. Those that he hadn't discovered were there because he had put the final stamp of approval on them.

And then the squad broke camp and started north, and Krichell moved north with them, and at last they were in New York and ready to open the season. And now Krichell was through with them for the season. His real work was to begin. Nowadays the Yankee office receives college schedules from all over the country, but in that time Paul, in a manner of speaking, worked at random, picking the games out of the daily schedules in the papers. And scanning a paper on a mid-April morning, he saw that Columbia was playing Rutgers at New Brunswick. If Fordham or New York University had been playing at home that day, Paul would have passed up the trip to New Brunswick, gone to see one of the other games, and waited for Columbia to play at South Field. But Fordham and N. Y. U. were idle that day.

"I might as well go to New Brunswick," Paul said to Edward Grant Barrow, then the Business Manager and now the President of the Yankees. "I might see somebody I like, although I haven't heard anything about either of those teams."

It happened that he caught the train that was bearing the Columbia team, and walking into the car reserved for the players he looked for Coakley and found him in a rear seat.

"Hello, Paul," Andy said. "It's flattering to see you with us. Whom are you after?"

Paul sat down, took out a cigar, and lighted it.

"I don't know yet," he said. "I'm just going for the ride, maybe. . . . Anybody on your ball club worth looking at?"

Coakley shrugged.

"We have a pitcher you might like," he said. "A big left-handed kid. He is a good hitter, too."

"A hitting pitcher, eh?" Paul asked. "And a left-hander."

"Yes."

"Is he going to pitch today?"

"He may," Andy said. "I don't know. I have another kid that may be ready. If he is, I'll start him."

"You wouldn't do an old friend a favor and start the left-hander, would you?" Paul asked.

"I'd like to," Andy said. "But I really want to save him for Pennsylvania on Friday."

"All right," Paul said. "I'll look at him then if he doesn't pitch today. You're playing Penn at home?"

"Yes."

Paul nodded.

"I'll be there, if necessary," he said.

When they reached the ball field at New Brunswick, Paul took his seat in the stands, and soon the game was under way. The other pitcher must have been ready, as Coakley had hoped, for there was a right-hander in the box for Columbia. Paul thought to watch him, but he soon forgot about him. There was a kid in right field who caught his eye. A broad-shouldered kid. A power-house hitter. A left-handed hitter who smashed the ball every time he stepped to the plate and twice hit home runs into the trees that bordered the field. That was his man. Never mind the left-handed pitcher Coakley had been talking about. Maybe he was good, too. But this kid in right field! That was the one he would go to South Field to see again on Friday. South Field! He'd go to the South Pole to have another look at a kid who could powder the ball like that! Why, Babe Ruth himself couldn't have hit a ball any better than the one he hit for his second home run.

The kid wasn't much of a fielder, seen through the eyes of a major league scout. He staggered around under a couple of fly balls, and Paul wasn't sure whether he would fall down or get hit on the head. He did manage to catch both of them. But his performance in the field was a triumph of tenacity over awkwardness.

Paul was on the station platform waiting for Coakley after the game.

"Who is that clown in right field?" he asked.

Andy laughed.

"I just wanted to see if you'd notice him," he said. "That's the kid I was telling you about. That's my left-handed pitcher."

"A pitcher!" Paul said. "A kid can hit like that—and you use him for a pitcher!"

"When it's his turn to pitch, I do," Andy said. "The rest of the time I play him in the outfield or on first base."

"So would I," Paul said. "I'd want that guy in my line-up in every game. What's his name?"

"Gehrig," Andy said. "Lou Gehrig."

"And he pitches against Penn on Friday?"

"Yes."

"I'll be there," Paul said.

That night Paul called Barrow on the telephone.

"Ed," he said, "I think I got something. I'm not sure yet. But I just want to see him do it again."

"Do what again?" Ed asked.

"Hit the ball like he hit at New Brunswick today. Ed–"

"Yes?"

"Ed, I think I've found another Babe Ruth!"

Barrow laughed.

"All right, Paul," he said. "Go to bed and get a good night's rest and you'll feel better in the morning."

"No, listen, Ed," Paul protested. "I'm not kidding. You know I don't talk like this as a rule. But I saw a kid today—"

"I know," Ed said. "Another Babe Ruth."

He laughed again and hung up.

On Friday Paul was at South Field. As his opponent on the mound that day, Lou drew Walter Huntzinger, the best college pitcher in the East that year, a tall, slim right-hander who subsequently joined the Giants. They waged an exciting duel. When Columbia went to bat in the ninth inning, the score was tied at 2-2–and Gehrig, wading into a fast ball, drove it out of the field and across 116th Street, where it bounded on the steps of the library.

As he jogged around the bases, the Columbia rooters swarmed out of the stands, picked him up, and carried him on their shoulders toward the dressing room in the basement of Furnald Hall, where Watt and O'Neill had talked to him nearly three years before. No wonder they were excited. The home run not only had won the game but it was the most amazing clout that ever had been seen on that field. It was a clout that they would talk about for years afterward.

Krichell struggled through the pack of delirious rooters, trying to reach Gehrig before he got down the steps to the dressing room. Pushing, panting, he finally made it.

"Lou!" he called. "Just a minute!"

Lou, beaming, laughing, turned to see who had called to him.

"Lou," Paul said, "I'm Paul Krichell. I scout for the Yankees."

Lou's eyes widened.

"Yes?" he said.

"Have you signed with any major league ball club?" Paul asked.

"Why, no," Lou said.

"Anybody else talk to you?"

"No. I never thought—"

"Well, I'm talking to you. I'm talking business to you right now. Would you like to play with the Yankees?"

Lou looked as though he couldn't believe what he had just heard.

"Are you serious?" he asked.

"Certainly, I'm serious," Paul said. "What do you think I'm doing? Amusing myself?"

"I'm sorry, Mr—"

"Krichell."

"Mr. Krichell. I'm sorry. I didn't mean to offend you. But, you see, I never thought that anybody—I mean any big league ball club—would be interested in me. Especially the Yankees. Why—why—I don't know what to say."

"Well, take it easy, son," Paul said. "Would you like to talk to your coach first?"

"Yes, I would," Lou said. "Here's Andy now."

Andy was pushing his way through the crowd packed about the top of the stairs. When he saw Paul, he grinned.

"Well?" he said.

And turning to Lou:

"That was wonderful, Lou. The Babe himself couldn't hit one any better than that. . . . Have you signed with the Yankees yet?"

"Why, no, Coach," Lou said. "Mr. Krichell just asked me if I was interested, and I'd like to talk to you about it."

"Come in with us, Paul," Andy said.

"No," Paul said. "I'd rather you two talked it over first. But I think I know how you'll advise the boy, and I'd like both of you

WIDE WORLD

Two famous Yankees—Lou Gehrig and Babe Ruth

to come to the office tomorrow morning and talk to Mr. Barrow. How does that suit you?"

"It sounds all right to me," Andy said. "What time?"

"How about ten o'clock?"

"Fine. We'll be there."

Paul shook hands with both of them and hurried across Broadway to the nearest telephone and called Barrow.

"I've got him, Ed!" he said.

"Who?" Barrow asked. "The second Babe Ruth?"

"Yes," Paul said. "And it's no joke. Are you familiar with South Field?"

"Yes."

"Well, today this kid pitched, went into the ninth inning tied at

2-2, and won his own game with a drive that not only went out of the field but across the street and landed on the steps of the library."

There was no raillery in Barrow's voice when he asked:

"And what about him—about him and our club?"

"Andy Coakley is going to bring him in to see you tomorrow morning."

"Fine," Barrow said. "Nice work, Paul."

Paul and Barrow were waiting at ten o'clock the next morning. But there was no sign of Coakley and Gehrig. Came ten-fifteen . . . ten-twenty . . . still no sign. Paul was getting nervous. Suppose Coakley, whom he knew to favor the boy's signing with the Yankees, hadn't been able to persuade him that that was the thing to do? Suppose the boy's parents didn't want him to play professional baseball? Suppose—Paul didn't know anything about the boy's family—suppose they had a lot of money and wouldn't be interested in the offer the Yankees were prepared to make him?

He paced Barrow's office nervously. Barrow looked up curiously from the papers on which he was working.

"I never saw you as steamed up as this about a kid before," he said.

"That's because I never saw a kid like this before," Paul said. "He's terrific, Ed. No fooling."

Just then the office boy came in.

"Mr. Coakley and another man to see you, Mr. Barrow," he said.

"Bring 'em in!" Paul roared.

The conference didn't last long. Terms were agreed upon and Lou signed a Yankee contract. It was arranged that no public announcement be made of the signing at that time because Lou wished to finish out the college season.

"You'll report to us in June, then," Barrow said.

"Yes, sir," Lou said. "The day after our last game I will be at the Stadium."

"Good," Barrow said. "And good luck to you, young man."

It was a great day for Lou. It marked not only his signing as a Yankee but also the beginning of a friendship with Barrow that was to last all the days of his life.

ST. FRANCIS OF ASSISI

God's Troubadour

BY SOPHIE JEWETT

Paintings from the Assisi frescoes by Giotto

As a wealthy young man, Francis Bernadone (1181–1226) enjoyed to the fullest the gay life led by his companions in Assisi. As he matured he became aware of the poverty and wretchedness in the world. Casting off his riches, Francis regained his joy in life by founding a religious order whose members walked the dusty roads to take Christ's message of love and hope to all men.

ONLY fifteen miles away from Assisi stands a larger city, called Perugia. It also is built upon a mountain, and the two towns seem to smile at each other across the green valley. But for hundreds of years there were only bitter looks and hatred between the two. Perugia, higher and stronger, lay like a dragon, ready to spring upon her small but furious enemy. Assisi, like a lion's cub, was always ready to fight. Sometimes the lion was victor; always it was fierce enough to make the huge dragon writhe with pain.

When Francis Bernardone was about twenty years old, there was war between the great dragon and the little lion. Down from one mountain came the Perugian army. Down from the other came that of Assisi. With the army of Assisi rode Francis and most of the company of friends who had been so merry together in times of peace. They were gay as ever, and eager to see what a real battle might be like.

The armies met in the plain, and fought by the riverside, near a tiny town called Ponte San Giovanni, the Bridge of St. John.

This time the Perugians were too strong for the Assisians, and the young soldier's first combat was a defeat. One day taught him all the horror of a field of battle. He saw men wounded and dying. He heard the terrified cries of riderless horses. He suffered from blinding sun and parching thirst. War, that he had thought so noble and glorious, seemed somehow confused and cruel and hideous.

The army of Assisi lost heavily that day. Many men were slain, many were made prisoners, and one of the prisoners was Francis Bernardone. He was too tired, too hungry and too thirsty to feel anything keenly except the need of sleep and food; yet he wondered how it had all happened. Could he be the same man who had gone about for days delighting in the song of a warlike Troubadour:

> Luck to the arm that's quickest,
> And, if at odds ye strive,
> Die where the field is thickest,
> But never yield alive.

He knew that he had not been a coward. He had not even been afraid, yet here he was unarmed and captive.

Because of his beautiful dress, and because of his courtly manners, Francis was placed, not among the common soldiers, but among the nobles. For a whole year he was a prisoner of war. It must have been a sad change from the free, wild life in Assisi. Captives, even if of noble rank, were not softly treated in old times; and, though Francis and his companions may not have suffered serious hardships, the long confinement was, in itself, a cruel thing to bear.

On Francis Bernardone, however, his misfortune sat lightly. The army of Perugia could not make a captive of his fancy. His fellow-prisoners were astonished to hear him tell of his hopes and plans for the future; of the battles he should fight; of the fame he should win; of the beautiful ladies who should smile on him. The brave knights whom he admired, Gawain, Tristram and Lancelot, had sometimes fallen into prison, but had won their way out again, to fight better than before.

So Francis still dreamed of war and glory, and boasted in

his pride: "You will see that, some day, all the world will adore me."

Though he was proud and boastful, Francis was still gentle-hearted, and quick to feel sympathy for all who were unhappy. Among the prisoners of war was one man so vain and ill-tempered that his companions would have nothing to do with him. The unfortunate creature sat gloomily apart, with a black frown on his face, and with black thoughts in his mind. The songs and jests and games with which the others whiled away the long hours made him seem all the lonelier in his silent corner.

The sight of the sad, bitter face was more than Francis could bear. Many times he slipped away from the noisy group of his comrades to speak cheerily to the solitary knight, and, little by little, with the friendliness that no one was ever known to resist, he won the heart of the miserable man. Through the good will of the boy whom everybody loved, the victim and his tormentors in the end became friends once more, and there was peace in the great prison.

All through the long winter, from across the valley, the sad eyes of the Lady Pica watched the towers of Perugia. In her heart she questioned what might have been her boy's fate. Was he ill, and suffering and lonely? When would he come back to her? She seemed still to hear him singing, as on the morning when he had ridden out so blithely to his first battle:

> Comrades, let each be ready
>   To give and take his part;
> Shields bright and lances steady,
>   And all men glad of heart.

If the breeze that swept down the long valley from Perugia could have carried the prisoner's merry voice, the mother might have been somewhat comforted.

In prison or out of it, the heart of Francis of Assisi was always the heart of the poet, the Troubadour. Because his companions remembered gratefully the songs and laughter that brightened their captivity, the story of his gaiety has come down to us across seven hundred years.

At last there came a day when the prisoners were set free

and Francis could return to his home. The wide valley, with its shining rivers, the far blue mountains and the green forest road must have been welcome to eyes that, for a long year, had looked at the world through prison windows.

We may be certain that Piero and Pica Bernardone were watching for their son, and that all the neighbors made merry at his coming. We know that his gay young friends received him joyfully and that the old life of feasting, drinking and rioting began again.

Perhaps, in his delight at being free once more, Francis was more reckless than ever. At any rate, it is certain that, a short time after his return to Assisi, he suddenly became seriously ill. When, after long days of illness, he began to crawl about slowly, weak and pale, and leaning upon a stick, he was strangely unlike himself. Instead of being happy to be out of doors again, instead of frolicking with his friends, he was silent and sad at heart.

He wondered why he cared so little for the feasts and games and songs that he had delighted in only a few weeks before. Now, they did not interest him. It seemed to him that a man ought to have something better to do than simply to eat and drink, and wear fine clothes.

Because of his own pain and feebleness he felt sorrier than ever before for the lame, and blind, and the hungry beggars who came to his door, and his only pleasure was in giving them money and clothes and food.

As he listened to the talk in the market place by day, and in his father's house at evening, he heard many stories of the wars. Men told how houses were burned, fields and vineyards trampled and ruined; how women and children and helpless old men were killed, or left to die of hunger and cold. When he lay sleepless at night, he seemed to see again the battlefield of San Giovanni, and the faces of cruel men attacking, and of miserable victims wounded and falling. In these hours Francis doubted if war could be the glorious thing it had always seemed to him.

But when his friends began to tell him of new fighting in the south of Italy, and of a company of soldiers who were going from Assisi to join the army of a famous knight called

FRATELLI ALINARI

Saint Francis giving up his earthly goods

Walter of Brienne, all was changed. The old love for battle and glory woke up in his heart, and Francis made haste to grow strong again that he might be ready to go to war.

These were exciting days for the invalid. The color came back to his cheeks and his eyes danced with joy at sight of the rich clothes he was to wear, the beautiful horse he was to ride, the bright shield he was to carry.

He forgot that he was but a page, and that his first fight had ended in defeat. He dreamed of winning great battles; of marrying a beautiful princess; of living in a magnificent palace, or riding to the wars at the head of knights and soldiers of his own.

Assisi was full of noise and battle in these days. Companies of soldiers rode through the narrow streets so recklessly that the folk on foot hurried into doorways, and stood open-mouthed with fear while the riders passed.

In the market place men talked in eager groups. The voices were loud and excited, but louder still rang out the sharp blows of hammer on anvil, for every smith who knew how to make or to mend armor was busy from morning to late at night.

Furnaces stood in the open square, where the fires looked pale in the sunshine. Gay esquires brought from their masters bent or broken pieces of fine wrought steel, common soldiers brought their own clumsier armor; and the small boys of the city stood in admiring circles about the sounding anvils, and thought that, next to being a soldier, one would like to be a smith.

All this hurry of preparation was strong medicine to Francis. He forgot that he had been sick. He forgot that war had ever looked an evil thing to him. With his friends he was once more the gayest of companions, and he needed no urging to sing to them, to their hearts' content. Over and over he sang:

I love the gay spring weather,
  And all the trees a-flower,
When a hundred birds together
  Make music every hour;
But it sets my heart a-beating
  To see the broad tents spread,
And bright-armed warriors meeting,
  And banners floating red.

When camp and street are stirring;
  When the city gates stand wide;
When bands of knights are spurring
  Through all the countryside.

I know a joy that's dearer
Than food, or drink, or rest,
When the battle-shouts come nearer,
When flash bright sword and crest;
When above the trumpet's braying
And shrill cries of distress,
I hear the mournful neighing
Of brave steeds riderless.

Francis seemed to have become more boastful and more gay than ever, so that even his friends wondered at him, and asked him laughingly: "What is it that makes you so merry?" and he answered proudly: "I know that I am going to be a great prince."

Vain as he was, however, Francis never quite forgot that brave deeds and not fine garments make a good soldier. Among the company of knights who were going from Assisi, there was one who had for years been a great fighter, but who had suffered misfortune, and was now so poor that his clothing was actually ragged. To him Francis gave his own new coat and mantle, and the other accepted the gift quite simply, knowing that rich clothes are worth little, but that kind hearts are worth much.

When the good-bys were said and the horsemen clattered out of the city gate, no heart in all the company was so light as that of Francis Bernardone.

His mother watched him with grave eyes, remembering how many times she had seen the towers of Perugia fade into the red sky at sunset, and had prayed that her boy might come back to her. Now, he was going again, not to Perugia, but far to the south, to a country that she had never known. She wondered how he could smile at her so gaily as he rode away.

Francis and his fellow soldiers were to spend the first night in Spoleto, a city about twenty miles south of Assisi, on the way to Rome. The road ran along at the foot of the mountain, sometimes through forests of oak and beech and walnut trees, sometimes between olive orchards and vineyards. Presently it struck across the plain to Foligno, a busy Umbrian town lying in the valley by the River Topino.

In the square of Foligno, Francis had often stood with his

FRATELLI ALINARI

Saint Francis giving his cloak to a poor man

father, selling goods at the fairs. Today he held his head high as he rode through the familiar market place. He thought: "I shall come back a famous soldier, and I will never, never sell things at the fair again." He blushed with pride when someone in the street pointed him out to a companion, saying: "That young man, who is dressed and mounted like a lord, is the son of Messer Piero Bernardone, the merchant."

At Foligno the company halted to eat and drink, and to rest through the hottest hours of the day. When they were in the saddle again, and had left the city gates behind them,

Francis no longer rode superbly, with his chin in the air. Instead, he went silently, with drooping head, and let his horse lag behind the others along the level stretch of road.

He could not himself have told what was the matter; nothing had happened; the woods were as green and the sunshine as bright as in the morning, but he who had been so proud and gay a few hours earlier felt strangely weary and sick at heart.

He lingered to let his horse drink from the clear, little river, Clitumnus, that comes dancing down from the mountain and glitters across the plain, but not even the song of the water made him merry. His comrades noticed his silence, but they were all too deeply interested in their own plans and hopes to think of anything else.

In the late afternoon they entered the glorious oak forest that filled the ravine where Spoleto lies at the end of the Umbrian Valley. Beyond, their way would be through a narrow mountain pass where, over and over again, armies had fought fiercely to hold the road to Rome. Deep in the cool woods, the birds were singing, and, for the first time in his life, it seemed to Francis that they sang not joyfully, but sadly.

Perhaps he had not grown strong after his long illness, and so could not bear the fatigue of the hard saddle ride. Whatever the reason may have been, it is certain that, when the party reached Spoleto, Francis took to his bed with fever, and that his companions rode on, next day, without him.

And Francis had no wish to follow them. As once before, but this time more powerfully and surely, there had come upon him a great horror of a soldier's life. As he lay burning with fever and sleepless with pain, all his dreams of glory faded. Instead of knights, with shining armor and bright banners, he seemed to see women weeping, little children begging for bread, beautiful cities ruined and desolate.

We do not know how he made his way home. It was a strange and sorry journey, and, at the end of it, he met with ridicule from those who had seen him ride away so bravely to seek his fortune as a soldier. But if his thoughtless friends mocked him, and his father and brother reproached him, his mother was glad to welcome and to care for him. Perhaps she, alone, understood the change in him.

The first days after his return were the most sorrowful that Francis had ever known. Though he was sure that he had decided rightly, it pained him sorely to know that his friends thought him weak, or, perhaps, even cowardly. Besides being hurt, he was puzzled, not knowing what he ought to do next. A week ago his path had lain clear before him, like the white road in the valley; now it had lost itself in a tangled forest.

We do not know how long his trouble lasted, nor what he was doing in these dreary weeks; but we know that, by and by, he began to see plainly again, and all his doubts and puzzles vanished. It was as if he had found his way through the forest and saw the path that he must take, a narrow path and rough, a lonely path, but straight to follow.

He did not know that in a few years hundreds of fellow travelers were to come and ask that they might walk with him along that narrow way; that instead of being, as he had dreamed he might, Francis Bernardone, the most famous knight in Italy, he should become Brother Francis, the man whom all men loved.

All that Francis knew was that, in the place of his old love for a soldier's life and his old desire to become a great prince, had come a new love and a new desire: a love for all the ragged and hungry and sick and sorrowful folk in the world, and a desire to feed, and clothe, and heal and comfort them all.

WOLFGANG AMADEUS MOZART

The Dream of Freedom

BY MANUEL KOMROFF

From child prodigy to a place as the greatest musical genius of his time—this was the destiny of Mozart (1756-1791). In 1763 Mozart's father took the seven-year-old, who had already composed symphonies and given concerts, and his sister Nannerl on a grand concert tour which lasted three years. It was the first of a lifetime of triumphs.

ITALY welcomed both father and son. Their tour of the Italian peninsula, which lasted a little over a year, was to prove one of the happiest periods in Mozart's life. Everything about it was good.

At Verona he played in the finest homes. A local nobleman was so impressed with the boy that he ordered an artist to paint his portrait. Mozart also played on the two organs in the old church of San Tomaso. Such a great crowd had gathered to hear him that he and his father could hardly get out of the coach.

At Mantua Mozart played in the Philharmonic Society's concert hall. It was here that, for the first time, he heard several of the great women concert singers of Italy. He accompanied them at the clavier in such a way as to best display their voices, and they were very pleased. When he was leaving Mantua one of the singers wept and another sent him a small jar of pomade for his chapped hands together with a little poem. They wanted to show their appreciation and genuine affection.

Wolfgang then gave successful concerts in Milan, Bologna, and Florence. As a result of all this, he was given a commission to write an opera for the Milan Opera House. The libretto was on the subject of "Mithridates, King of Pontus." The work was to be ready by the end of the year and he was to receive one hundred ducats and free lodgings during the rehearsals and production. This time he felt confident that his work would be appreciated. He would not be forced to face the humiliation he had suffered in Vienna. While at Bologna, he studied fugue with the great teacher and scholar, Padre Martini.

And so it was with light hearts that father and son worked their way down the Italian boot and arrived in Rome in time for Holy Week.

On Wednesday and Thursday they went to the Sistine Chapel at St. Peter's to hear the famous *Miserere* which had been written over a century before by the Italian composer Allegri.

So sacred was this composition that the Vatican singers and musicians were forbidden to carry home any part of the music on pain of excommunication. But young Mozart did not feel that this regulation applied to him. He sat in the Sistine Chapel under the famous Michelangelo ceiling and listened intently to the music. Not a single note escaped him. Then, hurrying back to the hotel, he took up pen and paper.

"What are you going to write?" asked his father.

"The *Miserere.*"

"Can you remember it?"

"The notes of every part are clear in my head. I can write it all out from memory."

After Wolfgang had written out the *Miserere,* he was eager to check its correctness. He and his father returned to the Sistine Chapel on Good Friday and with the score secreted in his hat, young Mozart followed the music. The notes he had written from memory were almost perfect. Only one or two minor corrections were needed.

The report that young Mozart had written down the music of the sacred *Miserere* quickly spread through Rome, and he was asked by the Vatican to produce his copy. It was found to be correct in every detail. Soon all Rome knew of this amazing feat.

When this news reached Salzburg, Mozart's mother and sister were filled with horror. They believed that he had sinned

BETTMANN ARCHIVE

Wolfgang Mozart at about the age of thirteen
Portrait by Thadäus Helbling

and would be excommunicated. However, Papa Mozart hastened to calm their fears. "We both had a good laugh when we read your letter," he wrote. "There is nothing to worry about. It is taken in quite another way. All Rome knows about it. Even the Pope himself. . . . There is certainly nothing to be afraid of for it has brought him great honor. . . . Be sure to show this letter everywhere in Salzburg so that the true facts are known."

Wolfgang was in high spirits. He wrote long letters home filled with little drawings, nonsense rhymes, and words that he invented only because he liked their sound. His heart was happy. He sprinkled his letters with Italian and Latin words and sometimes invented the craziest and most absurd expressions.

After visiting St. Peter's he wrote to his sister: "I have had the honor of kissing the foot of the statue of St. Peter, but since I have the misfortune to be so short, your good old Wolfgang Mozart had to be lifted up!"

From Rome Papa Mozart and his son traveled to Naples, where Wolfgang continued to give concerts and impress the public with his incredible talent. On one occasion an old woman in the audience called out: "It is all magic! And the magic is due to the ring on his finger."

To prove that she was wrong Wolfgang took off his ring and showed that he could play just as well without it. The audience broke into loud applause.

But his life in Italy was not all admiration and applause. After leaving the glamorous concert halls he and his father had to return to their simple little lodgings.

From Naples he wrote his sister:

"Vesuvius is smoking fiercely! Thunder and lightning and blazes! . . . Now I will describe to you how we live. I rise generally every morning at 9 o'clock, but sometimes not until 10, at which time we go out. We eat in a restaurant. After dinner I write, and I write until it is time for supper. And what do we eat? Half a fowl or a slice of roast meat. On fast days a little fish. After supper we go to sleep. Now you understand how we live. . . . In the opera house we often see the King of Naples. He is short and because of this he always stands on a stool so that he may look a little taller than the Queen. The Queen is beautiful and most gracious for she bowed to me a number of times."

After many successful concerts and pleasant adventures in Naples the father and son returned to Rome. This journey was usually made in slow stages and took over four days, but Wolfgang and his father took the fast coach and made the trip in only twenty-seven hours. And since they were able to get only two hours of sleep and very little food, they arrived exhausted and hungry.

The next morning as soon as it was known that the young Mozart had returned to Rome, a courier arrived from the

AUSTRIAN INFORMATION SERVICE

Mozart at twenty-one, wearing the medal of the
Order of the Golden Spur

Vatican inviting father and son to have an audience with the Pope. During this visit the Pope conferred on Wolfgang the Order of the Golden Spur. This order brought with it a gold medal and the title *Signor Cavaliere*. It was a very high honor and Wolfgang was very proud. Some years earlier the composer Gluck had also received this distinction, but he was forty-two years old when he was made a *Signor Cavaliere*. No musician fourteen years of age had ever before been so honored by the Vatican.

When Papa Mozart and his son returned to their lodgings they were in very high spirits. Mozart wrote a brief note to his sister just so that he could sign it with the following words:

"I have the honor to be your very humble servant and brother the Cavaliere Mozart."

All this was good fun. Papa Mozart often smiled when he heard people addressing his young son as *Signor Cavaliere*. He smiled because Wolfgang seemed such a little Cavaliere, but nevertheless he was very proud of the title and insisted that his son use it whenever he signed his name.

But young Mozart was very modest and felt that titles added little or nothing to a person's true artistic worth. He used the title merely to be obedient and please his father. However, he soon forgot about it and after a year or two he left it off completely.

A few months after Mozart had been honored by the Vatican, he received another honor which he prized above all. His fellow composers, members of the Academy of Bologna, subjected him to a very severe examination in which he was locked in a room by himself and asked to compose a section of a Mass on a given theme. This difficult task he did very easily, completing the work in half-an-hour, although three full hours were allowed.

After the work was examined by a committee of composers, young Mozart was unanimously voted a member academician of the Bologna Philharmonic Society. This was the highest honor his fellow musicians could bestow upon him. Of this honor he was truly proud.

Young Mozart was completely happy in Italy. He wrote long letters to his mother and sister and filled them with bubbling nonsense. He sent complicated messages to the dog and to the pet canary. However he had one regret—his bad handwriting. "I can't write any better for this pen is not a writing pen but a music-note pen. I do not have any other."

But if Mozart's music pen was not good for writing letters it was very fine for writing music.

During the short time that he spent in Italy he composed four symphonies in the Italian manner and a number of arias and other compositions, besides the opera which had been commissioned for the Milan Opera House. The great successes he had enjoyed in the past months and the appreciation he had received had encouraged him, and music flowed easily from his pen. Writing music was creation. And while creating he knew true happiness.

At length it was time to go to Milan to rehearse the singers and orchestra. And as is usual in every opera house, there were serious rivalries among the singers. Some thought they had not been given important roles to sing and others felt slighted because their arias were too short. The prima donnas were jealous of each other and the lesser singers all wanted to be prima donnas. Every day a new storm swept across the stage.

But young Mozart was very tactful. He was agreeable to everyone and tried to please all. For one singer he put in some extra high notes so that she could display herself and for another he wrote in a few sweet sentimental lines certain to bring applause. In this way all were eventually pacified, and everyone set to work to learn their words and music.

On the day after Christmas, in the year 1770, the opera *Mithridates, King of Pontus* was produced. Young Mozart conducted from the orchestra pit. The public was so pleased that many shouted as they applauded. They shouted "Bravo!" and "Long live the master!"

Here in Milan young Mozart had matched his musical talent with the best in Italy and had succeeded. Twenty performances were given.

Papa Mozart was very proud of his son. He felt that this success would establish Wolfgang firmly in the musical world. He believed the road would be easy from now on. With the reputation thus gained, commissions for musical compositions would come freely. The Italian critics had often said that it was impossible for a German to write an Italian opera. But here it was. The impossible had been accomplished. And with the impossible would come fame, glory, and money! The dream was now sure to come true.

Two good things did result from the success of this opera. The manager of the Milan Opera House commissioned the young composer to write another opera to be produced in the season of 1773. And Mozart also received a commission to write a dramatic serenade to be performed in honor of the coming marriage in Milan of the Archduke Ferdinand of Austria.

These honors mark the climax of Mozart's boyhood fame.

BETTMANN ARCHIVE

Mozart with his sister and father in 1780
Lithograph by Johann Nepomuk della Croce

He had spent his fourteenth and fifteenth birthdays in friendly Italy, and now he was no longer a boy. Gone were the days when he could be exhibited as a child prodigy by his proud and ambitious father! But with the great success of his opera and with many important compositions to his credit, he felt ready to take his place as a man in the musical world. The glory of his childhood triumphs was now behind him. Fresh glories, he was sure, lay ahead.

And so—basking in the warmth of success—the happy travelers left Italy and returned to their home in Salzburg.

Five months later, on August 31, 1771, Mozart and his father again left Salzburg for Milan to compose the pastoral and mythological serenade which Wolfgang had been commissioned to write for the marriage of the Archduke Ferdinand.

The trip was a gay and pleasant one. Wolfgang visited with the celebrated opera composer, Hasse, who had also been commissioned to prepare an opera for the festivities. Hasse is said to have remarked, "This boy will cause us all to be forgotten."

The music for the serenade was light and gay. It was tuneful. The characters were gods and goddesses of ancient mythology. And it was well received by the public.

On the strength of this success, and knowing how unhappy Wolfgang was at the thought of returning to work for the Archbishop, Papa Mozart approached the Archduke and suggested that he take Wolfgang into his service and appoint him concertmaster of his orchestra.

But the Archduke could not make up his own mind. He asked the advice of his mother the Empress. And she, the Empress Maria Theresa, who had once dressed Nannerl and Wolfgang in brocades, she whom the child Mozart had kissed, now wrote, warning her son. She wrote that he should not hamper his court by giving positions to "useless people," people who would only dishonor his name by running about like beggars.

With this sharp advice from his mother, the Archduke Ferdinand refused to give Wolfgang a place in his orchestra. And so the father and son were forced to return to Salzburg and resume their duties in the Archbishop's court, arriving December 15, 1771.

The day after Papa Mozart and his brilliant son returned to Salzburg, the good Archbishop died. He had been understanding and tolerant and proud of young Mozart. And now, much to everyone's surprise and disappointment, a very unpopular and mean dignitary was sent to fill his place.

The new Archbishop bore the imposing name and title of Hieronymous Joseph Franz von Paula, Count of Colloredo and Bishop of Gurk. This sounded very grand, but the man himself was stupid and petty. He had no conception of music or appreciation of Mozart's talent. And from the very first day the sensitive Mozart suffered under the pressure of this man's ignorance.

Nevertheless, Mozart performed his duties as *Kapellmeister* with full generosity. He did the very best he could, even composing an allegorical opera on a classical theme for the installation of the new Archbishop. Although he was taken seriously ill while he was working on this project he finished it in time: it consisted of ten arias, two choruses, and a full overture.

Mozart tried to please the new Archbishop, but it was impossible. He was not interested in music. He liked hunting, sports, and society. The brilliant young composer and musician working in his orchestra meant little or nothing to him. He did, however, recognize Mozart's ready pen and ordered him to keep busy writing new Masses and church music, as well as special pieces for the many holy occasions of the year. For this extra work Mozart should have received additional compensation, but the Archbishop extracted a full measure of services for the miserable wages of one hundred and fifty gulden a year which he paid him. This would amount to about two hundred and eighty dollars in our money. And although its purchasing value was greater in Mozart's day, it was barely enough, together with Papa Mozart's wages, to support the family. Servants were paid little less.

The tension was broken when Mozart and his father again left Salzburg in October 1772 for a third visit to Milan, to write the opera commissioned the preceding year. On this trip Leopold attempted to secure his son a post with the Grand Duke Leopold of Tuscany, but his efforts failed, and March 1773 they had to return to the Archbishop's oppressive court.

However, that summer young Mozart was again, for a short time, released from bondage. He and his father were given another leave of absence to go to Vienna. Wolfgang was now seventeen and his father was determined to make a final attempt to find him a patron. But again he failed.

Mozart was once more plunged into the routine work of the Archbishop's orchestra.

The past two years had been especially hard for Mozart because he had had to contend not only with the Archbishop but also with the jealousy of his fellow musicians at the court. When he was a "wonder child" they had accepted him and even been proud of him. But now they seemed to resent his presence. They looked upon him with envy because he had been received in the royal courts of Europe. They were quick to criticize, and they even poisoned the Archbishop's mind with false and malicious opinions. And the ignorant Archbishop in his crude and offensive manner set himself up as a critic and judge. "You know nothing about music," he said to Mozart one day. "You ought to go to a *conservatoire* in Italy and learn how to compose properly!"

In an atmosphere so highly charged with hostility and insult, Mozart found it difficult to work. He was of a very sensitive nature, and his feelings were easily hurt. His creative spirit was being crushed. He began to dream of escape.

While this period of Mozart's life was very unhappy, yet it was one in which his music made some very important strides. Scholars have pointed out that it was during those days that the first signs of that quality which we call Mozartean began to appear in his work.

Before reaching the age of fifteen Mozart had written over one hundred compositions. But much of this early work was conventional and cast in the accepted musical forms of the day. It showed promise, though hardly that rare quality of creative imagination so characteristic of his later work. There was little display of musical originality. As one critic remarked: "The fruit was more extraordinary than excellent."

However, during the two years that followed his fifteenth birthday, his work suddenly matured. At this time he wrote a great quantity of music, some of which has become immortal. He wrote six piano sonatas for the newly improved pianoforte. All these have become very well known and are today part of every good piano library. During this time he also wrote seven symphonies.

It should be noted here that some of these orchestral works show the influence of Joseph Haydn, whose compositions Mozart greatly admired. Haydn was twenty-four years older than Mozart and was well established as a composer. It was natural that Mozart should at this formative time have been influenced by his work. But this influence was only a stepping-stone to something more individual. His compositions soon lost all trace of Haydn's influence.

Haydn lived for eighteen years after Mozart died and it is interesting to see that his later music was definitely influenced by Mozart!

In both cases the influence was a healthy one and marked musical progress.

As the months and years ran by, Mozart's dream of freedom

grew stronger. He began to dislike everything in Salzburg, even the sight of its streets and its simple people.

The Archbishop must have sensed this, but he did not relent. In his deep ignorance he only became more and more critical and more and more demanding. At length Mozart could endure it no more and he wrote a long letter to the Archbishop resigning his position.

The Archbishop was furious. He knew that he could not replace young Mozart. And in anger he cried: "Both the son and the father can go seek their fortunes where they please!"

Papa Mozart was very upset. He feared that he would lose his position. He had no savings and desperately needed his small wages to support Mamma Mozart and Nannerl. It was a question of daily bread. But the Archbishop's anger soon cooled, and Leopold Mozart was permitted to keep his post in the orchestra.

Mozart, now free of his chains, began to make plans for the future.

He decided to go to Germany and Paris to seek his fortune. He was confident that somewhere abroad he would find an appreciative patron. After all, he was an accomplished artist. He was only twenty-one years old and he had already composed symphonies, operas, quartets, and concertos. He had written music for the piano, violin, horn, and other instruments. He had also written sacred music for the organ and church choirs. And he was justly proud of its quality; it could be compared with the best. Besides, he was a concert virtuoso. He could play the clavier and piano with grace and great technical skill. There was no one in Europe who could rival him in this!

Papa Mozart knew all this to be true, and he felt it was right for Wolfgang to leave Salzburg to seek his fortune elsewhere. Yet he did not like to be separated from his son and he feared to trust him alone in the big world. After all, Wolfgang had always led a sheltered life. The father had always been at his son's elbow, telling him what to do and what not to do. He had taken care of everything. How could the boy possibly manage alone!

And so Papa Mozart decided that Nannerl should stay in

AUSTRIAN INFORMATION SERVICE

Unfinished portrait by Joseph Lange, Mozart's brother-in-law

Salzburg to keep house for him, while Wolfgang, under his mother's protection, should journey forth to seek fortune from music's magic sounds.

On the twenty-third of September, 1777, Wolfgang and his mother left Salzburg. Mozart was happy to leave it behind. He was hopeful. He was certain that his talents would open many important doors.

Mozart was also happy to be traveling once more. He loved the rumble of the wheels, the sway of the coach, the sound of the horses' hoofs, and the moving landscape. These were things that he had originally heard and loved when he was six years old and had started out for the first time with Nannerl and his father. These were pleasant things which were part of his memories of the days when he and his sister were "wonder children."

FLORENCE NIGHTINGALE

Lonely Crusader

BY CECIL WOODHAM-SMITH

Florence Nightingale (1820–1910), "The Lady with the Lamp," brought sanitation, and scientific nursing, first to the nightmarish war hospitals of her day, and later, as her fame spread, to the world. Nursing was considered an undignified profession—certainly not proper for a young lady of high society. But Florence Nightingale, roused by the ills and sufferings of mid-nineteenth century Europe, had a mind of her own. She knew what she had to do.

IN March the Nightingales went to London for the season and took rooms at the Burlington Hotel, Old Burlington Street.

Florence was very gay. Though she was only twenty-two, she was becoming a figure in intellectual society. Her demure exterior concealed wit. She danced beautifully, yet possessed a surprising degree of learning, had great vitality, and was an excellent mimic. She had acquired a light touch and wrote of a dull party at which the Queen and Prince Albert were present that "the only amusement was seeing Albert taught to miss at billiards." She was "very much noticed," Fanny wrote, by the new Prussian Ambassador, the Chevalier Bunsen, and his wife. The Bunsens united intellect, good breeding, and wealth. The Chevalier (he was created Baron in 1857) was a Biblical scholar of European reputation, was extremely rich, and had a house in Carlton House Terrace besides a place in Sussex. The Bunsens were close friends of the Queen and Prince Albert and were liberal Evangelicals. Florence, who went constantly to their house, was addressed by the Chevalier as "My favourite and admired Miss Nightingale." He lent her books and discussed archeology and religion with her.

She had achieved a success and could not help feeling satisfaction, yet she reproached herself bitterly. "All I do is done to win admiration," she wrote in a private note. She cared too much for lights, pretty clothes, glitter, the allurements she called in her private notes "the pride of life." Over and over again she told herself that before she could hope to be worthy enough for God to reveal the path of service, the temptation to shine in society must be conquered.

In the summer of 1842 the temptation to shine was greatly increased. In May, at a dinner party given by the Palmerstons, Florence was introduced to Richard Monckton Milnes. In 1842, Richard Monckton Milnes was thirty-three. He was the only son of Mr. Richard Pemberton Milnes and heir to the estate of Fryston in Yorkshire. He had achieved a brilliant success in London society and was prophesied an important political career.

He wrote talented poetry himself but had an even greater talent for discerning poetic genius. Later he was responsible for the collection and publication of the first collected edition of the poems of Keats.

He diffused amiability. His kindness and generosity were based on love for his fellow men. His humanity expressed itself in philanthropic work. He loved children and worked for many years, against ceaseless opposition, to improve the treatment of young criminals. It was largely owing to his efforts that juvenile offenders ceased to be sent to jail with adult criminals and were sent to reformatories instead.

During the summer Richard Monckton Milnes came several times to Embley. He was falling in love with Florence, and he made himself the friend of Fanny, Parthe, and W. E. N. By the end of July, when the Nightingales went north to Lea Hurst, he was treated as one of the family.

The devotion of Richard Monckton Milnes left Florence unmoved. Sometime in the summer of 1842 she had taken the first step toward the fulfillment of her destiny. She had become conscious of the world of misery, suffering, and despair which lay outside her little world of ease and comfort.

The year 1842 was a terrible one for the people of England. The country was in the grip of what has passed into history as "the hungry forties." In villages, as in towns, there were starvation, sweated labor, ignorance, and dirt. Diseased scarecrows swarmed not only in the airless undrained courts of London, but in the "black filth" of rural cottages. Workhouses, hospitals, and prisons were overflowing. That summer Florence wrote in a private note: "My mind is absorbed with the idea of the sufferings of men, it besets me behind and before . . . all that poets sing of the glories of this world seems to me untrue. All the people I see are eaten up with care or poverty or disease."

She had progressed. She knew now that her destiny lay among the miserable of the world, but what form that destiny was to take she still had no idea.

In the autumn of 1842 Florence called on the Prussian Ambassador and his wife. The Chevalier Bunsen mentioned the work of Pastor Fliedner and his wife at Kaiserswerth, on the Rhine, where Protestant Deaconesses were trained in the hospital of the institution to nurse the sick poor. Florence's attention was not arrested; she had not yet begun to think of nursing.

But when, at the end of July, 1843, the Nightingales once more went north to Lea Hurst, her whole being was concentrated on the poor. She began to spend the greater part of her day in the cottages, began to badger her mother in and out of season for medicines, food, bedding, clothes. Fanny, who was generous in distributing charity, felt Florence was unreasonable. When the time came to go to Embley, Florence wanted to stay behind at Lea Hurst. Fanny would not hear of her remaining, and she had to come south. "It breaks my heart to leave Lea Hurst," she wrote to Aunt Mai in September, 1843.

When her mother had succeeded in getting Florence away, fresh difficulties arose. One of her friends died in childbirth, leaving a daughter. Florence demanded permission to cancel her engagements, give up London for the autumn season, and look after the baby. When Fanny refused, she fretted herself into an illness. Forced to give way, Fanny compromised by allowing her to go and look after the baby for a few weeks—at the height of the season when she should have been in London

CULVER SERVICE

Florence Nightingale

going to parties. Fanny was bitterly disappointed, and misery resulted on both sides.

Florence's misery was a thousand times increased by a terrifying discovery. She records in a private note that in the autumn of 1843 she suddenly realized the extent to which the habit she called "dreaming" had enslaved her. She fell into "trance-like" states in the midst of ordinary life, while, for instance, she was making conversation with the Ashburtons at Sir William Heathcote's dinner. She could not control herself, and she gave way with the shameful ecstasy of the drug taker.

Was there nothing for her but dreaming? Had she better close her eyes and find what satisfaction she could in a false paradise of consoling visions? And then, she wrote in a private note, "an acquaintance with a woman to whom all unseen things seemed real and eternal things near, awakened me."

Miss Hannah Nicholson, sister of Mr. Nicholson of Waverley, called Aunt Hannah by the Nightingales, was a deeply religious woman with the gentleness, purity, and limited vision of a nun. She did not understand Florence; there were depths, violences, capacities in her she was unable to grasp, but she knew Florence was ill, not on good terms with her family, and unhappy. She believed she could provide the solution. Union with God would bring reconciliation with earthly life. A close intimacy between the two women sprang up. Days were spent discussing the life of the soul and the way of the soul to God. Florence had an enormous amount of unexpended affection. In a private note, written at this time, she speaks of "those I love—and no one knows *how* I love." She adored Aunt Hannah, and became her disciple.

There was, however, an essential difference between them which Miss Nicholson did not appreciate. Though Florence sought union with God, she did not seek that state as an end in itself. Union with God was a necessary qualification for the performance of God's work, a preparation for action, not submission.

At the very moment when she seemed to be most thoroughly under Aunt Hannah's influence she took a secret decision of the greatest importance entirely opposed to everything Miss Nicholson hoped. Sometime in the spring of 1844 the knowledge

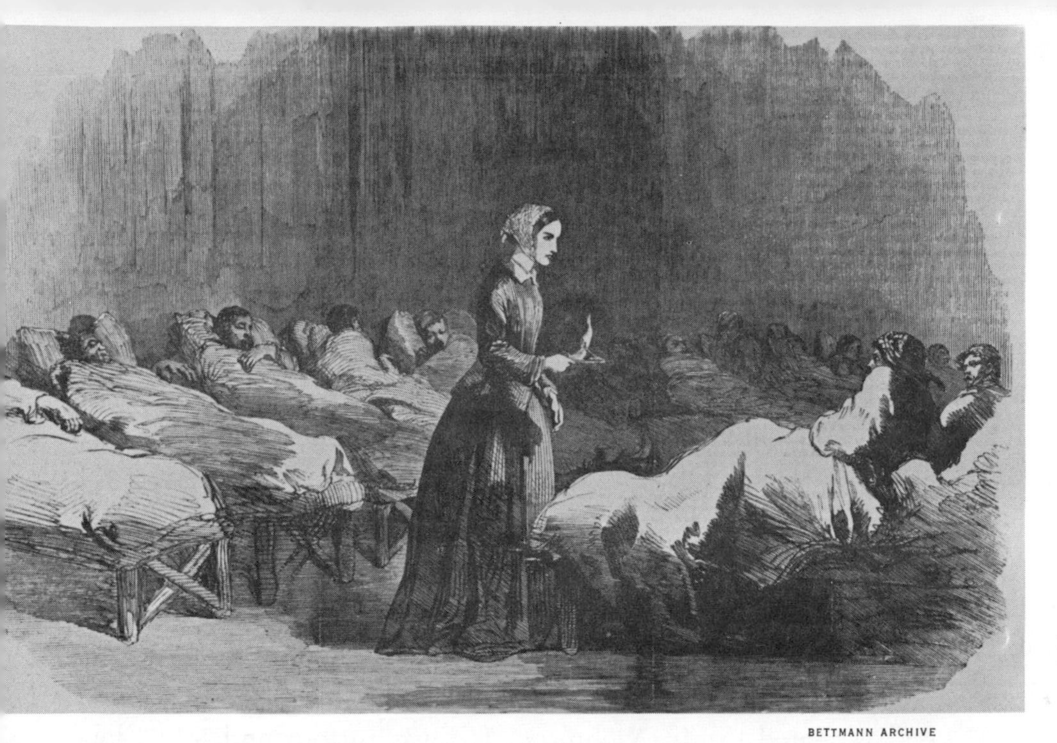
BETTMANN ARCHIVE

"The Lady with the Lamp"

came to her that her vocation lay in hospitals among the sick. At last, seven years after her "call," her destiny was clear. "Since I was twenty-four," she wrote in a private note thirteen years later, ". . . there never was any vagueness in my plans or ideas as to what God's work was for me."

In June Dr. Samuel Gridley Howe, the American philanthropist, and his wife Julia Ward Howe, later to become celebrated as the author of the "Battle Hymn of the Republic," came to stay at Embley. On the night of his arrival Florence came up to him in the drawing room. Would he meet her privately in the library for a few moments before breakfast? Dr. Howe consented. In the library next morning Florence went straight to the point: "Dr. Howe, do you think it would be unsuitable and unbecoming for a young Englishwoman to devote herself to works of charity in hospitals and elsewhere as Catholic sisters do? Do you think it would be a dreadful thing?" He gave a sincere answer: "My dear Miss Florence, it would be unusual, and in England whatever is unusual is thought to be unsuitable. But I say to you 'go forward,' if you have a vocation for that way of life. Act up to your inspiration and you will find there is never anything unbecoming or unladylike in doing your duty for the good of others. Choose, go on with it, wherever it may lead you and God be with you."

She had reached the turning point of her life, but she confided in no one. The word "hospital" had not yet been uttered to her family. She was well-advised to hesitate before introducing it; it was a dread word. She must think out some method by which her parents might be brought to consent to their daughter entering a hospital. Throughout the summer she meditated in secret. "I dug after my little plan in silence," she wrote.

That summer when she went north to Lea Hurst there was scarlet fever in the cottages, and she was forbidden to go near them. In October she coached William Nicholson, Henry's younger brother, in mathematics for an examination at Sandhurst, which led to a family unpleasantness. Parthe indiscreetly boasted that Flo was coaching William, and the indiscretion was repeated to Mr. Nicholson. He was furious and told Florence that William would be laughed out of Sandhurst if it got about that he had been coached by a girl. All through the autumn she was ailing, and when, at Christmas, Fanny and Parthe went to Waverley she was too ill to go. She stayed in bed at Embley pouring out letters, notes, analyses, plans. She was striving to find a way to get away from home to a hospital, striving to achieve the state of union with God in which Aunt Hannah assured her all difficulties would vanish.

On New Year's Eve, 1844, she was unable to leave her room and sat writing late at night with "a little black tea pot on the hob." Outside it was freezing hard, with a brilliant moon. She watched three hares playing on the whitened grass of the lawn. In the stillness the world seemed to be dead except for those three hares. At Waverley at this moment there was a ball. She sighed after the ball and the dress she had been going to wear, a pink dress with black lace flounces, ruefully aware that the "pride of life" was by no means dead. "I am convinced of it when I think of my black lace flounces," she wrote to Aunt Hannah.

In a fortnight or so she was convalescent, and Hilary Bonham Carter came to stay. She was another victim of family life. In the previous year Hilary had met Clarkey.* Through Clarkey

* Miss Mary Clarke, a major figure in the literary and political life of Paris.

she had taken drawing lessons in Paris and was pronounced to have genuine talent. Clarkey had implored Mrs. Bonham Carter to let Hilary work seriously. But Hilary could not be "spared." Now she was spending her life housekeeping, teaching her younger sisters, doing the flowers and, as a concession, attending a "ladies' studio" in London where so little was expected that lessons were taken "when social engagements permitted."

The girls were alone for two days; the weather was fine and still, and they made long expeditions into the New Forest, walking from breakfast until sunset, and talking all day. Florence poured out her heart, but she spoke neither of her determination to work in hospitals nor of the shameful secret of her "dreams"—that ever-growing terror.

But as week followed week, Florence became more wretchedly unhappy. Nearly a year had passed since her interview with Dr. Howe, and she was no farther forward. Eight years had passed since her "call" and she had accomplished nothing.

In the spring of this year, she received a shattering blow: Henry Nicholson proposed and insisted on a definite answer. She refused him. Henry was heartbroken, and the Nicholsons were furious. Florence had, they said with justice, encouraged Henry; Marianne ended her friendship with Florence, and the Nightingales and the Nicholsons ceased to be intimate. To Florence the loss of Marianne was a catastrophe; through the summer she suffered tortures. She did not blame Marianne; she wrote no recriminations; she blamed only herself.

She was approaching a mental collapse when two serious illnesses in the family saved her.

In August she went with her father to visit her grandmother, Mrs. Shore, found her seriously ill, and was allowed to stay and nurse her. Hardly was Mrs. Shore convalescent when Mrs. Gale, the girls' old nurse, was taken ill at Lea Hurst. Again Florence was allowed to nurse Mrs. Gale, and when she seemed too ill to be moved to Embley at the end of the summer, Fanny prepared to give up her winter gaieties and stay at Lea Hurst in order that the old nurse might not be separated from "her children." Mrs. Gale insisted, however, on being taken to Embley, and there, a week or so later, she died, sitting upright in her chair with Florence beside her holding her hand.

BETTMANN ARCHIVE

A pencil sketch of Florence Nightingale done in 1857
by Sir George Scharf

These two episodes brought a certain amount of emancipation. Since Florence had proved herself entirely capable in nursing her grandmother and Mrs. Gale, it was difficult to forbid her to continue to nurse. In the autumn there was an unusual amount of sickness in the village of Wellow, and she took an active part.

And now she moved forward another step—she realized the

necessity of training in nursing. The discovery came as a shock. Neither she herself nor anyone she had ever met had been taught how to nurse. It was universally assumed that the only qualification needed for taking care of the sick was to be a woman.

She too had thought that the qualities needed to relieve the misery of the sick were tenderness, sympathy, goodness, and patience. Now her short experience had already shown her that only knowledge and expert skill brought relief; and her destiny, which was to lighten the load of suffering, could be fulfilled only if she were armed with knowledge. She must learn how to nurse. How could she learn? There was perhaps one avenue by which she might succeed.

The idea was bold, but since she had achieved a little independence she had been becoming bolder. Her plan was to persuade her parents to allow her to go for three months to Salisbury Infirmary to learn nursing. Salisbury was only a few miles from Embley, the infirmary was a well-known hospital, and the head physician, Dr. Fowler, was an old friend. He held advanced views, and she thought he might support her.

In December, 1845, the Fowlers came to stay at Embley, and Florence proposed her plan. A storm burst. "Mama was terrified." Parthe had hysterics. Florence persisted, and her mother's terror passed into furious anger. In floods of tears Fanny wept that Florence wanted to "disgrace herself."

The Fowlers, embarrassed, "threw cold water." W. E. N., coldly disgusted, went away to London. Was it for this he had educated a charming daughter? Was this to be the end of the Latin and the Greek, the poetry and the philosophy, the Italian tour and the Paris frocks? Florence was left defeated, helpless, hopelessly depressed. "No advantage that I can see comes of my living on. . . . I shall never do anything and am worse than dust and nothing. . . . Oh for some strong thing to sweep this loathsome life into the past."

It was not surprising that the Nightingales were horror-struck. In 1845 hospitals were places of wretchedness, degradation, and squalor. "Hospital smell," the result of dirt and lack of sanitation, was accepted as unavoidable. Wards were usually large, bare, and gloomy. Beds were crammed in, fifty or sixty, less than two feet apart. Even decency was impossible. Fifteen years later, when some improvement had been made, Florence wrote in *Notes on Hospitals:* "The floors were made of ordinary wood which, owing to lack of cleaning and lack of sanitary conveniences for the patients' use, had become saturated with organic matter, which when washed give off the smell of something quite other than soap and water." Walls and ceilings were "of common plaster" also "saturated with impurity." Heating was supplied by a single fire at the end of each ward, and in winter windows were kept closed for warmth, sometimes for months at a time. In some hospitals half the windows were boarded up in winter. After a time the smell became "sickening," walls streamed with moisture, and "a minute vegetation appeared." The remedy for this was "frequent lime washing with scraping," but the workmen engaged on the task "frequently became seriously ill."

The patients came from the slum tenements called "rookeries," from hovels, from cellars where cholera lurked. Gin and brandy were smuggled into the wards, and fearful scenes took place. In certain hospitals it was not unknown for the police to be called in to restore order.

The sick came into hospital filthy and remained filthy. In 1854 Florence wrote: "The nurses did not as a general rule wash patients, they could *never* wash their feet—and it was with difficulty and only in great haste that they could have a drop of water, just to *dab* their hands and face. The beds on which the patients lay were dirty. It was common practice to put a new patient into the same sheets used by the last occupant of the bed, and mattresses were generally of flock [*i.e.*, stuffed with woolen or cotton refuse] sodden and seldom if ever cleaned."

Yet physically disgusting conditions were not the real obstacle to her scheme; the insuperable objection was the notorious immorality of hospital nurses. "It was *preferred,*" wrote Miss Nightingale, "that the nurses should be women who had lost their characters."

Drink was the curse of the hospital nurse, as of the patients. "The nurses are all drunkards," said the physician of a large London hospital in 1851, and in 1854 the head nurse of a London hospital told Miss Nightingale that in the course of her large experience she had never known a nurse who was not drunken.

One of the extraordinary features of Florence Nightingale's life is the passage of time. She started with a "call" in 1837. But what had she been called to do? What was her vocation to be? Eight years passed before, in 1845, she found out. Even then she was only halfway. Eight more years passed before she gained freedom in 1853 to pursue her vocation. Sixteen years in all, sixteen years during which the eager, susceptible girl was slowly hammered into the steely powerful woman of genius. The last eight years were years in which suffering piled on suffering, frustration followed frustration, until she was brought to the verge of madness.

Yet she endured year after year. She had the capacity to assert herself, but she did not. The bonds which bound her were only of straw, but she did not break them. Her temperament held her a prisoner. She could act only when she felt moral justification, and she felt no moral justification. She was convinced that the difficulties which confronted her were God's punishment for her sinfulness. She was unworthy, and by being unworthy she had brought her sufferings on her own head.

"What is my business in this world and what have I done this fortnight?" she wrote on July 7, 1846. "I have read the 'Daughter at Home' to Father and two chapters of Mackintosh; a volume of Sybil to Mama. Learnt seven tunes by heart. Written various letters. Ridden with Papa. Paid eight visits. Done Company. And that is all."

"Dreaming" enslaved her more and more. While W. E. N. was reading *The Times,* while she was making conversation with visitors or taking "a little drive" with Fanny, she escaped into a dream world. Her dreams centered upon Richard Monckton Milnes. She imagined herself married to him, performing heroic deeds with him.

Yet, in spite of her wretchedness, she was making progress. The philosophy which told her to submit did not tell her to relinquish her determination. Indeed, it gave her strength to persist, since she believed that as soon as she had attained a worthy state she would be released from submission. She began to equip herself with knowledge against that day.

She worked in secret. She got up before dawn and wrote by candlelight, wrapped in a shawl. Notebook after notebook was filled with a mass of facts, compared, indexed, and tabulated. She wrote privately for reports to M. Mohl in Paris; she procured information on hospitals in Berlin from the Bunsens. In the cold, dark mornings she laid the foundation of the vast and detailed knowledge of sanitary conditions which was to make her the first expert in Europe. Then the breakfast bell rang, and she came down to be the Daughter at Home.

Fanny had put her in charge of stillroom, pantry, and linen room. Twice a year she went through linen room, plate chest, china and glass cupboard, and storeroom, checking, listing damage, replacements, and repairs. In the stillroom she supervised preserving, and she wrote to Hilary Bonham Carter in September, 1846, that after a hard day's work she was "surveying fifty-six jam pots with the eye of an artist."

So month followed month—it seemed without progress or event, but in her character a profound change was taking place. "I feel," she wrote in 1846, "as if all my being were gradually drawing together to one point." She decided that her longing for affection, her susceptibility were too powerful for safety and she began deliberately to detach herself from human relationships. Love, marriage, even friendship, must be renounced.

In October the Chevalier Bunsen sent her the *Year Book* of the Institution of Deaconesses at Kaiserswerth. Four years earlier he had mentioned Kaiserswerth, but she had not then reached the knowledge that nursing was her vocation. Now with overwhelming joy she realized that Kaiserswerth was what she had been seeking. "There is my home, there are my brothers and sisters all at work. There my heart is and there, I trust, will one day be my body." There she could have training in nursing, and the objections raised against English hospitals did not apply. The religious atmosphere, the ascetic discipline placed the nurses above suspicion.

The *Year Book* became her treasure, but she did not dare mention Kaiserswerth to her mother. Fanny was busier, more successful than ever, and Embley was filled for autumn parties. Whenever Florence wanted "refreshment in the midst of this

WIDE WORLD

Florence Nightingale, when she first began to study nursing

table d'hôte of people at Embley" she went upstairs and secretly read the *Year Book* of the Deaconesses of Kaiserswerth.

Florence's destiny may have demanded that marriage should be put behind her, but the desire to be loved died hard. She could not bring herself to face losing Richard Monckton Milnes. Month after month she temporized, evading the moment when she must give him a definite answer. Fanny passed from impatience to anger, accusing her of godless ingratitude, perversity, and conceit.

At this point Florence found consolation in a new friend. The previous autumn, through Clarkey, she had met Selina Bracebridge, wife of Charles Holte Bracebridge, of Atherstone Hall, near Coventry. Selina understood her. In a retrospect Miss Nightingale wrote: "She never told me life was fair and my share of its blessings great and that I *ought* to be happy. She did not know that I was miserable but she felt it; and to me, young, strong and blooming as I then was, to me, the idol of the man I adored, the spoilt child of fortune, she had the heart and the instinct to say—'Earth, my child, has a grave and in heaven there is rest.'" Selina and her husband became family friends, and she was given a pet name by the Nightingales, the Greek character "sigma"—Σ—partly in compliment to the Hellenic traits of her character, partly in reference to her love for Greece.

In the autumn of 1847 Florence broke down completely. She wrote to Clarkey that she could not face "the prospect of three winter months of perpetual row." She collapsed, and took to her bed, coughing.

She was rescued by the Bracebridges, who were going to spend the winter in Rome; Σ persuaded Fanny to let them take Florence. The fussing was enormous: over the clothes she was to take, the books she was to read, the sights she was to see. Solemn farewells were said. Parthe was overcome at the idea of a separation, and for the last few days Fanny and W. E. N. withdrew from Embley and left the two sisters alone. Florence was apathetic. "Dreaming" had enslaved her even further during her illness, and she was terrified. In a private note she wrote: "I see nothing desirable but death."

On October 27 the party left England, going overland to

Marseilles and thence by sea to Civita Vecchia, the port for Rome.

"Oh how happy I was! I never enjoyed any time in my life as much as my time in Rome," Florence wrote. One of the great moments of her life was her first sight of the Michelangelo ceiling in the Sistine Chapel. "I did not think I was looking at pictures but straight into Heaven itself." She remained alone in the Sistine for the whole of one day and for the rest of her life had prints of the Sistine frescoes hanging in her room.

She danced out the old year of 1847 into 1848, and it was "the happiest New Year I have ever spent." In January she wrote: "This is the most entire and unbroken freedom from dreaming that I ever had." Her health recovered, and she was well all the six months she was in Rome.

And in Rome she met Sidney Herbert, half brother and heir presumptive of the Earl of Pembroke, who had already attained the rank of Cabinet Minister and was in Rome on a postponed wedding tour. Their strange and fatal intimacy began in picture galleries and churches; during strolls in the Borghese gardens and sight-seeing expeditions to Tivoli. Each was destined to exercise an extraordinary influence on the other; each in meeting the other had met his and her fate; but no portent indicated that this was the most important moment of their lives. The acquaintance opened with Florence's introduction by Σ to Sidney Herbert's wife. Liz was a woman of great charm. She was beautiful, with brilliant dark eyes and a glowing olive skin. She had a childlike eagerness, a simple power of enjoyment which made her a delightful companion. After knowing her for a few weeks, Florence wrote of "the great kindness, the desire of love, the magnanimous generosity" which distinguished her character.

Fate had heaped blessing upon blessing on Sidney Herbert's head. He was astonishingly good-looking—"a tall and graceful figure surmounted by a face of such singular sweetness as to be unforgettable." His hair was thick, waving, and light golden in color, his eyes dark and shaded with long lashes. Tall, broad-shouldered yet graceful, he was a superb shot, a remarkably good horseman, and an ardent rider to hounds. He had great wealth; he lived at Wilton, one of the most beautiful houses in

WIDE WORLD

Florence Nightingale in 1889

England, which he would eventually inherit; he had a house in Belgrave Square and vast estates in Ireland in addition. He was brilliantly clever; his wit and social talents were famous; yet he secretly belonged to an association the members of which were pledged to give away a large part of their incomes in private charity.

And yet—with so much goodness, brilliance, and beauty he was without zest for life. He longed only for quiet—the peace of Wilton. "There is not a spot about Wilton which I do not love as if it were a person," he wrote. "If one had nothing to do but consult one's own taste and one's own ease I should be too glad to live down here a domestic life."

It was impossible. Fate heaped on him glittering prize after glittering prize. Riches, high office, power, responsibility descended on him. He found the burden almost intolerable and turned for consolation to religion—both Sidney Herbert and his wife were devout Christians who consecrated their lives to philanthropic works. He built a new church at Wilton, he worked to improve the condition of the poor, he was in process of building and endowing a convalescent home, he was interested in a plan for emigrating sweated workers. Into these and other plans Liz threw herself heart and soul, worshiping her husband and desiring to share his every activity and thought.

In Rome the Herberts had a small circle of friends who met almost daily. One was Dr. Manning, Archdeacon of Chichester, who was wintering in Rome to improve his health, which had broken down under the stress of religious doubts; another was Mary Stanley, sister of Dr. Stanley, then Canon of Canterbury, later famous as Dean Stanley of Westminster. Florence formed a friendship with Mary Stanley because she was interested in nursing and had visited hospitals in England and Europe, and Mary Stanley developed a "passion" for her.

In April, 1848, Florence left Rome and reached home to find Fanny and Parthe occupied by the excitement and fuss of a family wedding: Laura Nicholson, Marianne's youngest sister, married Jack Bonham Carter, Hilary's eldest brother. The celebrations, in the Waverley manner, were colossal. Good will was in the air, differences were forgotten, and Florence and Parthe were bridesmaids.

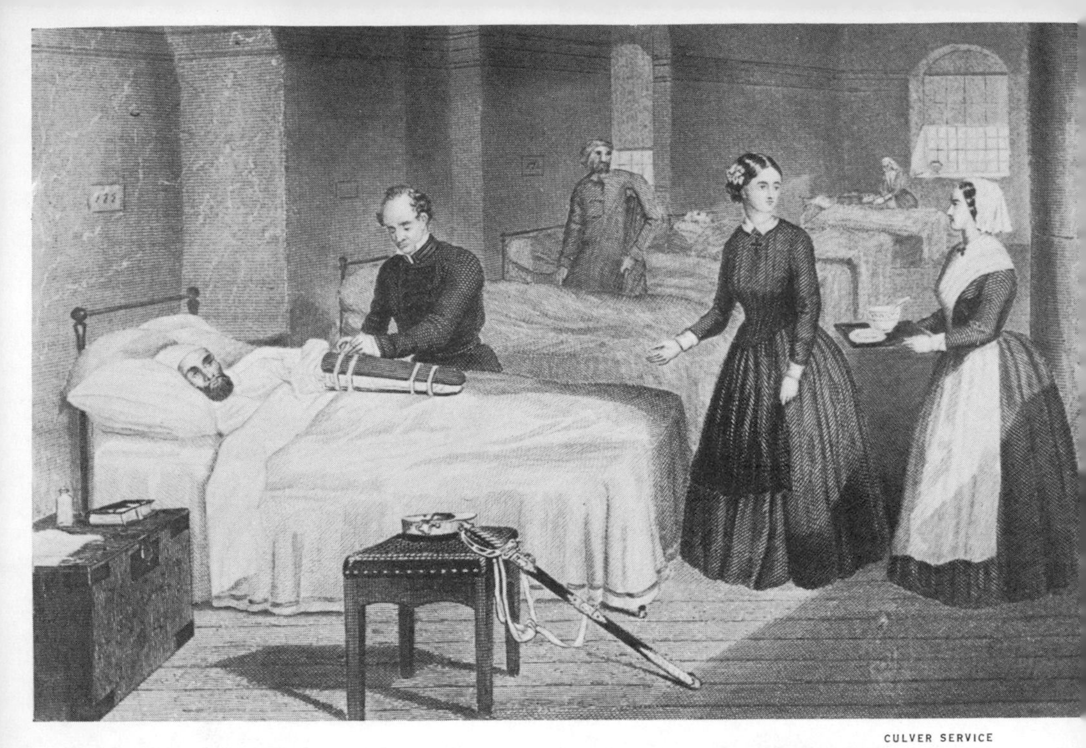

CULVER SERVICE

Florence Nightingale at the Army Hospital in Scutari, Turkey, 1854

Her friendship with the Herberts, a source of profound satisfaction to Fanny, grew closer. She stayed with them at Wilton where she met a circle of intelligent, socially impeccable, extremely influential people intensely interested in hospital reform. Public opinion was awakening; the Herberts and their friends were eager for information, and Florence, who had now been working for more than five years collecting facts on public health and hospitals, had an enormous mass of detailed information at her finger tips. She gradually became known as an expert on hospitals.

The Herberts knew of her plan to go to Kaiserswerth and approved, and the Bunsens were thinking of sending their daughter there. Once more the fulfillment of her desires seemed within the range of possibility. Who could disapprove of what the Herberts and the Bunsens approved? Surely her mother must allow herself to be convinced. But it was necessary to proceed cautiously—the very word "hospital" might be fatal.

In September, 1848, a heaven-sent opportunity offered. Parthe was ordered to take a cure at Carlsbad, and the Nightingales planned to go on to Frankfurt, where Clarkey, now married to M. Mohl, was staying with her husband. Kaiserswerth being near Frankfurt, Florence's plan was to leave her family for a week or two to "visit the Deaconesses and perhaps fit in a little training."

But 1848 was the year of revolution in Europe. When disorders broke out in Frankfurt, W. E. N. thought it wiser to stay in England, and the Nightingales went to Malvern instead of Carlsbad. "All that I most wanted to do at Kaiserswerth lay for the first time within reach of my mouth, and the ripe plum has dropped," Florence wrote to Clarkey in October.

Her reaction was violent. It was God Himself who had prevented her; God who had cut her off from Kaiserswerth because she was sinful. God wanted her to go to Kaiserswerth, but He could not let her go until she had reached a greater state of worthiness. She went down into the depths of depression; the short period of comparative happiness was over.

She dreamed of fame, of Richard Monckton Milnes. To escape from dreaming she sought relief in nursing the poor of Wellow, the village near Embley, and Fanny and Parthe became irritated. It was unnecessary for Florence to go into the "black filth" of the cottages, actually touching sick people and even making their beds. She would bring an infectious disease into the house and kill her sister. And she was always late for dinner. She visited her sick in secret, hurrying down the back drive so that she should not be seen from the house, running back breathless through the muddy lanes to be in time for dinner. W. E. N., who hated dirt, disease, and ugliness, was disgusted. He told Florence she was being theatrical.

In March, 1849, the Nightingales went to London for the season. Florence was in a mounting delirium of misery and frustration. Dreaming became uncontrollable. Agonies of guilt and self-reproach were intensified by the conviction that her worst fears were being realized and that she was going insane.

Again and again she made resolutions to end dreaming, to "tear the sin out," to "stamp it out"—but they were always broken. She turned on herself with savagery, hating herself, despairing her weakness. In this wretched state another blow fell on her. Richard Monckton Milnes would be put off no longer. He insisted on a definite answer—would she marry him or not? She refused him.

It was an act which required extraordinary courage. She was deeply stirred by him; she called him "the man I adored"; and she renounced him for the sake of a destiny which it seemed impossible she would ever fulfill. Desperately as she longed for him, she would not give way. "I know I could not bear his life," she wrote; "voluntarily to put it out of my power ever to be able to seize the chance of forming for myself a true and rich life would seem to me like suicide."

Fanny was severely disappointed and furiously resentful. Her obstinacy hardened; she determined that Florence should not have her own ungrateful way, and what had begun as genuine maternal solicitude for her daughter's welfare turned into a contest of wills in which love and kindess were forgotten.

By the autumn Florence's mental and physical state was pitiable. She was far from well and fainted on several occasions; sometimes her mind became a blank and she looked at people wildly and vaguely, not hearing what was said to her. Σ once more intervened. The Bracebridges were going to Egypt and then to Greece, and they persuaded Fanny to let them take Florence.

A journey to Egypt was an adventure in 1849. But she was in a state when Egypt, the desert, even the brilliant landscapes of the Nile itself meant as little as scenes painted on a backcloth. She was on the verge of mental collapse.

In a small black notebook she recorded her secret agonies; the entries are scribbled in pencil, in phrases which repeat themselves, in writing which wavers and becomes all but indecipherable. The weight of guilt laid on her conscience by dreaming was driving her insane.

Again Σ saved her. If Florence continued to be thwarted, she would go out of her mind. Σ acted on her own responsibility. They were to travel home from Greece by land; she chose a route through Prague and Berlin and suggested that she and her husband should spend a fortnight at Düsseldorf while Florence visited Kaiserswerth.

Florence was too exhausted, too wretched to be grateful. She found relief in the companionship of animals. On the Nile she had had two little chameleons which slept on her bed and had been "so sorry to part with them, they were such company." She

Florence Nightingale with her tame owl, Athena

was traveling now with two tortoises, a cicada named Plato, and Athena, a baby owl, which she had rescued from some Greek boys at the Parthenon. Athena was fierce, and Miss Nightingale had had to mesmerize her before she could be persuaded to enter a cage, but she became devoted to her mistress and traveled everywhere in her pocket. At Prague Athena ate Plato.

When Florence reached Berlin, she was still miserably depressed. "I had 3 paths among which to choose," she wrote on July 10, 1850. "I might have been a married woman, or a literary woman, or a hospital sister. And now it seemed to me as if quiet with somebody to look for my coming back was all I wanted."

But in Berlin she began visiting hospitals and charitable institutions, and her spirits instantly revived. "All at once I felt how rich life was." On July 31 she reached Kaiserswerth. "With the feeling with which a pilgrim first looks on the Kedron I saw the Rhine dearer to me than the Nile."

She stayed a fortnight. It was a visit of inspection, and she did not nurse but was shown the work of the institution and helped with the children.

On August 13 she left Kaiserswerth "feeling so brave as if nothing could ever vex me again." She was well, brimming with vitality, her powers of concentration had returned, and she performed the feat of dashing off a pamphlet of thirty-two pages in less than a week; telling the unwanted women kept in "busy idleness" in England, the women she saw on all sides "going mad for the want of something to do," of work, happiness, and comradeship waiting for them at Kaiserswerth. It was printed in 1851 "by the inmates of the Ragged Colonial School at Westminster" and issued anonymously under the title "The Institution of Kaiserswerth on the Rhine for the Practical Training of Deaconesses, under the direction of the Rev. Pastor Fliedner, embracing the support and care of a Hospital, Infant and Industrial Schools and a Female Penitentiary."

On August 21 she reached Lea Hurst and "surprised my dear people, sitting in the drawing room, with the owl in my pocket. Sat with Mama and Parthe in the nursery. Rode with Papa." Happiness lasted only a few hours. Fanny was furiously angry, the visit to Kaiserswerth was not to be spoken of, was shameful, a disgrace. The old resentments broke out, the old accusations were repeated. Parthe had hysterics; Fanny raged and wept. Florence must be forced to do her duty, made to stay at home, and engage in the pursuits proper to her upbringing and station.

Five years had passed since her attempt to enter Salisbury Infirmary; she was no longer a girl but a woman of thirty, and she had accomplished nothing. Only her determination persisted. "Resignation!" she had written in 1847, "I never understood that word!"

FRIDTJOF NANSEN

The Great Adventure

BY ANNA GERTRUDE HALL

Illustrations by Boris Artzybasheff

Not content with a remarkable career as a scientist and explorer of polar regions, Fridtjof Nansen (1861-1930) brilliantly served his country as a statesman, and mankind as a humanitarian. His work as League of Nations High Commissioner for Refugees won for him the Nobel Peace Prize.

THE World War awakened Fridtjof Nansen, as it did thousands of other sensitive people, to the fearfulness of warfare. The whole civilization of Europe seemed about to totter and fall in the fury of the struggle. There was nothing gallant or inspiring or noble in a devastating conflict that destroyed human beings as if they were vermin to be exterminated by any method. Ten years before, Nansen, like other people, had taken it for granted that nations should have armies and navies and should be ready to fight if it seemed necessary, but now he saw war as something so cruel, beyond all words, that he could only say: "If civilization is not to be destroyed, there must be *no more war.*"

He saw that small nations, like Belgium, like Norway perhaps, were lost if they happened to be in the way of the Great Powers. Their little armies and navies, their slender lines of fortresses would not save them; some other way must be found. All over the world, for years, men had dreamed of peace and friendliness among nations, but now the Peace Palace at The Hague stood empty and forsaken, while the nations that had built it pounded one another's borders with

guns and dropped bombs on defenseless villages. How could nations ever be friendly and trusting again, after so many years of fear and hatred? It seemed impossible. Perhaps it is impossible. The years since 1918 have often made it seem so.

To Nansen, the League of Nations was the answer. A new ship, he called it, "that sails on a new course with the future hopes of mankind on board"; but it would need to be a new ship, like the *Fram*, built on new lines to outride the shocks and pressures of the greed and pride of nations. The old ships, built of defensive alliances, balance of power, and secret treaties, had all foundered and sunk in the war. This ship must be something new; it must be built by all nations, small as well as large, the conquered as well as the conquerors, and it must be steered by the consent of all, and not by the few who were stronger.

From the time the League was first suggested, Nansen worked for it with his whole soul, not only in Norway but in the other Scandinavian countries. By the time the treaty-makers in Paris were ready to draw up the League of Nations Covenant, it seemed as if they would make it, after all, only one of the old ships, merely an alliance of the nations that had fought together under the name of the Allies; Germany and her supporters were to be left out; Russia could not come in because she had made peace while her Allies were still fighting; the little nations and the neutral nations, like Norway, were to be forgotten entirely. There was a sharp struggle before the Covenant of the League was finally completed in 1919. Nansen took part in the debates and helped open the League to the neutral nations. At home, he was able to persuade not only Norway, but other Scandinavian countries to join the League as soon as the membership was open to them.

The neutral nations had been shut out of the conferences on the treaty itself; Great Britain, France, Italy, and the United States had settled all the terms of the treaty, while the other nations looked on helplessly, feeling that a great many things should have been decided differently. The Covenant of the League of Nations did not please everyone; the United States refused to come into the League at all. In spite of everything that seemed wrong, however, Nansen urged his country to join the League, for it seemed to him the only hope for the future for small nations. If enough of them were in it, and were at all united in their demands, they might fare better than they could alone; and he was sure that the idea behind the League was right, that men and nations should join hands and work for the good of all, and that there should be no more war.

But he had given enough time to politics and diplomacy; his scientific work was calling him, and many plans had been waiting for the end of the war. Research and explorations, home and friends, and vacations in the mountains of Norway, these were the things he wanted in life, and he had lost too much time from them. The war was over and life could begin again.

But wars do not end when the guns stop; the miseries they cause live on for years, long after the armies have gone home, and the treaties are signed, and all the diplomats and their secretaries and their briefcases have left, and grass has grown over the battlefields, and even the names of the battles are forgotten. When the World War ended in 1918, there were more than half a million prisoners of war from twenty-six different nations scattered in desolate prison camps over Europe and Asia. Many of these men had been captured in the first year of the war. All of them had been cold and hungry and sick; they had been herded in camps or barracks, or shipped like animals in freight cars. Or rather, shipped in freight cars as no one of us would dream of shipping animals, locked in without food or water or heat, and left to live or die, as chance might be, while the trains rolled into Siberia. Nearly half of these prisoners, men from the armies of Germany and her allies, were scattered in Russia or western Siberia. The Russian revolution had thrown that country into such confusion that no one paid any attention to the prison camps. If ever in the world there were forgotten men, they were those war captives lost behind the turmoil of revolution, dying of hunger and cold and filth, going insane from grief and hopelessness. For years they had not heard from their homes; they did not know if they still had homes, or if their families still lived, or even if they still had countries to claim them. Many did not even know that the war had ended. They had no money to pay their way by railroad, and in many places there were no railroads, or they were no longer running. They could not walk, because they were too weak, or too ill, or the distance was too great. Many of the governments that had sent the men out to fight were no longer in existence, and there was no one to bring the exiles home.

This was the first task that faced the League of Nations when it opened its headquarters in Geneva. There was need for haste; men were dying in exile daily by the hundreds. The work should be put in the hands of some one person who could act quickly, someone who could manage great enterprises, and, most important of all, someone whom everyone would trust. An Englishman, Philip Noel-Baker, of the headquarters staff, or secretariat, suggested Fridtjof Nansen. Everyone had seen him at the conferences in Paris, the tall Norseman, head and shoulders above the crowd, with the quick, keen glance, the fearless voice, and the transparent

UNITED PRESS INTERNATIONAL

Fridtjof Nansen

sincerity and frankness. A great, simple, thoughtful man, "who could venture to say whatever he thought right to any prince, prime minister, or president in the world." He was the man for the task; would he take it?

To a telegram sent him in Christiania, Nansen returned an emphatic No. He was a scientist, a university professor, he could not take more time from his work; he had recently married for the second time, he wanted to be at home. Mr. Noel-Baker went to Christiania to see him. A month or two of his time, that was all the League would ask, just to make a plan for moving all these men, and to estimate the cost; the League would see to the rest.

How many prisoners were there? No one knew.

Would the Soviet government help at all? Mr. Noel-Baker could not say.

Where would the money come from? From the League? Perhaps, but the League at present had no money.

Where would they get food, clothing, medical supplies, trains, ships? No one knew; that was what the League wanted him to find out. And this time, Nansen said Yes. Was this, perhaps, the great work, the flash of lightning for which he had looked as a young man? He did not think so at the time, but as the years rolled on, he found himself in a work that he could not lay down. He was fifty-nine years old now; he no longer dreamed of storming the heavens; his life was full, and he was content; why should he turn to new work?

The reasons are not far to seek. His sympathies were touched by the sufferings of the prisoners as Mr. Noel-Baker described them, but also he saw here a chance to make the League truly the new ship on a new course. All over the world people were saying that a League of Nations was only the fanciful dream of a few visionaries, an idle waste of time and money that could serve no practical purpose. By returning these prisoners to their homes he would prove that the League could be practical, and that it was able to do things no one else could do, things that would make people friendly and happy again where for so long they had been sad and bitter.

It was April 11, 1920 when Nansen left Christiania. On

May 19, the first shipload of prisoners steamed across the Baltic from the Russian port of Narva to Swinemünde in Germany at the mouth of the Oder River. An almost incredible amount of work lay between those two dates. The first obstacle had been Russia, defiant, fighting with her back to the wall, torn by revolution and counter-revolution, and without a friend in Europe. Other nations had refused to recognize the new Soviet government; many of them were secretly helping its enemies; the treaty-makers at Versailles the year before, in spite of Nansen's efforts, had refused to send help to the famine-threatened districts of Russia except under terms that would have meant the defeat of the Soviet by the White armies. Naturally the Soviet government trusted no one, would not let relief workers from other countries enter its territories, and emphatically would not do business with the League of Nations. More than half the prisoners were either in Russia or must be moved across Russian territory. Nansen was blunt: Either the Soviet government must find some way to work with him, or else his train would leave Moscow in two hours, and the responsibility for those thousands of sick and dying men would lie directly at Russia's door. That brought Foreign Minister Chicherin to the point; the Soviet would work with Nansen gladly, but not with the League. Nansen asked: Would it work with him as representative of the separate governments involved, leaving the League out of the question? Yes. And would the Soviet undertake getting the necessary credentials from the separate governments, and allow him to go to work at once? Certainly. It took more than six months to get the credentials, but in the meantime Nansen had been at work, and the task was half done. Two years later Nansen reported to the League that the Soviet had worked with him in complete friendliness, that it had kept every agreement it had made, and had often done more than it promised.

The next problem was to find money. The governments of Europe were wrung dry with war costs; the League of Nations had no money as yet. An international loan, backed by the League, brought more than a million dollars to be used for transportation from the Russian border. The Soviet government provided free transportation within Russia. For other expenses, such as food, clothing, and medicine, a central committee was formed, called the Nansen Relief Committee, which could raise funds from private sources and use them wherever they were needed.

Trains to carry prisoners across Russia were furnished by the Soviet at the rate of two a week. For ships, Nansen turned to England, which held the surrendered German fleet. England refused to lend them at first, but finally yielded and let him use fourteen ships.

Every step of the way was set about with difficulties, with bitterness and jealousy. Nations do not fight for four years and then become all at once agreeable, friendly, and easy to get along with; they keep on fighting in their minds long after they stop actually killing each other. No one can ever know how much patience and steadfastness and courage Nansen showed day after day in meeting the petty quibbling, the cold indifference, the cruel opposition that lay in his way.

From the time the first ship left Narva on May 19, until Nansen made his first report to the League in November, one hundred and fifty thousand men had been sent home across the Baltic Sea. Others from southern Russia were brought out by the Black Sea and the Mediterranean. Fifteen thousand men who had escaped across Siberia to Vladivostok were sent home half around the globe by way of the United States. At the end of 1921, eighteen months after the work began, 427,886 prisoners had been returned to their homes. And, what was almost as important, they had brought no epidemics with them. Typhus, the louse-borne disease, was the scourge of every prison camp, but so well did the Red Cross handle the quarantine and disinfection camps at the ports that every prisoner reached home clean, warmly clothed, and free of lice and of infection. And the cost? The first estimates made by various relief agencies and the League secretariat had been about two hundred dollars per man, and to take them out by Vladivostok, if Russia had refused to work with them, would have cost about six hundred dollars per man. But this university professor, this dreamer of the brotherhood of man, no business man, no financier, had

brought all these men home at an average cost of eight dollars and sixty cents each!

Can we realize what this homecoming meant? Nearly half a million lost and ruined men returned to their homes, their families, to familiar work and play? If we think what it would mean for just one man, after six hopeless years, to come home to a family that had not known all that time whether he was alive or dead, we can begin to picture what it would mean to the five hundred thousand. Philip Noel-Baker said of the work: "There is not a country on the continent of Europe where wives and mothers have not wept in gratitude for the work which Nansen did." And Nansen himself said: "Never in my life have I seen so much terrible suffering as in this attempt to lessen it." But he was to see much more in the next few years.

Prisoners of war, then refugees. Probably never in the history of the world had there been so many people driven from their native lands by war and revolution as in the ten years after the Russian revolution. In September 1921 the League estimated that a million and a half Russians had fled from the revolution and were scattered over Europe and Asia. A few of these were wealthy, for they had foreseen the revolution, and had sent money, jewels, and securities to other countries before the storm broke. More of them had been wealthy and used to every luxury, but had escaped with nothing except their lives. A few of them were trained for occupations that they could follow in foreign countries, as teachers, musicians, artists, scientists, or technicians, but more of them had been army officers and government officials, who knew only how to give orders to others. Thousands were disabled soldiers, invalids, and old people, who could do only the lightest work, if any at all. Many were finding a living only in the underworld; others were doing work for which they were not fitted, or which was destroying their self-respect and self-confidence. In every country there were hundreds of such people, homeless, without money or work.

After the defeat of the White armies in 1920, it was plain to everyone that these Russians could never safely go back to Russia or recover their property; they must be given work and permanent homes somewhere else in the world. The countries nearest Russia, such as Poland, Turkey, Rumania, Lithuania, and Germany, were war-swept and distressed, with thousands of their own returned soldiers tramping the roads in rags looking for work, and it was in these countries that the refugees were gathered in greatest numbers, without means for going farther. Constantinople became the nearest asylum for refugees from all the countries to the east of it. From Wrangel's defeated army alone ninety thousand starving refugees descended upon the city. During the next few years the city received in all one hundred and seventy thousand Russians, seventy-five thousand Turks, and one hundred and fifty-five thousand Greeks and Armenians. Such masses of people in such poverty meant, not only unbelievable human suffering, but also two great dangers to the nations that sheltered them: political unrest and epidemics of disease.

In the spring of 1921, the Red Cross came to the League of Nations for help. Relief societies had been trying to take care of these refugees, but so many countries were involved that there must be some one person at the head of the whole work, someone who would have official standing and power to make agreements with the different governments, as had been done in the work for the prisoners of war. The Council of the League turned to Nansen. Would he act as the League's

High Commissioner for Refugees, uniting all these relief organizations and the work of the different governments in one plan? He could not refuse, for here was proof that the work he had been doing for the prisoners had shown the world that the League of Nations was needed, that it could do work that no one else could do, that it was already becoming important.

The work he began in 1921 was still unfinished in 1939 when World War II broke out. During those years exiles of many countries were cared for by a bureau of the League called the Nansen International Office for Refugees. The Nobel Peace Prize of 1939 was awarded this bureau, the first time the prize had been given to an organization instead of to an individual.

It would fill a whole book to tell all that the High Commissioner for Refugees did in those early years of the twenties when the need was the greatest. First, in September 1921, he called a conference of leaders from thirteen countries to discuss the whole situation and to make plans for working together. He then appointed his own officials in each country, giving them as their first task the gathering of facts about the exiles—how many there were, where they were living, what work they were able to do, how many were children, how many were sick, or aged, or disabled. He himself worked with the International Labor Bureau of the League, studying the labor needs and conditions in every country of the world, seeking places where more workers were needed.

There are great difficulties in moving large numbers of people from one country to another, especially when they are homesick and desperately unhappy. They want the same ways of living that they had at home, they do not understand the languages of the people about them, they do not like their ways, and they cannot make their new neighbors like and understand them. Many of us know how hard it is sometimes to move to a town only a few miles from home, or even to go to a different school in our own town, and can understand a little how homesick and unhappy these people were.

It was out of the question to put each one of these Rus-

sians in the place he might like best, but Nansen did try to send each one to a place where he could find work. A few thousand could go back to Russia, but the greater number neither could nor wanted to return. As far as he could, he sent children and young people where there were schools and colleges for them. Czechoslovakia took thousands; Bulgaria put five thousand children in Russian schools; before long, nearly every nation in the League had taken numbers of young Russians and placed them in schools. Many Jewish refugees were settled in Palestine and the United States. Yugoslavia, where war and typhus had killed the youngest and strongest, had room for fifty-five thousand refugees. In one year, out of Constantinople alone, the League moved twenty thousand refugees, settling them in forty-five different countries.

One obstacle to moving the refugees arose almost at once —they were no longer citizens of any country, they had no passports, and without passports they could not enter foreign countries. It was another of those times when all the wise men said: "It can't be done," and Nansen said: "There is always a way to do things that must be done." He called a conference of thirty-one countries at Geneva in 1922, and proposed that his office give each refugee a simple paper of

identification, and that the nations agree to recognize it as a passport. More than fifty nations finally recognized these "Nansen Passes" bearing Nansen's portrait, and hundreds of thousands of them were issued. Every holder of a Nansen Pass could renew it every year by paying a fee of about a dollar. The money paid for these renewals was used to care for refugees who could not find work or who were otherwise in need. With a Nansen Pass a homeless exile could travel from country to country until he found work and a chance for a permanent home.

No one person can ever tell the whole story of all the sufferings of these sad and broken people. Of just one group of two hundred and fifty whom Nansen found on a barren beach outside Constantinople the story is tragic enough to help us imagine something of the total sum of grief. Fleeing from Russia in 1920, with Wrangel's defeated army, they had come first to Constantinople, and from there had been sent by the League to Bulgaria, where workers were needed. A year later the Bulgarian government, suspecting them of being Bolsheviks, first shut them in a prison camp, then decided to send them back to Russia. Without notifying the Soviet government of what they were doing, they packed two hundred and fifty bewildered men, women, and children on a

small leaky vessel, barely large enough to carry fifty persons safely, with the scantiest of rations, and dispatched them across the Black Sea to Odessa. The port officials at Odessa, knowing nothing about them, refused to let them land and turned them back from the harbor, without allowing them even to obtain more food and water. There was nowhere for them to go, except back to Turkey, and after a voyage of twenty-six days, with the ship barely able to keep afloat, they reached Constantinople. Here the Turkish police refused to let them disembark and sent out a tug to tow them back into the Black Sea. By this time the ship was really sinking, and the terrified passengers were leaping into the water in a hopeless attempt to swim ashore. The captain of an English ship in the harbor interfered and forced the Turks to let the Russians land. The Turks let them land, but herded them onto a narrow, windswept beach, took away all their money, and left them without food or bedding. When Nansen was taken to see them, they were camped on the bare ground, as many as possible under an old boat house, the others outside, cold and soaked to the skin with rain. They were in rags, they had no blankets, no fuel, nothing. Their only food was a little bread and a cup of thin soup once a day, furnished by some charitable Englishmen in the city.

Such misery! And all Constantinople was full of tragic men and women! Nansen sent out an appeal for money to care for refugees like these until work could be found for them, and received it from all the world, and especially from the United States, whose American Relief Administration was working all over Europe. Nansen said once that the United States alone among the great nations did not "count on its buttons to see whether or not it was good policy to feed the hungry."

EDGAR ALLAN POE

Growing Pains

BY LAURA BENÉT

Illustrations by George Gillett Whitney

The weird contrasts of beauty and horror in the work of Edgar Allan Poe (1809-1849) rose not only from his fervid imagination but also from the sharp changes he suffered in life. Raised by wealthy foster parents, Edgar was given every advantage. But when he was sixteen, his beloved "Ma" Allan died, and he quarreled with his strict foster father. The rest of his life is an ugly story of bitterness and degradation. The following excerpt shows Edgar at the age of twelve, arriving home in Richmond after five years away at school in England.

WHAT did the old city or town look like to Edgar Allan Poe (for so he was now to be called, his foster father thinking it better to give him his own name)? The boy stared and stared, for after a five years' absence things no longer seemed familiar. First he was aware of the heat—a heavy, settling blanket that kept him sleepy most of the time; next of his old friends, the negroes. They seemed strange to him at first with their slurred speech and the grinning white of their teeth showing in the black faces. But they exhibited real joy in welcoming their "Marse Eddie" home again and exclaiming with cries of delight over his growth and sturdiness.

After the drowsy English village there was stirring life in this aristocratic little city. Carriages drawn by blooded horses passed up and down through the streets, especially in the cool of the day. Black slaves in livery drove or stood at the back of the carriages as footmen. The white houses of Richmond were of Georgian design, with colonial porticos and lawns and gardens. They were the homes of distinguished men—lawyers, divines, statesmen. How sweet these Southern gardens smelled, what beautiful and graceful manners the ladies had, what profusion of living there was everywhere. Outside the city there lay plantations, with dozens and dozens of field hands working the cotton and tobacco, summoned to their meals by the horn. Edgar was to develop a growing love for John Allan's country place, called the "Hermitage," a plantation not far from Richmond. He was to frequent the docks of the city and watch the ancient canal boats, mule-drawn. Above all, he was to know that he was a Virginian—elegant word. Soon, sooner than he would have believed possible, he was to lose all feeling of nostalgia for England. Life would have been satisfactory, highly so, if Pa had always been his old genial self and Ma less complaining of her health.

The Allans were compelled perforce, to visit for a while, until a house could be found for them. Mr. Ellis was glad to escape for a little vacation, leaving John Allan in charge. When he returned with his family, little Tom Ellis began to wander about with Edgar, to be his adoring slave, while the visitors remained at their home. Edgar, still feeling his way about this new territory, made Tom his guide and companion.

"Come along. Want to go exploring with me?" he said in a low tone to his hero-worshipper, one Saturday in the fall. "I'm going off for the day, beyond Belvedere to shoot game. Can you shoot?"

"No—not yet." Tom shook his head with a crestfallen expression.

"I'll teach you—and help you to swim, too, if we can find a good place." Edgar's eyes sparkled.

Thomas Ellis was several years younger and this invitation was an honor. He wanted nothing better than to follow in the footsteps of his idol. Ah, what a day that was for two prowling, mischievous boys! Belvedere was Judge Bushrod Washington's estate and the fowl they discovered there were not wild but domestic.

"Bang! Bang!" went young Edgar Poe's gun when he spied

them and to Tom's secret horror, the chickens went down like tenpins before him. Their corpses had to be secreted in the bushes.

"Now come, Tom," commanded the bigger boy, "we've got to pull the feathers off this chicken if we want to roast it!"

A fire was hastily built by the chief of this expedition of two and a chicken was at least partially roasted and devoured half raw by the hunters.

"Tom, you climb the fence and raid that turnip field over there. We'll have turnips with our dinner."

When dinner was over, small Tom, shivering with the hectic delight of this adventure, was taken to a stream with a waterfall near by and ignominiously thrown in.

"Strike out like a dog now! Paddle!" cried his teacher. And poor, dazed Tom did strike out—in the wrong direction and might have gone to the bottom. But Edgar plunged at once to his rescue and skilfully brought him up. His clothes had to be dried at a fire. Dark had fallen when they at last reached Richmond.

At home there was a lurid day of reckoning, for many of the dead game chickens accompanied the boys as lawful plunder. Pa, usually so proud of his foster son, flushed to the ears with wrath when he caught the boys sneaking out to the shed.

"Edgar, I hear you boys have been at Belvedere. May I ask if you were poaching on the judge's property?" He looked fairly distraught at seeing the limp bodies and bright feathers that Tom's little sister, Jane, was already pulling out of the knapsack the boys had tried to secrete in the outhouse. "Lad, I am amazed at such behavior, I am that. Your head's good enough. Why do you shame me in this manner? Leading Tom here off for the day and dark falling before your mother or Mrs. Ellis knew where you were. Edgar, you've not behaved like a gentleman. I am sadly disappointed. You must be chastised for this. Come with me at once"—and Mr. Allan went in search of a sharp switch.

Black James, son of Mrs. Allan's coachman, his eyes rolling in his head, commented upon the event thus, "Marse Edgar is a maunstous baid boy but he has an extry haid on him."

As for young Tom, he got off with a suitable and lengthy lecture and a mild whipping. Very mean he felt on hearing the sound of the old-fashioned switching Edgar was receiving in the shed. Never but that one time did his admirer see Pa whip Edgar. On the contrary, Edgar was his foster father's close companion. He took him about with him, read with him. They walked together. It seemed strange to Tom that the Allans wanted a daughter as well and begged constantly to be allowed to adopt his little sister, Jane. But of course Mr. and Mrs. Ellis would never consent to such an offer.

With the coming of fall, Mr. Allan found a new home, a house on "Clay Street beyond old St. James Church—a low wooden house with five rooms on the ground floor and a garret at the top." When his family was established in it, common sense told him that Edgar must lose no time in getting back to school. To a friend, the foster father remarked, "Edgar is wayward and impulsive but that is to be expected from genius. He will some day fill the world with his fame." And he himself took this boy who was his pride to be entered at Master Joseph Clarke's English and Classical School, as it was sonorously called. Otherwise it was the "Academy on the Hill," situated at Broad Street near Fifth.

Master Clarke was a bluff, gifted Irishman and a Latinist of the first order. After greeting Mr. Allan, he suggested, "Let your son put down his name on the school register."

Edgar hesitated a moment and said something in a low tone

to his father. Up to this time he had been "Master Allan." But his father nodded approvingly and he wrote "Edgar Allan Poe" in a distinct, small hand, wonderfully legible for a boy of twelve.

"Now let me see," said Master Clarke, addressing himself to the new scholar, "how far have you progressed in Latin?"

"As far as irregular verbs, sir."

"Decline some nouns—let me see—*penna, domus, res* and *fructus.*"

The speed and accuracy with which this was done gladdened the schoolmaster's heart.

"Now for some adjectives," he said. "*Bonus,* for instance."

"*Bonus,* a good man," rehearsed nimble-tongued Edgar, "*bona,* a good woman, *bonum,* a good thing."

"Excellent! I shall now know where to place you," Master Clarke exclaimed. There was something that drew him strongly to his new pupil. He shook hands with Mr. Allan and congratulated him on his son's ability.

"Yes," said the elder man, complacently, "Edgar is quite brilliant."

Master Clarke could afterwards testify that during the years spent with him at the Academy, Edgar "read Ovid, Caesar, Virgil, Cicero and Horace in Latin; and Xenophon and Homer in Greek but showed a stronger taste for classic poetry than for classic prose." His schoolmaster was to take a vital interest in all this boy said and did. Edgar was to study for him and to enjoy studying.

Among his school friends there was one, Robert Sully, a slender, frail lad, six years his senior, who was the son of the actor, Matthew Sully. Matthew Sully had once played in the Charleston Comedians with Edgar's mother. This was a special bond between the two boys. Robert had no taste for Latin and many were the whispered colloquies between the desks.

"I *can't* get this passage; I can't understand half the words!"

"Wait after school. I'll help you with it, Rob."

Rob waited many times and purposely, for the pleasure of Edgar's companionship, while Edgar took up the cudgels for his friend against onslaughts on the part of stronger boys who wanted to torment him.

One brilliant, frosty Saturday in the late fall, when Rob was doing nothing interesting but sat gazing listlessly out of his sitting room window, he heard a halloa from outside. There stood his friend Edgar, eyes dancing. What a handsome boy he was! His adopted parents were certainly sparing no pains with his education and manners. He was graceful, polished and bewitching.

"Come along with you, Rob," he called. "We are going to the Hermitage woods for chinquapins and you must come along with us. Uncle Billy is going for a load of pine-tags. We can ride in his wagon, so it won't tire you!"

To his real astonishment, the pale, sickly boy did actually go on the rough ride and enjoyed it as Billy rattled the wagon along at a brisk rate.

Yes, there were happy Saturdays spent with various friends at every season of the year, Saturdays when the harem-scarem quality in Edgar's blood ran high. Though Pa did not approve of his making a friend of the chum of his childhood, Ebenezer Burling, Edgar often spent nights at his cottage. It was low-built enough to enable prankish youths to climb in and out of a window. This gave a special feeling of adventure and he knew Ma or Aunt Nancy would cover up his disappearance.

After breakfast in the spring mornings and a hasty devouring of hot breads and sausage, Mrs. Burling would see that the boys had a good luncheon put up to take with them. Then

Ebenezer would begin, "Now for the boat. I swear, Edgar, I hope no one has borrowed it. I left it tied in a safe place last night. How far do you think you can swim now?"

During the summer, as Edgar had taught Tom Ellis, Ebenezer had instructed Edgar, product of an English playground, in a number of advanced strokes. Off went two boys to the reaches and quiet little inlets of the James River, so much larger and more satisfactory than the minute streams of England. A volume of their adored *Robinson Crusoe* was carried with the lunch basket. Utter liberty rejoiced both their hearts. There was no knowing whether they would swim, fish or act out their parts of Robinson Crusoe and Man Friday on some one of these islands. Perhaps they might not return till dusk. But there was always the window to climb in.

Once in the river nook they chose, they took turns at spying out passages in *Robinson Crusoe* that made their eyes dance, their hearts beat faster, as they planned explorations in their own skiff.

"The boat," read Edgar, "was really much bigger than I ever saw a canoe or periagua that was made of one tree, in my life. Many a weary stroke it had cost . . . and there remained nothing but to get it into the water; and had I gotten it into the water, I made no question but I should have begun the maddest voyage, and the most unlikely to be performed that was ever undertaken." He stopped, handing the book to Ebenezer.

"Though my little periagua was finished," continued Ebenezer, interestedly, "yet the size of it was not at all answerable to the design which I had in view when I made the first; I mean, of venturing over to the terra firma, where it was above forty miles broad. . . . As I had a boat, my next design was to make a tour round the island. . . ."

Here Edgar took up the exciting narrative. "It happened one day, about noon, going towards my boat, I was exceedingly surprised with the print of a man's naked foot on the shore, which was very plain to see in the sand. I stood like one thunderstruck or as if I had seen an apparition. I listened, I looked round me, I could hear nothing nor see anything. I went up to a rising ground, to look farther, I went up the shore and down the shore, but it was all one; I could see no other impression but that. . . .

There was exactly the very print of a foot—toes, heel, and every part. How it came thither I knew not."

"And there lies the mystery," cried Edgar with sparkling eyes. "Let us play that scene!" How delightfully the romantic river with its swirling currents and wooded islands lent itself to the play. Goats had to be left out of the drama—but that was all.

Edgar's mama was vague in her mind about these excursions; but then she had to lie on the sofa a good deal. Robust Aunt Nancy, well and cheerful, was the life of the household. Pa must *not* be told that Eddie had been on the river all day and spent the night with that Burling boy, who was said to be quite wild. The string of fresh fish Eddie often brought home would be consigned to a servant and hurried out of sight. Nevertheless both the ladies felt it was good that their darling had young companionship with those of his own age. They were genuinely troubled when he stayed up in the garret for hours with that verse-writing he had begun to do. Besides Ebenezer, their Edgar ran to Roberts; Rob Sully, Robert Cabell, little Rob Stanard were, with Jack Mackenzie, his best friends. He missed having neither brother nor sister to help him romp in the quiet house. More and more when he was not playing pranks about Richmond in his free time or going on the river to boat and swim, he retired to the garret, his own special domain. Then, all at once, there would be an overflow of animal spirits, caused no doubt by his being solitary for a while. But, whatever he did, he was the joy of Frances Allan's life!

Though letters had passed between the Poes and the Allans, Edgar was not for some time aware that his elder brother by two years, William Henry Leonard Poe, was growing up. This boy lived in Baltimore with his grandparents. General Poe, their grandfather, had wanted Edgar to come to them after their mother's death. But John Allan had refused by holding out promises to him of a fine education and certain other advantages for young Edgar.

Mr. Charles Ellis, senior partner at Ellis and Allan, had a whist party one evening, the august and regular meeting of the "Gentlemen's Whist Club." The aforesaid gentlemen, representing the cream of Richmond society, with nicely curled heads, blue broadcloth coats, ruffles, stocks, buckled shoes, were gazing absorbedly at their cards as they sipped rum punch and thought of their stakes. Suddenly there appeared among them as neatly and complacently as though his "walking" were a daily feat—a ghost!

There was a hush—then General Winfield Scott, who thought phantoms a minor incident, sprang toward the sheeted figure. But a physician, Dr. Thornton, was quicker. Being close to the door, he tried to force a retreat on the part of the "ha'nt," endeavoring to tweak its nose. But the ghost, versed also in the noble art of self defense, whacked him over the shoulders with a singularly familiar-looking cane, thus holding him at bay.

After a few minutes, however, the unlucky specter got more and more deeply involved because of the muffling sheet which threatened to trip his feet.

The gentlemen, outraged at the delay of their game, fell upon the figure in a body, robbing him of robe and mask and—a delicious laugh, with something of the eerie in it, rang through the room. The night visitant was (they might have known it) Edgar Poe, of the charm, the good manners, the remarkable, long-lashed gray eyes.

Wayward, graceful, thoughtless Edgar, with a lithe body and ever too active mind, was too brilliant to be intimate with the majority; and, because of his adopted mother's health, was never allowed or encouraged to bring schoolfellows home to spend the night with him as other boys did. So, in the seclusion of his room verse-making went on, addressed (for the sake of practice) to various and sundry of the "young ladies" in Miss Jane Mackenzie's aristocratic boarding school on Franklin Street, with its high garden wall. Quick-witted Eddie soon discovered that Rosalie, his sister, anything but bright in other directions, was a good-natured messenger. He made use of her ability in this direction.

"Rose, take this drawing and note to Miss So-and-so," he would breathe in her ear, pressing it into her willing hand, "and tell her" (the particular "she" might be Sally or Jane or Bessie) "to send me back a lock of her hair. Don't fail now."

Rosalie did not fail her brother; she was too much thrilled at the importance of such an errand.

These missives and attentions began to seriously worry Miss Jane Mackenzie, who wished to keep her exclusive dovecote of young ladies free from any such intrusions. By nature she detested Boys. Shaking her elegant cap with the lavender ribbons and the "frisette," stately Miss Jane told her sister-in-law, Rosalie's foster mother, "that that Edgar Poe, whom the Allans had mistakenly adopted, was a wild, bad boy and would come to no good end."

Edgar's passionate and growing love for literature and all its works, found an outlet in a most unexpected place—the dusty second story of Ellis and Allan's counting house! Here, perched on a box or stool or perhaps stretched his full length on the floor, an eager-faced boy dipped into the firm's liberal store of foreign periodicals. One of his favorites was the many-volumed *Critical Review of Annals of Literature,* fresh from England.

Absorbing information as a sponge soaks up water, Edgar, content and happy in his realm of books, might be summoned downstairs by an intruding bell. Often he served as messenger between his father and his father's partner, Mr. Ellis.

"Here," the clerk in charge would say, "Mr. Ellis wants you to carry important papers to Mr. Allan."

Or again, he would be entrusted with some package of valuables to deliver to a client. He always executed these commissions well.

Again his foster father would decide to give Edgar, for his own good, some clerking experience in selling goods over the counter or casting up accounts. Here, too, he was apt, realizing that his future might be with the firm. Customers, many of them friends of the Allan family, loved to transact their business with Edgar on the other side of the counter.

"What beautiful manners he has! How courtly he is!" the elegantly shawled and bonneted ladies would murmur.

Literary lights of the town, dropping in for tobacco, would often invite him to recite a poem for the pleasure of seeing his dark eyes roll dramatically. Clerks would cry, "Give us a song" —and as he had sung unaffectedly for his parents' pleasure as a child, so he would sing for them. Employees at Ellis and Allan's were all by way of being his friends.

But—a clerk in one of the principal dry-goods stores of the town suddenly became the victim of Edgar's rooted dislike. Why? Because this fellow had dared to lift his eyes, he was actually making advances to one of the fluffy damsels to whom Edgar sent notes. Furthermore, Edgar believed him to be one of those in the town who often sneered at him "for being the son of strolling players." This was a bitter pill. But he would put that rascal Pitts on a hot griddle; he would get even with him, that he would. Clenching his teeth, Edgar made up his mind to punish his rival in subtle fashion. Besides writing romantic verses, he could write satire when he pleased and was not slow in setting to work. Pitts would not cast even furtive sheeps' eyes upon the lady of his choice any longer.

CULVER SERVICE

Engraving of Poe at the age of 19, from a painting by H. Inman

A few days later, after much scribbling and burning of candles, a long satire with the title, "Oh Tempora! Oh Mores!" appeared in the Richmond local paper. As if by chance, the very night it was printed, Edgar strolled over to Miss Mackenzie's school to see his sister. Rosalie ran to him at once. Several girls were chatting in the parlor. She led him there and before them all, thrust a paper at him.

"Do, Eddie, read this aloud to us. It is *so* funny—that is, if you can see by this light." (For the light in the parlor was quite dim.)

Seated in the sofa corner, Edgar gallantly complied and read distinctly and without peering at the text,

> "For at a ball what fair one can escape
> The pretty little hand that sold her tape,
> Or who so cold, so callous, to refuse
> The youth who cut the ribbon for her shoes!"

and so on to another verse,

> "At me in vengeance shall that foot be shaken—
> Another proof of thought, I'm not mistaken—
> Because to his cat's eyes I hold a glass
> And let him see himself a proper ass?
> I think he'll take his likeness to himself,
> But if he won't *he shall,* the stupid elf,
> And, lest the guessing throw the fool in fits,
> I close the portrait with the name of Pitts."

By this time the girls, who had listened innocently enough, thought their friend singularly perfect in his reading. All at once the secret was out and several merry voices cried in chorus: "*You* wrote it, Edgar!"

Edgar, pleased as Punch, did not deny that he had. Alas for Pitts, the dry-goods clerk. He attained such local notoriety that he soon found life intolerable and left Richmond for another town. Ridicule was a weapon that Edgar (if in the mood) could use with great skill—though he hated to have it directed at him.

Other eyes were looking critically at his verses. One afternoon, pompous old Master Clarke, the school teacher, about to retire in the fall of 1823, was visited privately by John Allan himself, the redoubtable Pa of Edgar's life. Admitted to the parlor, this respected gentleman cleared his throat, extended his hand. "Master Clarke," he began.

"'Pon my soul," said the fiery Irishman, looking sharply through his spectacles. "Mr. Allan, sir, be seated. How can I serve you?"

Mr. Allan wiped his high forehead with an initialed lawn handkerchief, and laid a little bundle of papers on the schoolmaster's knee. "Edgar's work," was the worthy merchant's comment. He seemed secretly pleased, though he would not admit it.

"Ah, what have we here? Writings, verses, 'pon my soul."

Mr. Allan cleared his throat. "I must inform you that Edgar wishes to have this book—as he is pleased to term it—published. I promised to do what I could, after first submitting it to your approval. Friends to whom I have read some of these, call them trash—but I swear I like the imagery of these lines on the Lake, describing the Tarn of Arran. We went there, ye know. It is overshadowed by a great mountain and at sunset is truly a wonderful sight. They call it 'the cauldron of the geese.' I am Scotch born, myself, ye see"—and leaning over, he pointed to the lines:

> "In youth's spring it was my lot
> To haunt of the wide earth a spot
> The which I could not love the less;
> So lovely was the loneliness
> Of a wild lake, with black rock bound,
> And the tall pines that towered around . . .
> But when the night had thrown her pall
> Upon that spot as upon all,
> And the wind would pass me by
> In its stilly melody" . . .

"True; it's haunting," agreed Joseph Clarke. Then, addressing himself to the bundle, he unfolded the first poem and began to read, then to roar with laughter. "Calf love has caught your boy early," he spluttered. "The rogue! Yet it can hardly be called *calf love,* since numerous damsels are mentioned in these effusions. Faith, sir, Mr. Allan, he is writing to all Richmond. Look at the names here, 'Louisa, Susan, Eliza, Jane, Myra.' He must be making trouble for Miss Mackenzie and the virgins in her boarding establishment."

"I fear so—he has made that feather-headed sister of his the bearer of these missives," said Mr. Allan, smiling in spite of himself.

The Irishman chuckled and kept on chuckling as he read further. "Does he ask for locks of hair and send candy along with the notes? He draws pictures of the ladies, that I know, from the specimens I have found among his papers."

"Yes, yes," replied the foster father testily, striking the floor with his stick. "The question is—what shall I do with Edgar,

Master Clarke? You've had him under you for two and a half years. Are you of the opinion that he has a good head on him? He goes for long walks alone and picks flowers and draws pictures and, except for girls, he cares only for Rob Sully and that worthless, wild son of the widow Burling."

Bewildered anger stood in the merchant's eyes. Since his return home three years before and the breakdown of his health, he was a changed being. He had become far harder, grasping and more inflexible than the man who once rode a certain bright, attractive little boy on his knee.

"Edgar writes late at night upstairs," he continued.

A serious, almost prophetic look had come over Mr. Clarke's face. "Mr. Allan, if you'll excuse me, sir," were his words, "you take that boy a trifle too hard. Remember, he's growing up and growing up is a difficult business for the young. After these next few years are over he'll be—or I am very much mistaken—a credit to you and Mrs. Allan, your lady. A grand credit! He has a brain and the germ of a rich imagination, is ridden by it and may startle the world. As bright a student as I ever had in my charge."

"Sometimes, ye ken, I think him promising," answered Mr. Allan, much gratified but not showing it, and relapsing into the Scotch burr, as he always did when moved. "But the young scoundrel's fond of girls and their ways."

"Why would he not be at his age? He has a sweet disposition —is always cheerful and brimful of mirth—and a very great favorite with his school mates. I never have occasion to speak a harsh word to him, much less to make him do penance. He has, I assure you sir, the ambition to excel."

This statement, as even strict John Allan had the wit to know, was high praise from the schoolmaster.

"Yet," resumed Master Clarke, "I should certainly not have his verses go into print just now. At his age such a step might do him no good. He is too excitable and easily flattered to be pointed out now as the author of a volume of verse."

Mr. Allan agreed that publication at the moment was not the part of common sense; shook hands heartily and took his leave. Thus the common bond of interest in Edgar's writing that might have kept father and son close was gone forever.

But if Edgar could not print his original verses, he could do poetic translations from Horace. All the boys in his class—Jack Preston, Robert Mayo, Channing Moore, Nat and William Howard, John Brockenborough, Rob Sully, Richard Ambler, Creed Thomas, Joseph and Miles Selden, Robert Cabell—were admiring and almost envious of his powers.

One day Schoolmaster Clarke gave Edgar free rein, telling him to read and render into English one of his favorite passages from the Odes of Horace. Edgar began almost lovingly, for his favorite rhythms were the iambic and sapphic. He read gravely and musically:

> "*Non ebur neque aureum*
> *Mea renidet in domo lacunar*" . . .

"Yes, translate it," said Master Clark, genially, beating time with his quill pen.

The clear, well-modulated voice went on: "Not ivory nor a fretted ceiling adorned with gold, glitters in my house."

"Good. Now we will double cap some verses. Get into line" —for before school hours ended for the day, all Latin scholars went through this rigid drill, several times a week.

Usually Edgar Poe was head of the line. But today Nat Howard headed it. He gave out a Latin verse. The next boy, Edgar Poe, was supposed to give another, beginning and ending with the same letters as the first verse.

Poor Jack Preston was never good at this test. How his legs trembled under him! The verse recited by Nat began with a "d" and ended with an "m." This being a "double capping" day, a verse containing two m's and two d's was required. His knees began to give way altogether for, to his amazement, Edgar Poe failed to get it. The next boy in the line blundered, then the next.

It was now Jack's turn and he always failed in this test of cleverness. All at once a line of Virgil came suddenly to his lips: "*Ducite: ab urbe domum, mea carmine ducite Daphnim.*"

"Excellent, Preston!" shouted Master Clarke and Jack went above his much-admired friend, Edgar, dizzy with the surprise of such an achievement.

He was still more stunned as he sat by his idol one day in

school, to have Edgar show him some verses on which he was working and actually ask his opinion of them. "Would the word 'groat' properly rhyme with 'not'?" mused Edgar, nibbling the end of his quill pen. "What do you think, Jack?"

To himself the admiring Jack, comparing Edgar and Nat Howard in his own mind, said: "Howard studies harder but Edgar Poe is smarter. He is a swift runner and a wonderful leaper. And how he can box! I'm certainly glad that of all the older boys, *he* took a fancy to me. Still, he is not the favorite here. Howard is that. Perhaps what makes Poe fierce and haughty at times is that word has gone around the school that he is the son of players. And he is so proud!"

Preston had judged his friend aright. There was a great aloofness about Edgar—but no one was allowed to get the better of him. On one occasion, though he had had meagre training as a boxer, he permitted the strongest of his school fellows to hit him with full force on the chest. He stood up under this blow by filling his lungs to their utmost capacity and then letting the air out of them the instant he was hit. Once, too, Jack Preston saw Edgar in a twenty yard run on level ground, leap a distance of twenty-one and a half feet.

But there came a day when baleful silence reigned among the occupants of the desks just before the beginning of school. Edgar Poe was unusually quiet and Creed Thomas who was his desk-mate whispered portentously behind his hand to others: "Selden told so-and-so that Poe was a liar and a rascal. They're going to fight after school in the lot."

Latin and other tasks over, the school gathered in the vacant lot at the rear of the building where they usually played ball. Poe's close friends worried about his slightness and rather delicate, though wiry, frame. Selden was big, sturdy and much heavier. After they grappled, he pounded Poe hard, especially about the head. Edgar continued patiently to lose ground. Then Selden, thinking the fight won, relaxed his grip on him. The boys stared, eyes popping out of their heads for—Edgar suddenly turned about, fell upon Selden and whipped him soundly. Cries of triumph rose: "Look, look! Poe's won! He's *won!*"

"Why did you let him knock you about so long?" asked the victor's comrades, rushing to shake his hand.

"I was waiting for him to get out of breath," explained Edgar, triumphantly pointing to the other. "Then I knew I could show him a few things about fighting."

Edgar's swift-footedness was also well known to his mates. One day the classical Academy was challenged by another school in Richmond. Two boys were to race. Let the Academy send a champion. Votes were taken and the vote fell on Edgar. Alas, this time, he was beaten! But, as Jack Preston sensibly said, "Poe ran well but the other boy was a long-legged Indian-looking fellow who would have outrun anybody."

There was another fact known about Edgar. "Why is it," envious ones would remark in school, "that Master Clarke never canes Poe? Everyone else catches it sooner or later. He *never* does."

But all good things reach an end. At the close of the term in 1823, there was a turnover in Richmond's Academy for Young Gentlemen. Master Joseph Clarke resigned as head master and was to be succeeded by one Master William Burke of a more forbidding personality but said to be more soundly versed in learning. Farewells to their schoolmaster were in order among the old scholars. The hall was filled for the little ceremony of the day. Parents and friends took their seats, ladies adjusted hoops and bustles, gentlemen settled their canes. All were listening and attentive. Several pupils performed but the banner role was taken by a youth named Edgar Poe who was to read an ode.

Fourteen now, easy of carriage, handsome, broad of brow, there was something in the boy's pose, in his rendering of the lines by which he sought to do his friend honor, that drew and held the attention of Richmond's aristocracy. Master Clarke had genuinely and truly favored him, as the school knew. Though somewhat garrulous and inclined to the dramatic, Master Clarke was a fine old fellow. Edgar would miss his teacher. Would the teacher guess at once that his pupil had written every line of the ode himself?

The final words were delivered, the goodbyes said. Tears stood in the eyes of the recipient. He grasped Edgar's hand and wrung it. "You always had a great ambition to excel—and you certainly excelled when you wrote those lines to an old man

like me," said Clarke, choking huskily. "Last vacation, d'ye remember, you and Nat Howard each wrote me a Latin letter—and yours was in verse? I assure you I shall always remember and treasure it—and now this. You have gone far, Edgar. You will go farther yet—and bless you."

For an instant the warm-hearted scholar of Dublin saw what he had never seen since his childhood—a sinister something threatening Edgar Poe's radiant appearance and brilliant achievement. A look of wild tragedy seemed to emanate from this shade, striving to eclipse the joy that overspread the young face at the sincere words of praise.

"But young Poe does not see it," thought Master Clarke. "Thanks be to the saints! My liver must be troubling me again." Indeed he had a genuine fit of the creeps.

LOUIS ARMSTRONG

The Boy with the Horn

BY JEANETTE EATON

Illustrations by Elton C. Fax

Who could have guessed in 1912 that the ragged boy hawking newspapers on a New Orleans street corner would become famous playing melodies in a style yet unknown? Louis Armstrong (b. 1900) had not put his first cornet to his lips, nor taken his first bow as a jazz musician. But one day his genuine New Orleans jazz and mastery of music were to bring him the acclaim of audiences throughout the world.

IT was at his mother's home that the holiday began for Louis. Sleeping late, he dawdled luxuriously over the breakfast his sister cooked for him. It was almost noon when an explosion of firecrackers down in the street made Louis jump up from the table. He snatched up a package and dashed out. In another moment he was in the middle of the crowd of youngsters gathered on the sidewalk. The exciting odor of smoke, the bang and splutter of firecrackers, and the sharp smash of torpedoes made the street seem like a battlefield.

In a twinkling Louis unwrapped his package, lighted the fuse of a giant cracker, and flung it into the middle of the street. From that moment he was in the center of action. Noise, laughter, mischief, and merriment filled the afternoon hours. Grown-ups and children, white and colored, set off crackers, popped toy pistols, blew penny horns, and paraded in crazy costumes. The whole ward, usually so sleepy in the daytime, was one hilarious carnival.

As light faded into dusk, Louis rounded up his three singers.

“We gotta start our p’formance,” he commanded, “befo’ it gits late.”

“Dat’s right,” agreed the drummer. “I got my drum box right over here. But, Dipper, we ought to have sump’n’ to make a real noise for startin’ off. Ain’t you got no mo’ cannon crackers left?”

Louis’ black eyes sparkled and his teeth gleamed in a triumphant grin. Now at last was the moment for his big surprise.

"Jes' you-all wait a minute!" He dashed off and raced back to the house.

Meanwhile, his troupe of three had sauntered on. They were almost at the corner of Perdido and Rampart Streets when Louis caught up with them. Before they could yell their amazement at the huge object he was carrying, he tipped it skyward and pulled the trigger. The tremendous bang that followed dwarfed all other sounds for half a block. Then came cheers from his friends and laughter from bystanders. Louis noticed with triumph that several members of the Perdido Street gang were gazing at him enviously.

"Look at that!" cried one man. "The kid's gun is bigger than he is!"

"Whar'd you git dat, Dipper?" screamed the minstrels in chorus.

Louis fondled his weapon with pride. "It's my daddy's old thirty-eight. Mammy hid it away, but I found it sho' nuff."

"You could kill a dozen men wid dat," declared the drummer fearfully.

"Naw," laughed Louis. "It's loaded wid blanks. Come on now. Let's get goin'. We'll sing 'Mister Moon.' "

As the last note died away amid applause and a shower of pennies, a small white boy came swaggering down the sidewalk. He was snapping away with a little cap pistol.

"Look at him!" sniffed Louis. "I'll show him what a real gun can do." Aiming high, he fired twice.

The little boy, quite unaware of anything but his own gun, was almost facing Louis when the blast went off. Stopping dead, he began to scream with terror. Louis, dumbfounded at this unexpected reaction, stepped forward to reassure him.

At that instant a heavy hand fell on his shoulder. A harsh voice cried, "Shooting at a white boy, are you? You come along with me!"

Twisting about, Louis saw a policeman towering over him. In vain he babbled that he had shot into the air, with blank cartridges. In vain his three friends shouted, "Mister, he didn't do nothin'!"

Impelled by a powerful grip, Louis was hustled down the street and shoved into the back of a big steel box on wheels.

With a bang of the rear door, darkness closed in. And now Louis realized what was happening. Often he had seen this wagon carry off drunks and cutthroats from Perdido Street. "De Black Maria! Dey's takin' me to jail!" he moaned.

Shock and anxiety blurred the details of the next hour. Later he remembered the wagon's jolting along the street with its bells ringing. It stopped shortly and then he was mounting steps beside the policeman. Near the entrance of the building a man in a shabby uniform exchanged comments with the policeman. Next, Louis found himself shoved into a sort of cage with only a cot inside. He stood shivering in the lonely dark. What was going to happen to him? The sign above the doorway—*Detention Home*—had told him where he was, and he had heard the guard say, "Guess the judge will hear the kid's case in the morning." Then what, he asked himself in dread. Even when he stretched out on the cot, he could not sleep. Out of each doze he would start up at the sound of groans and curses from nearby cages. A blend of horrid smells piercing the odor of disinfectant almost stopped his breathing. How had such a fate befallen him?

Never had he been more thankful to see morning light at last. There was a long wait, however, before anything happened. First, a tray with food was shoved into his cage. Then, after he had been heartened by the bun and the cup of milk, the man in uniform escorted him into a big, dim room. Several youths and girls, both colored and white, sat on benches in front of a platform on which a big table was perched. Behind it, facing the room, sat a grave, quiet middle-aged man. One by one, each culprit was summoned by a policeman to stand beside the table while the officer read out his or her misdeeds in a loud voice. At last it was Louis' turn.

"Judge Wilson," said the policeman sternly, "here is one of the worst hoodlums in the Perdido Street gang. He was caught red-handed, shooting at a little white boy. This was the weapon, sir." He held aloft the confiscated gun.

"It ain't so!" bawled Louis. "Dey was blank cartridges and I was aimin' high. I was *not* shootin' at him!"

Looking straight at him with keen blue eyes, the judge asked in a low tone, "What is your name and how old are you?" After hearing the choked-out answers, he said, "Well, Louis Armstrong, we have a lot of trouble with residents of Perdido Street, young and old. Even if you didn't shoot to hurt the white boy, you were risking other people's safety by firing that gun. A boy of thirteen ought to have more sense. You are going to be taught how to behave where I am going to send you. Here, Officer"—the judge wrote out a slip—"have this boy taken to the Colored Waifs' Home."

Again a trip in the wagon, a longer one than before. Again Louis was told to get out and hurry up a flight of steps. In the hallway of the big building a colored man stepped forward. Through his cloud of terror Louis could hardly make out his face. Would he be kept in another cage or in a dark cell?

"Howdy, Mr. Jones," said the driver of the police vehicle. "I've got a fine case for you here—one of them Perdido Street gangsters. Here's Judge Wilson's slip."

During this introduction, Mr. Jones had waved them into a small office. He sat down at a desk, drew out a big book, and entered Louis' half-sobbed replies to questions as to his name, age, address, and schooling.

As soon as the policeman left, Mr. Jones got to his feet and said, "Come upstairs to the dormitory, Louis, and I'll show you your locker. You get yourself thoroughly washed, and then put on the blue jeans and shirt I'll give you."

Louis stared into the big room at the top of the stairs. Some fifty cots, neatly made, stood in two rows down its length. At least it was not a cell! His guide laid a sheet of paper bearing Louis' name upon a cot near the middle of the room.

"This will be your bed," said Mr. Jones. "Here is your locker just behind it. Put those clothes you have on in it. Through that door is the washroom. I'll put your new clothes on your bed. When you're clean and dressed, come down to my office."

The comfort the boy felt at being clean again was immediately blotted out by his interview with Mr. Jones. First Mr. Jones talked about the Perdido Street gang and their crimes, and how shocking it was that Louis at his age had such bad associations. Next came a long list of rules to follow. Finally Louis was warned that he must obey orders instantly or expect severe punishment. Louis' replies were meek and quiet, but

they disguised the wild rebellion in his heart. How could he get out of this awful place? There must be some way to escape to freedom!

A bell rang loudly through the hall. Doors opened on each side, and boys in blue jeans came marching in lines toward a central room with wide-open double doors. "It's lunchtime," said Mr. Jones. "I'll take you along to the dining room."

To the man at the entrance Jones said, "Here's a new boy. I guess he'd better sit with the older group."

"All right, I'll attend to him." The speaker's eyes bored into Louis. A firm hand pushed him across the threshold. "Sit on that right-hand bench. And mind you behave yourself!"

Louis slid into place before a smoking plate of stew. He stared at it, feeling that he could not swallow a single mouthful.

The boy opposite him pushed a pitcher of milk and a glass in his direction and said, "Well, happy New Year!"

Glancing up, Louis felt his lips tremble at the sound of the first friendly words he had heard in eighteen hours. Unburdened by a sense of irony, he managed to respond to the greeting with a feeble grin. "What's your name?" he asked.

"Jim Glass. What's yours?"

After telling him, Louis asked fearfully, "Who dat man at de door?"

"Him? One of de teachers—Mr. Peter Davis. Watch out for him, kid. He got a bite like a wolf!"

The terrifying effect of this statement made Louis feel even worse than before. Unable to eat, he looked about the room. What he saw surprised him. The long rows of faces looked cheerful. Subdued talk and giggles made a low murmur through the mild clatter of dishes and cups. Didn't these boys mind being in such a place? Curiosity made him turn back to Jim Glass. "Dey all crooks an' gangsters here?" he inquired.

Jim laughed. "Not me. Not most of 'em. Lots has no homes, like me. My dad and mammy got sick and died. I hadn't no place to go. Course, some of de kids was brought in by de police. How 'bout you?"

Louis choked and nodded his head. He was glad when lunch was over. Forlornly standing by the wall outside the dining room, he watched the boys stroll by twos and threes into the playground. Only curious glances were flicked in his direction as they passed. Used as he was to sociable companionship, he was chilled to the bone by his sense of isolation. When the bell rang, the boys hurried into classrooms. Presently a woman who, he learned later, was Mrs. Jones, wife of the head of the home, told him to go downstairs to Mr. Alexander's carpentry class.

He pushed open the door shyly. In spite of poor lighting, the big room had a cheerful air, filled as it was with the sound of hammers and saws. Louis felt his spirits rising. But when the teacher placed him with a group engaged in making a bookcase and he tried to take part in the work, he was once more made to feel unwelcome. The boys were openly hostile. Eying him suspiciously, they hurled low-voiced contempt at his efforts. "Dumbbell, dat ain't de way to do it!" "Watch him wid de saw. He t'inks it's a jackknife." Mr. Alexander's kindly help did little to alleviate his misery.

In the arithmetic class, held upstairs, the teacher, Mr. Jones, seemed determined to show up Louis' ignorance. Unreproved, the others laughed loudly at his mistakes. So large grew the lump in his throat that he could hardly speak at all.

Still more desolating was the reading and spelling class taught by Mr. Peter Davis. His hard, reproving eyes frightened

Louis and there was good reason for his fear. After class, for no reason he could discover, he was given a whipping. Gritting his teeth, he managed not to cry, even when the teacher said, "We have no use for boys like you and the rest of the Perdido Street gang." In sarcastic tones he told Louis to cure his aches by joining the boys in the garden, where Mr. Alexander was having them prepare a place for growing spring vegetables.

Sipping his soup at supper, Louis thought of the red beans his mother would be cooking. Never in his life had she let him go hungry. And right this minute she would be worrying about him and feeling sad because of his imprisonment. Not a single boy, not even Jim Glass, said a word to him that evening. It was a relief when, in bed at last with lights out, he could smother his face in the unsympathetic pillow and sob out his unhappiness.

Waking next morning was abrupt. Hands were shaking his shoulders. Voices were crying, "Hey, wake up! De bell's done rung!" Sitting up with a start, Louis stared at the boys on each side of his bed. One of them was Jim Glass, who said gruffly, "Hustle, kid! Dey beats you if you're late to breakfas'!"

The long, dimly lighted room was alive with figures hastily pulling on their clothes. Subdued murmurs filled it. Louis dressed in a twinkling and rushed through his washing in time to join the tail end of the march downstairs.

That day and the days that followed were grim. Twice Mr. Davis gave Louis a beating. The boys treated him like a pariah. Bitter resentment filled his soul. He longed to fight each one of them separately and then make a dash for freedom.

On Sunday the first streak of light crossed his dark sky, for in the afternoon the school band gave a concert and all the boys attended. Louis had heard the blare of practicing now and then and was eager to discover what the performance would be like. He planted himself on the front bench to watch and listen. The band, eighteen strong, consisted of horns, cornets, triangles, and drums. The conductor was Peter Davis. Louis, whose ear was trained to band music, was happily surprised by the snappy pace and clear tones the boys achieved. He knew the credit belonged to the bandmaster, whose authority and enthusiasm were inspiring the players.

Louis stamped and clapped lustily after every number. He had forgotten his wretchedness for this one absorbing hour. But when, at its end, the leader turned to bow, his stern glance fell upon Louis. With a shudder the boy stopped applauding and dropped his eyes. He thought, Bet dat man don't like me to take pleasure in his music. Bet he finds a chance to beat me tomorrow.

The phophecy came true. Again, for no reason that was explained to him, Louis was given another beating. As before, he suffered in silence. Worse than physical pain was the aching sense that this man whom he could admire, with whom he longed to talk about music, hated him. The fact made the dark days darker, loneliness still more bitter.

It was almost impossible for Louis to slip into the groove of discipline. He had never known restraint. He obeyed commands sullenly, but he could not remember all the rules and was forever breaking them. One evening he committed the sin of strolling out after dark into the playground. When Mrs. Jones screamed at him to come right back, he waved his hand to her, meaning that it was all right, he was not going to run away. But Mr. Jones rushed after him, caught him by the collar, dragged him into the office, and beat him with a leather strap.

If he missed his place in line when the bell rang for a meal, he was forced to miss the meal. Yet, in spite of his hatred of all the rules, he did realize that when he obeyed them he received smiles and kind words from Mr. Jones and his wife and from Mr. Alexander.

Moreover, he rather liked gardening and began to take an interest in making or painting some useful object in the carpentry class. His stupefying fear of Mr. Davis made him dread his class, yet he found himself reading and writing with increasing ease. The Waifs' Home would have begun to feel like a school instead of a prison if only the boys had been companionable. True, they had stopped laughing at him in class and calling him a dumbbell, but they still kept their air of watching him suspiciously. He was determined not to show his hurt and anger and to resist his longing to pummel the most offensive snubbers. Stoically he kept to himself.

Then came a day when the ice thawed. It started in the carpentry class when Mr. Alexander gathered the boys around Louis to admire the bench he had made and painted a bright red. And they did. "It's sure slick!" said one. "Dat's a real gay seat!" said another. Louis grinned with satisfaction over his very first success.

"Look at dat fella smile, Mr. Alexander!" crowed Jim Glass. "Why, he got a mouth big as a satchel."

Amid laughter another youngster cried, "Jus' look at Satchel Mouth. Bet he could swallow his own bench."

Louis chuckled delightedly. He was thrilled an hour later on the playground to be drawn into a ball game by the cry, "Come on, Satchamouth! See if you can catch wid ya teeth!" When a member of the band changed the name to Satchmo, Louis approved it heartily. Instinct told him that a nickname meant he was at last included, accepted as one of the group.

Not long after this baptism, Jim Glass openly adopted him as a friend. "Say, Satchmo," he said one afternoon as they left the reading class, "I couldn't see why Mr. Davis hit you today. You was doin' all right. He's mean to you, ain't he? I bet you hate him like a black snake."

"No, I don't!" replied Louis instantly. "Dat Mr. Davis sure knows music. He kin play every instrument in de band. I jes' wish . . ." His voice trailed off.

Jim looked at him curiously. "You's funny, Satchmo. I'd sure hate anybody dat beat me up like dat. Why, you don't do nothin' bad." He whacked Louis on the back. "I think you're as good a fella as we got."

This, indeed, was the salutation of fellowship. From then on Louis Armstrong began to relax and regain his shattered sense of fun. One night when the lights were out in the dormitory and only moonlight streamed through it, Louis was seized by irresistible gaiety. Softly, but in his old clowning way, he began to sing "Tiger Rag." In spasms of laughter the other boys rolled on their cots.

At that moment Peter Davis entered the room. With one stride he was beside the performer's bed. "So!" he cried, seizing Louis by the arm. "I might have known it was you stirring up mischief. Get into bed now and no more tricks!"

As the door closed behind him, Louis leaned over to Jim's cot. "What you t'ink o' dat?" he whispered. "He jus' tole me to git into bed. Not even one whack! I sure b'lieved he'd beat de daylights outa me."

Although he sank back on his pillow in puzzled relief, Louis did not interpret the incident as marking a change in the teacher's feeling toward him. Every contact with Davis put him tensely on the defensive.

Sitting happily absorbed in supper one evening, he saw Peter Davis come walking through the dining room. With spoon halted in mid-air, the boy watched him fearfully. To his horror, Mr. Davis stopped right beside him. Was he to be dragged away for another punishment? An upsurge of bitterness swept away all the pleasant memories of the last weeks.

But the tone of Mr. Davis' voice was unfamiliar. And the words—no, they couldn't be meant for him. Looking up incredulously, Louis met the eyes which had so often sent shivers down his spine. It was not the stern teacher looking at him, speaking to him, but the bandmaster. Davis was saying with a friendly smile, "How would you like to play in my band?"

Louis could only gasp in amazement. But he leaped to his feet and his eyes were twin lamps of joy.

"Come over to the window, Louis," urged the pleasant voice. "I want to talk to you." And never had the boy obeyed a command so swiftly.

"I've been watching you, Louis," began Davis, "and I've decided you aren't really one of the Perdido Street gang. I happen to know that pennies and pencil boxes and other things get left around that you could have stolen. But you don't steal and you don't pick fights. You don't lie or tell on other boys. It isn't your fault you had to live in a bad neighborhood. So!" He dropped a hand on the boy's shoulder. "Come along now and I'll give you a lesson on the bugle. I think I'll start you on that."

Stepping into the band's practice room was the beginning of a new life for Louis. The moment he lifted the bugle to his lips he felt as if something wonderful was being born in him. Patiently and skillfully Peter Davis showed him the rudiments of bugle blowing, illustrating every point himself. At the end of half an hour he stopped the lesson.

"That's enough for tonight," he said. "I truly believe, Louis, that you have talent. Your breath control is good. We'll have another lesson tomorrow. I think you'll learn fast."

After a few joyous skips down the hall Louis looked back to see his teacher watching him with a smile. The boy's heart gave an extra bound. Him and me's goin' to be frien's, he thought ecstatically.

Louis did indeed learn fast. Within a week he was sounding the bugle calls for meals, classes, and band rehearsals. Every day his tones grew clearer and more accurate. He played taps for bedtime and reveille for rising.

Often Louis lay awake to wonder how all this had happened. It was a true fairy tale. A wand had been waved and at once the Waifs' Home was turned into a castle of delight. The dreadful ogre had become a prince and the hostile inmates of the castle were now friends.

When he had made a really good start as a bugler, Louis had a glorious reward. He was made a member of the band. To qualify for the honor, he had to learn to play the tambourine and the small drum, and his quick mastery of both instruments won praise from the conductor.

But Louis did not desert the bugle. In early summer the Colored Waifs' Home Band was asked to play for a parade in New Orleans. The uniformed boys marched in good form and at their head was Louis, the proud bugler. He had written his mother about his part in the parade and hoped she could watch it. As the band reached Canal Street, Louis gazed at the handsome hotels, banks, and stores with the interest of a foreign visitor. How he had longed to see that street again! But he had never dreamed of doing so in such glory.

As the band neared Perdido Street, Louis cast swift glances left and right. Could he possibly distinguish his plump mother and little Mamma Lucy among the cheering crowds? Then, during a pause in the music, he heard a piercing scream—"Louis! Louis!" A red handkerchief wildly waved from the sidewalk marked his sister and mother. He waved his cap. At last they were proud of him! This was the great moment of the afternoon.

It was some time after the parade when the most thrilling event in Louis Armstrong's short life took place. After band practice one afternoon Peter Davis asked Louis to stay a few moments. Wonderingly he waited by the window while the bandmaster fussed with something at his table. Suddenly he turned and said, "Louis, I have a present for you." And before the boy's bulging eyes he waved a cornet.

"Mr. Davis!" roared Louis. "You *givin'* me dis?" He held out both hands, palms upward, with an air of receiving something unutterably precious.

"Yes, I'm promoting you," laughed his teacher. "Take care of this cornet. It's yours as long as you stay here. You'll have to work hard to make it do its best."

Then and there the ecstatic boy was given a first lesson in fingering. There was never a more ambitious pupil. He drank up instruction as if he could never get enough and practiced so continuously that before a week had passed he was permitted to play in the band as second cornetist. He was so nervous that Sunday afternoon that he made mistakes, but the conductor indicated by a smiling shake of the head that he understood why. Before he went to bed that night Louis wrote his mother about the wonderful gift, and signed himself, "Your loving cornet-playing son."

The bandmaster's exacting standards were too much for the patience of many of the players, but never for Louis. He enjoyed going over and over a piece to perfect the rhythm or

improve the tone. His zest was so contagious that the leader declared the band was playing better than ever before.

No longer did Louis have to struggle with homesickness. Perdido Street tricks seemed merely childish now. That year of 1914, a year filled with tragedy for the world, brought happiness and satisfaction to Louis Armstrong. He responded so wholeheartedly to every responsibility that Davis made him assistant band leader, with a distinctive uniform. When the others donned their blue coats and white trousers, he wore blue trousers and a cream-colored jacket. Such elegance was not wasted on school concerts, of course, but saved for adult audiences.

During the spring of 1915 Mr. Davis often took his band into New Orleans to play for church sociables and club meetings.

The members were much excited one week to learn that they had been engaged to entertain a group of people going on an all-day picnic up the Mississippi.

Early in the morning of the day for the picnic Mrs. Jones lined up the band members to inspect their well-pressed uniforms and polished shoes. "Boys, you certainly look fine," she said with motherly pride. "Now try to keep your suits from getting all messed up."

As she spoke, Peter Davis came rushing from the office. "Boys," he said, "I've been called to a meeting of the trustees of the Home. I can't go along with you. Louis!" He turned to him solemnly. "I'm putting you in charge. I trust you to see that everything goes just as it should."

Louis stepped to the head of the line. With a glowing look of pride he said, "Yes, sir, Mr. Davis, you sure can count on me."

Armed with directions for meeting the picnic party, Louis marched off with his band. Not for the world would he show a sign of the nervousness which brought beads of moisture to his forehead. Since the meeting place was near Baton Rouge, the boys had to take a steamboat from New Orleans. Once he had shepherded the band on board, he could relax for a time and enjoy his first long trip on the mighty Mississippi. From the boat deck he thought the river looked bigger than ever before. Leaning over the rail, he marveled that the pilot could steer so surely against the powerful current.

At Baton Rouge, Louis marshaled the band for landing. Then he formed them in marching order to reach another wharf where the party waited to ferry across to the picnic place. As they came in sight of the crowd, Louis shouted, "Get ready now! 'Stars and Stripes Forever!' One, two, three! Strike up!"

From the waiting crowd handkerchiefs waved and hands clapped. Just as the marching boys reached the wharf, a loud whistle from the ferry urged the party on board. There was a merry jam of moving figures, bumping picnic baskets, laughter and talk. Words of welcome greeted the band members. "Thank you, boys!" "That's great, boys!" "Glad you're with us!"

Across the muddy river the ferryboat landed the passengers on a muddy shore, but a rough road led up to higher ground where open country was bordered by woods. Louis looked eagerly about at the wild magnolias and flowering shrubs glowing in the spring sunshine. Beyond the picnic grounds lay a cypress swamp with a mass of colorful azaleas framed in dark, twisted trees.

Louis grouped his players on a little rise and opened the program. Solemn and intent, they launched the band's most ambitious piece, an arrangement Mr. Davis had made for them of part of the overture to "Tannhäuser." The listeners were so spellbound that they did not even open the picnic baskets until the last note had died away, drowned in applause. To prove their versatility, the band then played the "St. Louis Blues," a jazz song so recently popular in New Orleans that Louis was startled to hear half the crowd joining in with the words. After that, requests for tunes were shouted from women setting out food and men opening ginger-ale bottles. The band never failed to respond, and after almost an hour of heroic blowing and drumming the call to luncheon was a sound of piercing sweetness to all the boys.

Louis stared at his plate of fried chicken, spoon bread, cold ham, potato pie, and biscuits. Rolling his eyes, he sighed ecstatically. "Ma'am, dis sho' is heaven!" Yet before he touched a bite he made sure all the other boys had been served.

"Now, you musicians, just do as you please!" said the leader of the picnic group. "We're going to take naps, stroll, and laze around. No more music until we board the ferry again to go home. You've given us fine entertainment, boys, so just relax and take it easy now."

After all the plates were empty Louis instructed his charges. "You-all on your own now, fellas. But mind you don't git lost an' lef' behind."

"What you doin' yo'se'f, Satchmo?" someone asked.

"Me? I'm fixin' to take a look at dat ol' cypress swamp."

"Den you's de one to git lost!"

Waving his hand airily, Louis set off. As he reached the edge of the swamp, he pushed aside the delicate curtains of moss hanging from the trees and crept along between moss-covered stones and fallen logs. Everywhere about him ran narrow streams of inky water. All was weirdly still beneath the lofty canopy of interlacing branches. Just in front of his lifted foot a snake swirled its long, heavy body over a log and noiselessly swam away. The fragrance of azaleas growing on tiny islands accented the dank odors of rotting wood. For some time, as Louis made his cautious exploration, he enjoyed the fantastic scene. Then suddenly weariness overcame him and he stretched out on a bed of moss between the knobby knees of a sprawling cypress. The responsibilities of the day slipped from his shoulders. In two minutes he was sound asleep.

With a start of fear he awoke. Was it night? He could hardly see from one tree to another. Had the crowd gone without him? Grasping a low-hung branch, he jerked to his feet. From which direction had he come? He looked this way and that. Tales of men lost for weeks in cypress swamps rushed through his mind. If he missed the ferry, he would never get back to New Orleans that night and then . . . Mr. Davis! He would have failed him!

A faint cry cut through his anguish. Surely it was a boy's shout. Louis scrambled through the twisting paths, stumbling, pulling himself along with the help of drooping branches. And all at once he was out of the blackness. The sun was shining. He caught a glimpse of moving figures. They were still there. At full speed he ran up the slope, then stopped short. Swiftly he assumed a casual grin and a swagger in his walk as he strolled toward the crowd.

"Satchmo!" yelled the bass-horn player. "Whar you been?"

"Just in time, boy!" interrupted a cheerful voice. "We're all ready to start."

A blast from the ferry whistle saved Louis from explanations. He snatched up his cornet from the table where he had left it and strode down the road. Mixed with his grateful relief was a resolve never again to stray from the path of duty. And he kept this resolution during every excursion that summer.

As time went on, Louis found new stimulus from a rival in the band. His name was Kid Rena and he played the cornet too. It became a game with the two to see who could play the loudest and hit the highest note.

The activities of that speeding summer blotted out entirely from Louis' mind the fact that he had been sent to the Colored

Waifs' Home as a punishment. He felt much as any boy does about a private school where he is happy. Loyalty to the Home and a will to make good were his unconscious impulses. As a natural result, the faculty of four had become his warm friends. Often Mr. Jones and his wife invited him to their study to share a dish of ice cream or a thick chocolate layer cake. Mr. Davis had finally converted Louis to the idea that reading might actually be fun. Finding that he was a regular patron of the small collection of shabby volumes glorified by the name of school library, Mr. Davis gave him a book of his own.

"I sure like dat story 'bout Huck Finn, Mr. Davis," reported the convert. "But how did dat Mark Twain writer know our ol' Mississippi River like dat? He had every trick—good and bad—of dat river by heart."

"Well, sonny." Davis smiled. "First of all, Mark Twain was brought up in a Mississippi River town. When he was a young man he became a river pilot of one of the regular steamboats, so he had to learn everything about that big river, every island and shoal. He wrote a book about that, too."

Louis' eyes snapped with interest. "Some day I'd sure like to go up to where the river begins. Say, Mr. Davis, de bes' would be ef I ever could be in a band on one of dem river boats."

"Just you keep on with the cornet, Louis, and maybe you could join such a band."

One morning in early autumn Louis was called from class to Mr. Jones's office. As he stood waiting to find out why, he thought the head of the Home was looking at him in a rather odd way. After a moment he said, "Get your bugle, Louis, and call everyone into the hall. We're going to say good-by to somebody who's leaving us."

At the imperative notes of the bugle, boys hurried out of classes and in from the garden to form ranks for the roll call. Both Mr. Anderson and Mr. Davis came in also.

"What dis all 'bout, Satchmo?" whispered one boy after another. The answer spread through the ranks as wind sweeps through a wheat field. One of the boys was leaving the Home. But who? Wondering eyes rolled from face to face. Shoulders shrugged. Nobody knew.

Mr. Jones came from his office at last. "Well, this is a special occasion," he began. "One of our boys is leaving today. He has worked hard and behaved well. He has shown a marked sense of responsibility for the good of our school. So we have decided to let this boy go back home."

There was a long pause. Again heads turned this way and that, seeking the answer to the mystery.

"I'm sure you'll all be glad when you hear who this boy is," went on Mr. Jones deliberately, "although we'll miss him here. We certainly wish him luck. Louis Armstrong, you are the boy!"

Louis dropped the bugle with a clatter. "Me?" he gasped.

Smiling at his astounded look, Mr. Jones said, "Go up and get your things together, son. You're leaving right away."

Leaving the band! Giving back his cornet! Leaving Mr. Davis and Jim Glass and Kid Rena and his other pals! Dazed with shock, numb with a strange ache in his heart, Louis stumbled upstairs to his locker. Boys crowded around him, looking solemn, looking envious, all trying to joke. As he came down with the bundle of his possessions under his arm, cries rose from below and were echoed from above. "Good-by, Satchmo!" "Don't forgit us, Satchmo!" "Luck, ol' Satchmo!"

Louis' responses were choked-out murmurs and feeble grins. When Mr. Davis stepped from his door to shake hands, Louis dropped his bundle and seized the bandmaster's hand in both his own. "Mr. Davis," he stammered, "I—I—will I ever see you again?"

BROWN BROTHERS

Louis Armstrong

Assuring his cornetist that he would always be welcome as a visitor, Davis patted him on the back. Louis turned away quickly. He felt split asunder. It was like being expelled. All at once he saw his mother approaching from the end of the hall. A rush of gladness carried him into her outstretched arms. "Mammy," he cried, "it's sure sump'n' to see you again!"

It was good also to walk freely along the old streets on the way home. A lunch of his favorite red beans and rice, cooked only as his mother could prepare them, was nothing less than glorious. Yet that night in the dark Louis took a glance at the future with leaden heart. What now? No more cornet playing, or classes, or excursions. He had to go out and hunt for a job. A groan escaped him. He had been catapulted into manhood.

MARIE CURIE

The Discovery of Radium

BY EVE CURIE

Translated by Vincent Sheean

A Polish girl who married a French physicist, Marie Curie (1867-1934) is remembered here by her daughter, Eve, as a woman so full of love and energy that she raised her family and pursued the secrets of radiation at the same time. Working with her husband Pierre, Madam Curie succeeded in isolating the element radium and was twice awarded the Nobel Prize.

WHILE a young wife kept house, washed her baby daughter and put pans on the fire, in a wretched laboratory at the School of Physics a woman physicist was making the most important discovery of modern science.

At the end of 1897 the balance sheet of Marie's activity showed two university degrees, a fellowship and a monograph on the magnetization of tempered steel. No sooner had she recovered from childbirth than she was back again at the laboratory.

The next stage in the logical development of her career was the doctor's degree. Several weeks of indecision came in here. She had to choose a subject of research which would furnish fertile and original material. Like a writer who hesitates and asks himself questions before settling the subject of his next novel, Marie, reviewing the most recent work in physics with Pierre, was in search of a subject for a thesis.

At this critical moment Pierre's advice had an importance which cannot be neglected. With respect to her husband, the young woman regarded herself as an apprentice: he was an older physicist, much more experienced than she. He was even, to put it exactly, her chief, her "boss."

But without a doubt Marie's character, her intimate nature, had a great part in this all-important choice. From childhood the Polish girl had carried the curiosity and daring of an explorer within her. This was the instinct that had driven her to leave Warsaw for Pairs and the Sorbonne, and had made her prefer a solitary room in the Latin Quarter to the Dluskis' downy nest. In her walks in the woods she always chose the wild trail or the unfrequented road.

At this moment she was like a traveler musing on a long voyage. Bent over the globe and pointing out, in some far country, a strange name that excites his imagination, the traveler suddenly decides to go there and nowhere else: so Marie, going through the reports of the latest experimental studies, was attracted by the publication of the French scientist Henri Becquerel of the preceding year. She and Pierre already knew this work; she read it over again and studied it with her usual care.

After Roentgen's discovery of X rays, Henri Poincaré conceived the idea of determining whether rays like the X ray were emitted by "fluorescent" bodies under the action of light. Attracted by the same problem, Henri Becquerel examined the salts of a "rare metal," uranium. Instead of finding the phenomenon he had expected, he observed another, altogether different and incomprehensible: he found that uranium salts *spontaneously* emitted, without exposure to light, some rays of unknown nature. A compound of uranium, placed on a photographic plate surrounded by black paper, made an impression on the plate through the paper. And, like the X ray, these astonishing "uranic" salts discharged an electroscope by rendering the surrounding air a conductor.

Henri Becquerel made sure that these surprising properties were not caused by a preliminary exposure to the sun and that they persisted when the uranium compound had been maintained in darkness for several months. For the first time, a physicist had observed the phenomenon to which Marie Curie was later to give the name of *radioactivity*. But the nature of the radiation and its origin remained an enigma.

Becquerel's discovery fascinated the Curies. They asked themselves whence came the energy—tiny, to be sure—which uranium compounds constantly disengaged in the form of radiation. And what was the nature of this radiation? Here was an engrossing subject of research, a doctor's thesis! The subject tempted Marie most because it was a virgin field: Becquerel's work was very recent and so far as she knew nobody in the laboratories of Europe had yet attempted to make a fundamental study of uranium rays. As a point of departure, and as the only bibliography, there existed some communications presented by Henri Becquerel at the Academy of Science during the year 1896. It was a leap into great adventure, into an unknown realm.

There remained the question of where she was to make her experiments—and here the difficulties began. Pierre made several approaches to the director of the School of Physics with practically no results: Marie was given the free use of a little glassed-in studio on the ground floor of the school. It was a kind of storeroom, sweating with damp, where unused machines and lumber were put away. Its technical equipment was rudimentary and its comfort nil.

Deprived of an adequate electrical installation and of everything that forms material for the beginning of scientific research, she kept her patience, sought and found a means of making her apparatus work in this hole.

It was not easy. Instruments of precision have sneaking enemies: humidity, changes of temperature. Incidentally the climate of this little workroom, fatal to the sensitive electrometer, was not much better for Marie's health. But this had no importance. When she was cold, the young woman took her revenge by noting the degrees of temperature in centigrade in her notebook. On February 6, 1898, we find, among the formulas and figures: "Temperature here 6°25." Six degrees . . . !* Marie, to show her disapproval, added ten little exclamation points.

The candidate for the doctor's degree set her first task to be the measurement of the "power of ionization" of uranium

*About 44° Fahrenheit.

rays—that is to say, their power to render the air a conductor of electricity and so to discharge an electroscope. The excellent method she used, which was to be the key to the success of her experiments, had been invented for the study of other phenomena by two physicists well known to her: Pierre and Jacques Curie. Her technical installation consisted of an "ionization chamber," a Curie electrometer and a piezoelectric quartz.

At the end of several weeks the first result appeared: Marie acquired the certainty that the intensity of this surprising radiation was proportional to the quantity of uranium contained in the samples under examination, and that this radiation, which could be measured with precision, was not affected either by the chemical state of combination of the uranium or by external factors such as lighting or temperature.

These observations were perhaps not very sensational to the uninitiated, but they were of passionate interest to the scientist. It often happens in physics that an inexplicable phenomenon can be subjected, after some investigation, to laws already known, and by this very fact loses its interest for the research worker. Thus, in a bady constructed detective story, if we are told in the third chapter that the woman of sinister appearance who might have committed the crime is in reality only an honest little housewife who leads a life without secrets, we feel discouraged and cease to read.

Nothing of the kind happened here. The more Marie penetrated into intimacy with uranium rays, the more they seemed without precedent, essentially unknown. They were like nothing else. Nothing affected them. In spite of their very feeble power, they had an extraordinary individuality.

Turning this mystery over and over in her head, and pointing toward the truth, Marie felt and could soon affirm that the incomprehensible radiation was an *atomic* property. She questioned: Even though the phenomenon had only been observed with uranium, nothing proved that uranium was the only chemical element capable of emitting such radiation. Why should not other bodies possess the same power? Perhaps it was only by chance that this radiation had been observed in uranium first, and had remained attached to

BETTMANN ARCHIVE

Marie Curie in her laboratory

uranium in the minds of physicists. Now it must be sought for elsewhere. . . .

No sooner said than done. Abandoning the study of uranium, Marie undertook to examine *all known chemical bodies,* either in the pure state or in compounds. And the result was not long in appearing: compounds of another element, thorium, also emitted spontaneous rays like those of uranium and of similar intensity. The physicist had been right: the surprising phenomenon was by no means the property of uranium alone, and it became necessary to give it a distinct name. Mme. Curie suggested the name of *radioactivity*. Chemical substances like uranium and thorium, endowed with this particular "radiance," were called *radio elements.*

Radioactivity so fascinated the young scientist that she never tired of examining the most diverse forms of matter, always by the same method. Curiosity, a marvelous feminine curiosity, the first virtue of a scientist, was developed in Marie to the highest degree. Instead of limiting her observation to simple compounds, salts and oxides, she had the desire to assemble samples of minerals from the collection at the School of Physics, and of making them undergo almost at hazard, for her own amusement, a kind of customs inspection which is an electrometer test. Pierre approved, and chose with her the veined fragments, hard or crumbly, oddly shaped, which she wanted to examine.

Marie's idea was simple—simple as the stroke of genius. At the crossroads where Marie now stood, hundreds of research workers might have remained, nonplused, for months or even years. After examining all known chemical substances, and discovering—as Marie had done—the radiation of thorium, they would have continued to ask themselves in vain whence came this mysterious radioactivity. Marie, too, questioned and wondered. But her surprise was translated into fruitful acts. She had used up all evident possibilities. Now she turned toward the unplumbed and the unknown.

She knew in advance what she would learn from an examination of the minerals, or rather she thought she knew. The specimens which contained neither uranium nor thorium would be revealed as totally "inactive." The others, containing uranium or thorium, would be radioactive.

Experiment confirmed this prevision. Rejecting the inactive minerals, Marie applied herself to the others and measured their radioactivity. Then came a dramatic revelation: the radioactivity was a *great deal stronger* than could have been normally foreseen by the quantity of uranium or thorium contained in the products examined!

"It must be an error in experiment," the young woman thought; for doubt is the scientist's first response to an unexpected phenomenon.

She started her measurements over again, unmoved, using

the same products. She started over again ten times, twenty times. And she was forced to yield to the evidence: the quantities of uranium and of thorium found in these minerals were by no means sufficient to justify the exceptional intensity of the radiation she observed.

Where did this excessive and abnormal radiation come from? Only one explanation was possible: the minerals must contain, in small quantity, a *much more powerful radioactive substance* than uranium and thorium.

But what substance? In her preceding experiments, Marie had already examined *all known chemical elements.*

The scientist replied to the question with the sure logic and the magnificent audaciousness of a great mind: The minerals certainly contained a radioactive substance, which was at the same time a chemical element unknown until this day: *a new element.*

A new element! It was a fascinating and alluring hypothesis—but still a hypothesis. For the moment this powerfully radioactive substance existed only in the imagination of Marie and of Pierre. But it did exist there. It existed strongly enough to make the young woman go to see Bronya one day and tell her in a restrained, ardent voice:

"You know, Bronya, the radiation that I couldn't explain comes from a new chemical element. The element is there and I've got to find it. We are sure! The physicists we have spoken to believe we have made an error in experiment and advise us to be careful. But I am convinced that I am not mistaken."

These were unique moments in her unique life. The layman forms a theatrical—and wholly false—idea of the research worker and of his discoveries. "The moment of discovery" does not always exist: the scientist's work is too tenuous, too divided, for the certainty of success to crackle out suddenly in the midst of his laborious toil like a stroke of lightning, dazzling him by its fire. Marie, standing in front of her apparatus, perhaps never experienced the sudden intoxication of triumph. This intoxication was spread over several days of decisive labor, made feverish by a magnificent hope. But it must have been an exultant moment when, convinced by the rigorous reasoning of her brain that she was on the trail of new matter, she confided the secret to her elder sister, her ally always. . . . Without exchanging one affectionate word, the two sisters must have lived again, in a dizzying breath of memory, their years of waiting, their mutual sacrifices, their bleak lives as students, full of hope and faith.

It was barely four years before that Marie had written:

> Life is not easy for any of us. But what of that? We must have perseverance and above all confidence in ourselves. We must believe that we are gifted for something, and that this thing, at whatever cost, must be attained.

That "something" was to throw science upon a path hitherto unsuspected.

In a first communication to the Academy, presented by Prof. Lippmann and published in the *Proceedings* on April 12, 1898, "Marie Sklodovska Curie" announced the probable presence in pitchblende ores of a new element endowed with powerful radioactivity. This was the first stage of the discovery of radium.

By the force of her own intuition the physicist had shown to herself that the wonderful substance must exist. She decreed its existence. But its incognito still had to be broken. Now she would have to verify hypothesis by experiment, isolate this material and see it. She must be able to announce with certainty: "It is there."

Pierre Curie had followed the rapid progress of his wife's experiments with passionate interest. Without directly taking part in Marie's work, he had frequently helped her by his remarks and advice. In view of the stupefying character of her results, he did not hesitate to abandon his study of crystals for the time being in order to join his efforts to hers in the search for the new substance.

Thus, when the immensity of a pressing task suggested and exacted collaboration, a great physicist was at Marie's side—a physicist who was the companion of her life. Three years earlier, love had joined this exceptional man and woman together—love, and perhaps some mysterious foreknowledge, some sublime instinct for the work in common.

CULVER SERVICE

Pierre and Marie Curie

The available force was now doubled. Two brains, four hands, now sought the unknown element in the damp little workroom in the Rue Lhomond. From this moment onward it is impossible to distinguish each one's part in the work of the Curies. We know that Marie, having chosen to study the radiation of uranium as the subject of her thesis, discovered that other substances were also radioactive. We know that after the examination of minerals she was able to announce the existence of a new chemical element, powerfully radioactive, and that it was the capital importance of this result which decided Pierre Curie to interrupt his very different research in order to try to isolate this element with his wife. At that time—May or June 1898—a collaboration began which was to last for eight years, until it was destroyed by a fatal accident.

We cannot and must not attempt to find out what should be credited to Marie and what to Pierre during these eight years. It would be exactly what the husband and wife did not want. The personal genius of Pierre Curie is known to us by the original work he had accomplished before this collaboration. His wife's genius appears to us in the first intuition of discovery, the brilliant start; and it was to reappear to us again, solitary, when Marie Curie the widow unflinchingly carried the weight of a new science and conducted it, through research, step by step, to its harmonious expansion. We therefore have formal proof that in the fusion of their two efforts, in this superior alliance of man and woman, the exchange was equal.

Let this certainty suffice for our curiosity and admiration. Let us not attempt to separate these creatures full of love, whose handwriting alternates and combines in the working notebooks covered with formulae, these creatures who were to sign nearly all their scientific publications together. They were to write "We found" and "We observed"; and when they were constrained by fact to distinguish between their parts, they were to employ this moving locution:

> Certain minerals containing uranium and thorium (pitchblende, chalcolite, uranite) are very active from the point of view of the emission of Becquerel rays. In a preceding communication, *one of us* showed that their activity was even greater than that of uranium and thorium, and stated the opinion that this effect was due to some other very active substance contained in small quantity in these minerals.
>
> (Pierre and Marie Curie: *Proceedings of the Academy of Science*, July 18, 1898.)

Marie and Pierre looked for this "very active" substance in an ore of uranium called pitchblende, which in the crude state had shown itself to be four times more radioactive than the pure oxide of uranium that could be extracted from it. But the composition of this ore had been known for a long time with considerable precision. The new element must therefore be present in very small quantity or it would not have escaped the notice of scientists and their chemical analysis.

According to their calculations—"pessimistic" calculations, like those of true physicists, who always take the less attractive of two probabilities—the collaborators thought the ore should contain the new element to a maximum quantity of one per cent. They decided that this was very little. They would have been in consternation if they had known that the radioactive element they were hunting down did not count for more than a millionth part of pitchblende ore.

They began their prospecting patiently, using a method of chemical research invented by themselves, based on radioactivity: they separated all the elements in pitchblende by ordinary chemical analysis and then measured the radioactivity of each of the bodies thus obtained. By successive eliminations they saw the "abnormal" radioactivity take refuge in certain parts of the ore. As they went on, the field of investigation was narrowed. It was exactly the technique used by the police when they search the houses of a neighborhood, one by one, to isolate and arrest a malefactor.

But there was more than one malefactor here: the radioactivity was concentrated principally in two different chemical fractions of the pitchblende. For M. and Mme. Curie it indicated the existence of two new elements instead of one. By July 1898 they were able to announce the discovery of one of these substances with certainty.

"You will have to name it," Pierre said to his young wife, in the same tone as if it were a question of choosing a name for little Irène.

The one-time Mlle. Sklodovska reflected in silence for a moment. Then, her heart turning toward her own country which had been erased from the map of the world, she wondered vaguely if the scientific event would be published in Russia, Germany and Austria—the oppressor countries—and answered timidly:

"Could we call it 'polonium'?"

In the *Proceedings of the Academy* for July 1898 we read:

> We belive the substance we have extracted from pitchblende contains a metal not yet observed, related to bismuth by its analytical properties. If the existence of this new metal is confirmed we propose to call it *polonium,* from the name of the original country of one of us.

The choice of this name proves that in becoming a Frenchwoman and a physicist Marie had not disowned her former enthusiasms. Another thing proves it for us: even before the note "On a New Radioactive Substance Contained in Pitchblende" had appeared in the *Proceedings of the Academy,* Marie had sent the manuscript to her native country, to that Joseph Boguski who directed the little laboratory at the Museum of Industry and Agriculture where she had made her first experiments. The communication was published in Warsaw in a monthly photographic review called *Swiatlo* almost as soon as in Paris.

Life was unchanged in the little flat in the Rue de la Glacière. Marie and Pierre worked even more than usual; that was all. When the heat of summer came, the young wife found time to buy some baskets of fruit in the markets and, as usual, she cooked and put away preserves for the winter, according to the recipes used in the Curie family. Then she locked the shutters on her windows, which gave on burned leaves; she registered their two bicycles at the Orleans station, and, like thousands of other young women in Paris, went off on holiday with her husband and her child.

This year the couple had rented a peasant's house at Auroux, in Auvergne. Happy to breathe good air after the noxious atmosphere of the Rue Lhomond, the Curies made excursions to Mende, Puy, Clermont, Mont-Dore. They climbed hills, visited grottoes, bathed in rivers. Every day, alone in the country, they spoke of what they called their "new metals," polonium and "the other"—the one that remained to be found. In September

CULVER SERVICE

Marie Curie and her two daughters, Eve and Irène

they would go back to the damp workroom and the dull minerals; with freshened ardor they would take up their search again. . . .

One grief interfered with Marie's intoxication for work: the Dluskis were on the point of leaving Paris. They had decided to settle in Austrian Poland and to build a sanatorium for tubercular sufferers at Zakopane in the Carpathian Mountains.

The day of separation arrived: Marie and Bronya exchanged brokenhearted farewells; Marie was losing her friend and protector, and for the first time she had the feeling of exile.

> *Marie to Bronya, December 2, 1898:*
> You can't imagine what a hole you have made in my life. With you two, I have lost everything I clung to in Paris except my husband and child. It seems to me that Paris no longer exists, aside from our lodging and the school where we work.
> Ask Mme. Dluska if the green plant you left behind should be watered, and how many times a day. Does it need a great deal of heat and sun?
> We are well, in spite of the bad weather, the rain and the mud. Irène is getting to be a big girl. She is very difficult about her food, and aside from milk tapioca she will eat hardly anything regularly, not even eggs. Write me what would be a suitable menu for persons of her age. . . .

In spite of their prosaic character—or perhaps because of it—some notes written by Mme. Curie in that memorable year 1898 seem to us worth quoting. Some are to be found in the margins of a book called *Family Cooking*, with respect to a recipe for gooseberry jelly:

> I took eight pounds of fruit and the same weight in crystallized sugar. After an ebullition of ten minutes, I passed the mixture through a rather fine sieve. I obtained fourteen pots of very good jelly, not transparent, which "took" perfectly.

In a school notebook covered with gray linen, in which the young mother had written little Irène's weight day by day, her diet and the appearance of her first teeth, we read under the date of July 20, 1898, some days after the publication of the discovery of polonium:

> Irène says "thanks" with her hand. She can walk very well now on all fours. She says "Gogli, gogli, go." She stays in the garden all day at Sceaux on a carpet. She can roll, pick herself up, and sit down.

On August 15, at Auroux:

> Irène has cut her seventh tooth, on the lower left. She can stand for half a minute alone. For the past three days we have bathed her in the river. She cries, but today (fourth bath) she stopped crying and played with her hands in the water.
>
> She plays with the cat and chases him with war cries. She is not afraid of strangers any more. She sings a great deal. She gets up on the table when she is in her chair.

Three months later, on October 17, Marie noted with pride:

> Irène can walk very well, and no longer goes on all fours.

On January 5, 1899:

> Irène has fifteen teeth!

Between these two notes—that of October 17, 1898, in which Irène no longer goes on all fours, and that of January 5 in which Irène has fifteen teeth—and a few months after the note on the gooseberry preserve, we find another note worthy of remark.

It was drawn up by Marie and Pierre Curie and a collaborator called G. Bémont. Intended for the Academy of Science, and published in the *Proceedings* of the session of December 26, 1898, it announced the existence of a second new chemical element in pitchblende.

Some lines of this communication read as follows:

> The various reasons we have just enumerated lead us to believe that the new radioactive substance contains a new element to which we propose to give the name of RADIUM.
>
> The new radioactive substance certainly contains a very strong proportion of barium; in spite of that its radioactivity is considerable. The radioactivity of radium therefore must be enormous.

OLIVER WENDELL HOLMES, JR.

A Lawyer's Oath

BY CLARA INGRAM JUDSON

Illustrations by Robert Todd

Son of a famous poet and physician, Oliver Wendell Holmes, Jr. (1841-1935) achieved his own fame as a defender of human rights. So often did he differ with his fellow Justices of the United States Supreme Court that he became known as the great dissenter.

WENDELL Holmes' starry-eyed view of the law was badly jolted by the end of his first week as a student. The subjects of lectures sounded fascinating. How did the three elderly lecturers manage to be so dull? Listening was as wearisome as Dr. Holmes had predicted—but Wendell was not ready to admit that to his father. He did walk over to see Uncle John Holmes.

After the death of Grandmother Holmes, the big old house had been sold, and John had taken a small place on Appian Way, nearby. John was at home when Wendell dropped in that Friday afternoon.

"You're a lawyer, Uncle John," Wendell began as he stepped inside the door. "How did you keep your first thrill when you studied law?"

Uncle John stared at Wendell; then he roared with laughter. "You need food, Wendell," he said, a moment later. "I've got bread and cold corned beef. Let's eat." He led the way to his tiny kitchen, where a housekeeper cooked on certain days; on other days John Holmes looked after himself. Now they made man-sized sandwiches, ate cookies and apples, and Wendell did feel cheered.

"All the same, Uncle John . . ."

"You cannot expect a college to supply thrills," John interrupted. "Read the catalog. Did it promise excitement? No. Those 'elderly professors' you mention are brilliant men—a lawyer, a judge, a jurist. They give you facts. You will have to hunt your own thrills in yourself or in the books you read outside the lectures. Courses simply give direction to your reading and thinking. You'll never make a lawyer if you can't last out a week of dull stuff. I'll wager you don't understand all the words those men use."

"Sometimes I think they must be talking a foreign language," Wendell admitted, subdued by his uncle's tirade. "Equity. Common law. Trespass. Negotiate. I thought I knew those words, but in the lecture meanings seem different."

"Of course. Words have different meanings in every profession. Get out your dictionary. Look along the definitions till you come to the words 'In law.' Read that meaning and remember it. You must know words to listen intelligently."

"You talk like Mr. Emerson," Wendell suddenly remembered. "He told me I'd have to take over myself; to read and think. That's what you mean, isn't it, Uncle John?"

"Exactly. And talk with young lawyer friends. John Ropes will help you. You like John Gray, too. Have an evening with them now and then. They'll help you get on the right trail."

Wendell acted on this advice. His mother invited the two young men to supper. Of course Dr. Holmes led talk there, but he was interesting. Afterward Wendell took his friends up to his study, and they talked till midnight.

On this first evening, and others following, they asked each other many questions.

"What is law?" Wendell wanted to know. "Is it restraints by means of which men in power try to control other men?"

"I'd say that law is rules that have grown out of long experience," Gray suggested.

"Do laws change men?" Ropes asked. "Or do men change laws?"

Such questions could not be answered quickly. Wendell searched in books for answers. He thought he learned more in these evenings than in school. But he admitted that lectures gave him new ideas to discuss. Sometimes other friends joined the lawyers; William James and Henry Bowditch were medical students. Charles Peirce was making mathematics and logic his life work. On such evenings talk ranged over the whole universe; they called it "the Cosmos" in an intimate way that amused and challenged them.

The young men went to campaign meetings now and then, especially if George Shattuck was the speaker. Shattuck was handsome, dark haired, a fine speaker. Wendell enjoyed him and his arguments for voting for Abraham Lincoln.

On election day, Wendell Holmes along with a majority of his fellow citizens voted for Lincoln. War still raged, but the end did seem nearer.

Before Christmas Mr. Robert Morse, a well known Boston lawyer, called at the house on Charles Street.

"I've come to see your son Wendell," he said to Dr. Holmes. "I hope I catch him at home?" Wendell was called.

"Good afternoon, Holmes," Mr. Morse said. "I won't keep you long. I need help in my office. How would you like to work there—afternoons when you haven't a lecture?"

Dr. Holmes opened his lips to say "Yes." Then he caught his wife's eye and swallowed the word. Morse went on.

"There's no pay. But you will see how law school theories apply in practice. Like the idea?"

"I like it very much, sir," Wendell said. "And I thank you for asking me." Dr. Holmes relaxed. Wendell had *some* sense.

"May I start tomorrow?"

"Just what I hoped you would say," Morse replied. Talk turned to weather—which was bad—and Morse left.

Wendell had no doubt as to how this opportunity had come to him. But by this time, he had learned that his father was right on one point: experience as well as theory was valuable. He welcomed a job in a good office.

Daily Wendell Holmes went back and forth between Cambridge and Boston. The winter seemed the coldest in memory. Way into March, feet stiffened with cold in spite of piles of straw on streetcar floors.

In Washington, Lincoln's second Inaugural Day was bleak and windy. But crowds gathered, expecting wise suggestions for ending the war. Many were disappointed. This second address was thoughtful and religious rather than political or practical. It sounded like a gentle preparation for peace without harshness.

At Dane Hall students gathered to talk.

"Lincoln's fine words are well enough, but I wish he had spelled out his position," a second year student said. "How is all this going to be done?"

"And the war not yet over," grunted another.

"It will be soon," Wendell Holmes felt sure. "Likely Lincoln has plans he can't tell till then."

Richmond fell on the second day of April. Lee surrendered on the ninth. When this news came, Boston stopped work to celebrate. Crowds thronged the Common, jubilantly retelling the good news. Women with long black mourning veils met women whose men would return and tears of mourning and thankfulness mingled. Mrs. Holmes watched her tall son, alive by a miracle—by three miracles.

"The Union's saved! Now Lincoln can do something!" This idea in various words was repeated over and over.

Someone began to sing "The Union forever, Hurrah, boys, Hurrah!" The crowd took it up and sang happily. Youths joined together, hands on shoulders and snaked through the massed people, singing and whistling loudly. It was a wonderful day. The nation's troubles were over.

One week later Abraham Lincoln was dead. Flags dropped to half mast. Black crepe streamed from windows as a stunned nation mourned.

Incredibly, Andrew Johnson took the oath of office—who had ever thought that *Johnson* would be President? But in time, national and personal business was resumed as usual.

Work filled Wendell Holmes' days and evenings. Mornings he heard two or three lectures and worked in the law library. Afternoons he sat on a stool before a high wall desk in Mr. Morse's office and copied documents. Often he did errands; to the courthouse, another lawyer's office, to the library. Lawyers called this "leg work," a true name.

In spite of chores, Wendell liked work in the office. Mr. Morse had a large and varied business. Wendell learned to have respect for the man's quick decisions; for his careful preparation of a case.

Evenings, Wendell studied a while after supper. Then friends

dropped in, or he went out to see them. Dr. Holmes always noticed when Wendell took his hat from the rack.

"Where are you going, Wendell?" he'd call.

Wendell told him, politely. But he came to hate the ever watchful eye that sent him back to childhood. He seemed to have less independence than Amelia. She was a young lady, now, a member of one of the elite Boston Sewing Circles. She came and went as she pleased. Wendell, still a student, seemed a boy to his father.

"Who lectured this morning?" he would ask.

"What books did you take from the library today?"

"Anything new in Morse's office?"

When she was near, Mrs. Holmes came to her son's rescue and changed the subject. One evening she drew Wendell into the dining room after supper and talked to him anxiously.

"Your father is interested in you, Wendell. You mustn't mind his curiosity. He is proud of everything you are doing."

"I know, Mother," Wendell said with good humor. "It's just Father's way."

But it was a "way" that fretted Wendell. He considered leaving law school and earning some money—but that was silly when his tuition and living made no hardship for his parents. He should be patient and finish his education.

By late spring the long hours of work began to show on Wendell's health. His father fussed about his loss of weight, his paleness. Dr. Holmes rented a house on Nahant—a long strip of sandy beach thrust out into the bay—and he insisted that Wendell stop all work for a while.

Nahant was a popular place with friends of the Holmes family. Their house was invaded by young men eager to enjoy Amelia's company; Wendell saw his little sister with her following. She was "little," but very much the ruler of her world.

"I can't believe this grown-up young lady is the fat little girl I used to drag to parades," Wendell remarked to his mother.

"*I* can't believe you are the same little boy," she teased him. "Your father can't undertsand how you got to be so tall when both your parents are small. Have you passed six foot three yet, Wendie?" Wendell grinned. He wasn't going to get into that conversation.

The Dixwells had a summer house at Nahant, too, and Wendell dropped in there often. He never planned ahead; just took it for granted that when he came Fanny would want to see him. And she always did.

At the summer's end the same full program of work began—school, office, study and talk. In the back of his mind all this time Wendell felt the need for a special book about law. He did not find it. He spoke to Uncle John about it.

"I want to find out how *law* came to be," he said. "I don't mean laws passed by Parliament, Congress, or legislatures. I mean *law*; law for all people, beginning ages ago, I should think. Did law have a small beginning and grow by logic? Or by man's experience? Is the foundation of law the same anywhere?"

Uncle John puffed at his pipe thoughtfully.

"I don't think I ever heard of such a book," he finally decided. "No. I doubt if there is one. Likely you'll have to write it yourself, Wendell." They had a good laugh at that silly idea.

Wendell dropped in around the corner to tell Fanny about

the book he could not find. Not that Fanny knew anything about law; a girl wouldn't, of course. But she listened well. Wendell even repeated Uncle John's remark—that Wendell should write the book himself. She didn't laugh.

"Of course you will, Wendell," she said, amazing him.

Wendell Holmes received his degree in law late in the winter of 1866. He was through with lectures. The degree did not allow him to practice law in the courts, but it was a big step in that direction.

His parents astonished him with a surprise they had planned. He was to go to Europe before he settled down to further study. He could hardly believe his good fortune.

"Now I can talk again with Leslie Stephen," Wendell said. He had enjoyed that young Englishman who had visited in Boston. "And maybe I can see men whose books I have read. You are very kind and generous to me. I do thank you."

Dr. Holmes wrote a couple of letters which might pave the way for such meetings as his son wanted. The doctor had recently been abroad himself, to meet many readers of his books and to receive honors and a degree. Wendell's trip promised many pleasures and added education.

Shortly before Wendell was to sail, Mr. Shattuck sent a message; would Wendell Holmes kindly call at the office?

"I've been watching you, young man," Shattuck said as he greeted Wendell. "You'll want to study for your bar examinations when you come back, won't you?"

"Yes, sir. That is my plan."

"I suggest that you do your reading in my office. We'll have a corner for you. Someone can stop to answer a question—you'll have many."

"Oh, thank you, sir!" Wendell flushed with pleasure. "I can't imagine anything that would please me more."

On his way home he marveled again at his good fortune—a trip and the added joy of a definite task on his return.

He sailed away in high spirits.

Fanny Dixwell, looking lovely in spite of being thin and pale, spent the summer at the beach, being determinedly gay. She fooled most people—but not Mrs. Holmes, Edward, or Uncle John.

Wendell Holmes liked London. His letter to Leslie Stephen brought that one-time Boston visitor calling at once. The next day he came again with his brother Fitzjames, the judge; with true friendliness they planned sightseeing and parties so that the visitor could meet interesting people.

As he went about, Holmes saw that Leslie Stephen's reputation as a philosopher and critic had grown; he was highly esteemed. He found, too, that people liked his father's books. They talked of the "Breakfast Table" essays, now grown to several volumes, and of the novel *Elsie Venner*. Soon they liked Wendell for himself.

"An attractive young man; modest, too," was said of him.

Holmes saw famous sights, visited museums and galleries, and did a daily round of parties.

"When you first came," Leslie Stephen recalled one day, "you said there was one man you must see—who is he?"

"John Stuart Mill," Holmes replied. "His work fascinates me. Am I being too bold to want to meet him?"

"Indeed, no," Stephen assured him. "But Mill lives out of London. I'll write and plan the call at his convenience."

As he awaited the interview, Holmes thought over various books of Mill's that he had read. John Stuart Mill was a philosopher and economist; he was interested in wages and hours of labor and other practical matters. The man must have a rare mind, Holmes thought. It was said that he read and understood Plato before he was ten years old. Knowing something of Plato himself, Wendell was eager to meet a man who turned philosophy to problems of business.

The day came. The great man was cordial to his young visitor and talked freely. Mill was older than Mr. Emerson; he fidgeted, was bald and nervous.

"I tell you as I told Parliament," he said, "we must think of the greatest good for the greatest number. For this I am called a radical. Some day they will see that I am right."

Holmes listened avidly to new thoughts about labor. He tried to remember each sentence so that he could mull it over later.

In a few days the Stephen brothers and Holmes crossed the channel for sightseeing on the continent. They ended the tour with a stay in Switzerland. The rugged Alps were a revelation of beauty to the New Englander. The snowy heights, the fertile valleys, the industrious people, charmed him.

The three young men joined a group of mountain climbers, and since Holmes enjoyed the climb so much, they went again on a more difficult expedition. This was the first sport that Wendell Holmes had ever really enjoyed. He liked to be roped in line; it was a challenge to clutch at an icy ledge with numb fingers as his toes in clumsy shoes groped for foothold. He felt a kind of exaltation in these great efforts.

"It it the philosopher in you?" Leslie asked, half teasing.

"Maybe." Holmes had no breath for talk. As he paused, looking around at the vast panorama, a new thought came to him. Our struggle upward here is like life; tied to fellow men, searching a safe place to stand, ever reaching higher.

"This is like life," Leslie said, as though he shared Wendell's unspoken thought, "struggle, and success at the summit. Every person needs the thrill of success—we will experience it in another hour."

Wendell Holmes left Switzerland reluctantly.

At home, in September, no one seemed excited about either John Stuart Mill or Switzerland. For a few hours Amelia listened, prodding Wendell to talk about London parties and fashions. Dr. Holmes was pleased to hear that his English readers wanted a sequel to *Elsie Venner*. Edward, now an important senior at Harvard, was in Cambridge. Wendell felt quite left on his own.

Uncle John will listen, he thought, and set off for Cambridge. John Holmes' first words surprised his nephew.

"Get a file of back newspapers, Wendell, and catch up on doings in Boston. There's been a printers' strike. Talk about an eight-hour day stirs the city. Employers can't see what a workman will do with his spare time if he works only eight hours, six days a week."

This caught Wendell's attention.

"What do workmen say?" he asked.

"You'd be surprised. Some say a man can do more and better

work in eight than in ten hours. One bold fellow says that a workman's time, after work, is his own. Amazing! Why, it's not long since mill owners said women had to work twelve hours a day to keep them out of mischief. I tell you, Nephew, the world is changing. Seen Fanny yet?"

"Well, not yet." The shift of topic surprised Wendell.

"I do not understand you, Wendell," Uncle John exclaimed. "Coming here to talk to an old man when a pretty girl awaits nearby. Get along with you, or I'll disown you!"

After he got to the Dixwells', Wendell regretted that he had not come the first day he was at home. Fanny was so pretty, so interested in his talk. He told her about Mill and Switzerland. Mrs. Dixwell invited him to stay to supper; he had a wonderful time.

On Monday morning, Wendell Holmes went to the office of Chandler, Shattuck, and Thayer to start his studies for the bar examination. On passing this he would be allowed to practice law. Young lawyer friends had assured him that the examinations were easy.

"Just memorize everything that has been asked before."

"If you'd had the sense to read in Shattuck's office instead of going to law school you might have got by without an examination," another said.

Wendell doubted this. He would not even have liked "getting by." He needed all he had learned at law school. Now, this morning he met the three partners and was assigned to a desk.

"I have a list of books for you, Mr. Holmes," Thayer said. "Coke on Littleton, Montesquieu on the spirit of the law, Mill on logic, Stephen on criminal law."

"It will be fine to reread Mill and Stephen since I have met them," Holmes said and settled to work.

Holmes liked the feeling in the office. He liked Mr. Thayer, and he very much liked being called "Mr. Holmes."

Autumn passed, and the holidays. February had nearly ended before Mr. Shattuck decided that Holmes was ready for the bar examination. He wrote the letter of character recommendation required and made arrangements.

Holmes wondered if he would be frightened. The ordeal was

not a written examination; it was oral. The examining lawyers were to ask him anything they chose.

But when he faced his questioners around a table, he was not frightened. His mind was clear, his thoughts quick. They did ask some tricky questions; but he had the answers. After a couple of hours the thing was done.

"You pass with flying colors," one said, smiling.

"But it was so easy," Holmes protested, surprised.

"Few find it easy. You were well prepared. That makes all the difference in the world. I predict a fine future for you in law, Mr. Holmes."

Wendell could hardly wait to get outside where he could show his delight and relief. He wanted to run around the Common, to shout his glee. Instead he went back to the office—but he got generous congratulations there.

"Our senior partner will go with you Monday when you take the lawyer's oath," Mr. Shattuck said, pleased with Holmes.

Monday, March 4, 1867, was a bleak day. A chill wind blew as Mr. Chandler and Wendell Holmes walked to the Suffolk County Court House. This was the building where Anthony Burns had been jailed almost thirteen years before. Holmes had gone in and out hundreds of times in his years of studying law. But as he walked between the marble pillars this day the old building seemed to take on a new dignity.

They entered the Superior Court room of the County of Suffolk of the Commonwealth of Massachusetts. They sat in the lawyers' seats, at right angles to the bench behind which was the great chair for the judge.

Holmes glanced around. Only a few sat in the seats for the public, this early Monday morning. Dr. Holmes was among these in the second row. He had not spoken of coming; Wendell was pleased to see him.

Judge Lord entered, his curly hair well brushed. His long black robe fluttered as he took his place.

The clerk stepped forward.

"Hear ye! Hear ye!" he called in the traditional way. "The Court will now attend to the taking of the oath."

This was Holmes' cue. He stepped forward and took his place before the bench. All the people stood up.

Judge Lord stood, holding a Bible in his hand. He looked solemn, but friendly, too, as Holmes laid his right hand on the sacred book and repeated from memory the words of his pledge:

"I solemnly swear that I will do no falsehood or consent to the doing of any in Court; I will not wittingly or willingly promote or sue any false, groundless or unlawful suit, nor give aid nor consent to the same; I will delay no man for lucre or malice; but I will conduct myself in the office of an attorney within the Court according to the best of my knowledge and discretion, and with all good fidelity as well to the Courts as my clients. So help me God."

Judge Lord bowed. The clerk stepped forward and motioned Holmes to sign the register. The ceremony was over.

"March 4. Oliver Wendell Holmes, Junior," the new attorney wrote. The final word ended in a flourish.

Mr. Shattuck had invited several friends to drop in at the office. There was much congratulating and handshaking.

When he got away, Wendell stopped at a printer's shop and left an order. A couple of days later he opened the small parcel the printer's boy delivered and studied the new cards:

OLIVER WENDELL HOLMES, JR.
Counsellor at Law

On a sudden impulse, he enclosed one in an envelope and sent it to the secretary of the Class of 1861, Harvard. Now I shall be something besides a poet, he thought.

The next few days seemed blank, dull. He had worked so hard toward that examination that he felt aimless, now, by contrast. Books were still there to be read—but where should he begin?

At home, Edward was hunting through back newspapers to collect articles about the suggested impeachment of President Johnson.

"Why are you interested, Neddy?" Wendell asked. "It's a political matter." Wendell had little interest in politics.

"There's a legal aspect we're supposed to study," Edward said, laughing. "Maybe you're not interested in law?"

Thus prodded, Wendell did study the matter. It helped fill empty days.

While he had been studying for the examination, Wendell had neglected his friends. Now he found they were scattered or too busy for visiting. Will James was in Europe in the hope of improving his health. Wendell missed Will. Their minds stimulated each other. They even liked the same girl.

"I hear Will James went to Europe to keep from falling in love with Fanny Dixwell," Amelia said pertly, at supper. "That gives you a clear field, Wendie. Fanny liked Will, but he thought you had first chance."

"*Mother!*" Wendell was shocked. "How can you let Amelia gossip like that?"

"Is it gossip, Son? For all I know it may be true."

Months dragged by. November had come when he got his first case. His client wished to sue the New York Central Railroad for the accidental death of her husband.

"I'll help you in court," Mr. Shattuck promised. "But you must do all the work of preparation."

Wendell went at that case as though his life depended on winning it. He had every fact verified and ready. Mr. Shattuck was brilliant as usual in court. But they lost the case. Holmes was actually numb with surprise. He had worked so hard; had believed so firmly that their case was just—what sort of law could decide against them?

Late in that miserable day he went to see Uncle John.

"So you lost," John said, glancing at his nephew. "Well, that's law for you, but you would have it. Come with me to the Dixwells'. I promised to come over."

Wendell dragged along, feeling blue.

"You lost?" Fanny exclaimed as she saw Wendell. "Well, cases have been lost before. Don't take it so hard."

"But Shattuck was wonderful! I had all the facts . . ." Wendell was still dazed with that verdict. The evening was not a success.

More months went by. Edward was in law school and doing well. He was a handsome youth; not as tall as his brother, and thin. He had asthma like his Uncle John. Edward had a cordial manner; Wendell seemed a plodder by contrast.

Both his sons were still dependent, but Dr. Holmes did not mind. He prospered as did many other Americans at this time. He lectured, wrote books and essays, saved money and bought stock in companies that were developing America.

General Grant was elected President in the fall of 1868, and the country rolled along easily.

Dr. Holmes, with other Bostonians, had been watching changes in his city. Land had been made by filling in along the Back Bay, making a whole new section, much of it desirable for homes. He bought a lot and built a new house—number 296 Beacon Street. It was one of a row of narrow four-story brick houses, high, in the fashion of the day. His sons had rooms on the third floor.

Lawyer Holmes had little interest in the new house except to be glad his mother was so pleased. He was in the depths of discouragement. Three facts taunted him; he was a dependent in his father's house, he hardly earned his spending money. And he would soon be thirty years old.

While a soldier, Wendell Holmes had often been cold and wet, ill-fed and hungry, but his dreams had sustained him. Now comforts surrounded him, but where were the dreams? Had he aimed too high for his capacities? Was he marked for failure? These questions haunted him, and he found no answers.

A message rescued Wendell Holmes just when he had reached the end of his patience, waiting for clients. Mr. Thayer would like to see him about some editing. Holmes went at once to Thayer's office.

"A new edition of Kent's *Commentaries* is to be published," Mr. Thayer began, "and I am to be the editor. I would like to have you assist me."

Holmes' eyes sparkled, and new life seemed to flow into him. This would be work of importance. James Kent of New York was a great judge and jurist; many lawyers considered him the founder of American law. His four-volume work, *Commentaries on American Law,* published in the late 1820's, explained the laws of his country and commented on court decisions. Kent himself had kept his work up to date until his death in 1847; there had been, in all, eleven editions of the *Commentaries.*

"I'll do my best, sir," Holmes said.

"Good. I'm glad you will undertake the job." Mr. Thayer was pleased. "It is no easy task that I am giving you," he added. "You will have to search American and English court records for cases that have a bearing on laws Kent included. The pay is trifling. The work will be tedious—probably take two years."

"Only two years!" Holmes exclaimed.

"Can't give you more time."

"I'll do my best, sir," Holmes promised again. He could hardly wait to start on volume one.

Wendell Holmes liked this new work. It was hard; but it was his own. He searched through masses of court decisions to see what laws were still useful. The nation was constantly changing. A new edition of Kent would show judges which laws were being followed.

Will James returned from Europe and expected long evenings of talk. Holmes was glad to see him. But his interest in the Cosmos was slight compared with his fascination for Kent. Will wrote to his brother Henry that Wendell Holmes was studying "like a person possessed. He seldom goes out even on Saturday nights!"

Another friend wrote that Holmes carried a green bag with him—his precious Kent and notebook inside—on the rare times when he was persuaded to accept an invitation.

"He sets this bag under his chair at the dinner table," this letter continued. "He looks thin and pale."

So much of the work on Kent was thinking, deciding. It had to be done alone. And those two short years made him work every possible minute.

Meanwhile, Edward Holmes graduated with honors from Harvard Law School. There had been no argument as to where he should study. Since Wendell entered that school, it was already gaining in prestige. After Edward was admitted to the bar, Wendell resigned from Chandler, Shattuck, and Thayer and the brothers opened their own office, Holmes and Holmes.

Both were determined to build up a good practice. But there were difficulties. Edward's easy way was attractive, but dreadful asthma threatened his health. Wendell was absorbed by Kent evenings and some days.

"I don't know about this partnership," Dr. Holmes fretted to his wife. "Edward will do his share, but Wendell is so slow, so possessed with study . . ."

"Wendell is the kind that gets a slow start," she said loyally.

"A slow start! Where is he going when he does start?"

No one, not even Wendell, seemed to notice that from the time it was known that he had begun on the *Commentaries*, work came to him. He was invited to review new law books. At first these reviews were unsigned. Then his signature was used, showing that the review had value because it was his opinion. This pleased his father.

The brothers enjoyed being together. They worked hard. But to Wendell, clients were an interruption to the important business of editing Kent.

"Wendell was right, long ago," Mrs. Holmes remarked to Amelia. "He likes study; he wants to be a jurist, not a practicing lawyer. But how is he to earn a living?"

Amelia laughed. Earning a living did not bother her. Dr. Holmes' varied work and dividends continued to bring prosperity. In time business improved for Holmes and Holmes, too. Wendell got his first case and won it. Edward was very happy.

"We're going forward from now, Father," he said at supper. "You will be proud of your sons yet."

Soon Edward's engagement to Henrietta Wigglesworth, of a wealthy Boston family, was announced. Amelia had a steady beau and talked about a wedding. Only the older brother was untouched by romance. Oh, he liked Fanny, but that was no romance, though Amelia teased him unmercifully.

Wendell hardly heard her. His reviews of law books won him a place on the editorial staff of the *American Law Review*. He could not refuse that distinction, even for Kent.

Charles W. Eliot, a tutor, then a professor, had been chosen president of Harvard in 1869. His new ideas made quite a stir in the university's sedate halls. He was promptly called a "radical" because his ideas differed from traditional ways. Eliot organized new courses. He gave credit for work in science and started new methods of teaching.

In a couple of years he got around to the law school. For it, he engaged younger lecturers, among them Wendell Holmes and Wendell's wartime friend, John Gray.

"I want you to show students how law has developed in America," Eliot told Holmes in their interview. "You are working on that as you edit Kent." Holmes was pleased that Eliot had noticed the work with Mr. Thayer.

"I accept with pleasure," Holmes said. "I'll try to make students see that while English law is our foundation, we adapt it to American life—that's what you want?"

"Exactly!" The men parted, both satisfied.

Later in the day Wendell told Edward about the talk.

"If lecturing didn't fit with Kent, I suppose you would have refused the Harvard appointment," Edward said. His voice had a trace of bitterness.

"Of course! Kent is important.

Edward sniffed. Perhaps it was just his asthma.

Soon Edward and then Amelia married, the weddings not many weeks apart. In the big house at 296 Beacon Street, dinners and suppers were gay as ever; Dr. Holmes always had guests. But Wendell missed his sister and brother at breakfasts.

"What are you teaching today, Wendie?"

"Are your classes larger?"

"What do the students think of Eliot's frills?"

The doctor hardly waited for answers. He had no confidence in Wendell's observation of such matters.

With his sister and brother gone, Wendell began to feel another loss. He missed Fanny Dixwell. For years, except when at war or in Europe, Wendell Holmes had seen Fanny every week—often several times each week. While at college and law school, he often dropped by to see her. After he began work on Kent, he stopped going to Cambridge except to rush out to give a lecture.

But he often saw Fanny in his own home, having tea with Amelia; he came to count on it. After Amelia was married, Fanny went to her new home, not to 296 Beacon Street.

"Have you had a quarrel with Fanny?" he asked his mother one day. "She hasn't been here all week."

"All week!" his mother was amazed. "She hasn't been here since Christmas. Why should she come? Amelia no longer lives here. Have *you* quarreled with Fanny, Wendell?"

"Of course not! She should come to see you. Why not ask her to tea, Mother?"

"Well, I could." Mrs. Holmes' tone was doubtful. She wondered whether it had always been too easy for Wendell to be with Fanny. "But you know, Son, streetcars run both ways between Boston and Cambridge."

"Oh, streetcars! Ask Uncle John to drive her over. I'd like to see him, too."

When they came to tea a few days later Mrs. Holmes was shocked at Fanny's appearance. Thin, pale—she looked defeated, quite unlike the glowing Fanny.

Mrs. Holmes drew her toward the fire in the parlor; the

March day was chilly. John Holmes lingered, hanging up his coat and muffler as Wendell came down the stairs. He had not been feeling well of late.

"What's the matter with you, Uncle John?" Wendell exclaimed.

"I have a dumb nephew who worries me," John Holmes said in a brusque tone. "The fellow can't see beyond a printed page. Likes a book better than a pretty girl who's loved him for years. If there's one thing above another makes me sick, it's a dumb man named Holmes."

"Uncle John!" Wendell stared at this tirade.

"See for yourself—if you've not forgotten how," John said and stepped into the parlor, shutting off talk.

Wendell followed. His face and neck were scarlet, his manner shaken and confused. His mother served the tea and cakes, and the three chatted. Wendell sat silent, eyeing Fanny. Yes, she *was* thin. She looked weary.

Fanny saw his covert glances; she was oppressed by his silence. Finally she could stand it no longer.

"I really must be going," she said.

"Oh, not yet!" John Holmes exclaimed. "I haven't finished the cakes." Fanny had only crumpled hers.

"Uncle John!" Wendell stood up, nearly shattering his teacup. "You stay here with Mother. If Fanny has to go, I'll drive her home and come back for you."

Fanny looked up in surprise. She did not object.

In a masterful, direct way his mother had not seen for a long time, Wendell got Fanny's wraps and his own and they went off. Uncle John stayed for supper. He stayed on, and on. And still Wendell—and the borrowed horse and buggy—did not return.

Mrs. Holmes was about to suggest that John had better stay for the night when Wendell arrived.

"Fanny and I are going to be married," he announced without preamble. "Do you mind if we live here a while, Father? You know how little my lecturing pays, and writing, and the few cases we have. Do you *mind*, Father?"

Anxious eyes studied his father's face. Lack of income affected Wendell deeply. It made no difference that his father had plenty. He wanted to pay his own way.

"Mind?" the little doctor got up and slapped his tall son's shoulders. "I'd like a daughter in the house again. It's about time you got around to this step. Do you realize that you are thirty-one?"

"I didn't notice, Father. I guess I've always meant to marry Fanny, but I forgot to tell her. We . . ."

The three waited, silent.

"If it's all right, we'll be married in June."

"This is wonderful news," Mrs. Holmes said and pulled her son's face down to kiss him. Uncle John grinned. Why hadn't he prodded the boy before? Hated to meddle, likely.

"I'll get at cleaning and fixing up the third floor rooms," Mrs. Holmes planned. "With Neddy gone, you and Fanny can have the whole floor to yourselves. We'll like that, Son."

"I can tell all my old stories," the doctor boasted. "Fanny's not been here for so long, I may have new ones. She'll laugh even if they are old. Wonderful girl." Dr. Holmes continued to be pleased with his world.

Now that plans were made, Wendell was radiantly happy. Why had he waited so long? He didn't know.

On the seventeenth of June, 1872, Fanny Dixwell and Oliver Wendell Holmes, Jr. were married. They did not take a grand tour, as fashionable brides and grooms were doing then.

"Fancy taking a tour with Kent in a green bag!" Fanny confided to a friend. "My Wendell has work to do. That's more important than a tour."

Mrs. Holmes had made the third floor charming in her own way. Now Fanny, without the slightest fuss, deftly made it hers. She loved the entrancing view. She valued the kindness that surrounded her. She did not mind when Dr. Holmes asked his usual question, "Where are you going now, Fanny?" as she came down the stairs. He was just interested; she understood him.

Evenings, Wendell's friends took to dropping in again.

Fanny made them welcome, and the talk was good. Gently, skillfully, she guided it from the Cosmos to law, and Wendell did not miss an evening away from Kent. He wrote better for these changes.

Young Mrs. Holmes was making a good beginning.

NATHANIEL BOWDITCH

The *Astrea* to the Rescue

BY JEAN LEE LATHAM

Illustrations by John O'Hara Cosgrave II

*As a Salem seaman, Nathaniel Bowditch (1773-1838) applied his keen mathematical mind to the problems of navigation. He discovered new ways to measure latitude and longitude by the stars and found thousands of errors in the old tables. So he wrote a book—*The American Practical Navigator*—which is still the basic text for seafaring men. Nat began his book on board the* Astrea *shortly after marrying Elizabeth, a pretty, spirited girl who understood him as no one else could.*

WHEN Nat went aboard the *Astrea,* two sailors handled his gear for him, staggering under the weight of an extra sea chest.

Mr. Collins said, "What have we here, Mr. Bowditch? A private store of cannon balls?"

"Books and charts," Nat told him. "I'm starting now to check every figure in every table that's published. Just to see how many errors are in them."

Collins stared. "Man, that'll take you a year!"

"I'll be lucky if it doesn't take three years."

"But why in the name of sense should you slave over—"

Nat bellowed, "Because they ought to be right! That's why!" He started for the companionway. Someone in ducks and a striped jersey grinned and saluted. For a moment Nat didn't recognize him. "Johnny!"

Johnny swaggered. "Johnny Gorman, able seaman, sir!"

"Congratulations!" Nat told him. He hoped Prince wouldn't feel too bad about the loss of a cabin boy. He was going to feel bad enough about the loss of Lem. He went below, stowed his gear, and returned to the deck. Tom Owens was busy at one of the guns. Maybe Tom would console Prince about the loss of Lem; Tom was a mighty handy man, too, with the guns.

Once more the crew froze to attention; once more Captain Prince came on board, and whipped that stern glance around, seeing everything, looking at no one.

It's just his go-to-sea face, I guess, Nat decided. He probably won't smile between here and Cadiz.

Nat was right; he didn't.

A month later Spain loomed on the horizon. A blockade of British ships stood between the *Astrea* and the harbor of Cadiz. Captain Prince answered the hail of a British ship, ordered his longboat overside, and he and Nat went to present their papers to the British captain.

The Englishman scanned their papers, asked dozens of questions, and gave them a pass to enter Cadiz and trade. "Watch out for French spies," he told them. "They're everywhere. We even found a Frenchman in one of our crews, with a plot to blow up our powder room. Luckily, his pronunciation gave him away."

"The way he'd say—well—for instance, 'commencement'?" And Nat gave the word its French pronunciation.

The British captain raised his eyebrows. "Exactly. You mean, you speak French?" He looked at Prince. "Congratulations, sir, on having an educated man on board. Not the usual thing on a—a—merchant ship, you know."

Prince's eyes glinted. He was probably thinking that what the Englishman almost said was, "Not the usual thing on an American ship." He drawled, "Yes, an educated man is handy. For instance—when there are errors in Moore, he can find them."

"Errors in Moore!" The Englishman stared.

"Not really Moore's fault," Prince said soothingly. "The mistakes were in one of Maskelyne's tables." And he returned to the *Astrea* looking very pleased with himself. "Mr. Collins, call the men aft—down to the last one—even the cabin boy!"

Then men gathered. Little Charlie Waldo, the new cabin

COURTESY OF PEABODY MUSEUM, SALEM (BETTMANN ARCHIVE)

Nathaniel Bowditch

boy, listened big-eyed while Prince explained the danger of French spies. "Mr. Bowditch will tell you how you can spot them by their accent. Keep your ears cocked. If a man with that accent wants to come aboard for any reason—call Mr. Bowditch."

As Nat explained, he watched Charlie's face. I'll bet, he thought, Charlie finds himself a spy before we leave Cadiz.

The next day when they anchored off Cadiz the health officers came aboard. Nat saw Charlie edging around, his head cocked, listening. Then something jerked Nat's attention from Charlie.

The Spanish officer picked up their logbook in one gloved hand, wheeled, and tossed it overboard.

Nat roared at him in Spanish. The health officer smiled and explained. They always dumped logbooks overboard. Didn't the señor know that salt water would purify the book and banish disease? They fished up the book, dripping wet, scanned it, and bowed to Nat. Everything was in order and safe. The *Astrea* could trade with Cadiz.

That night Nat smiled when he wrote to Elizabeth about the salt-water cure for their logbook. He was glad when he had things like that to tell her.

The next night, after he had visited Cadiz, he had things he could tell her, too—about the city of stone, built on a rocky promontory, jutting out into the blue sea.

They must whitewash every building every year. Everything is so white that the glare hurts your eyes. The streets are so narrow, and the buildings so tall that you feel hemmed in when you walk here. No wonder they have such tall buildings, though. They have nowhere to go but *up*.

He stopped writing, and stared at the paper. When would Elizabeth get this letter, he wondered? No chance to send it back to her, unless they hailed a ship coming from the Mediterranean, going back to America. Maybe he'd just have to carry it home, and they'd read it together. When he got home . . . Nat sighed. Already the time seemed long. He laid his letter aside and went on deck for a walk before he turned in.

Charlie Waldo was on deck, talking to himself.

"Good for you, Charlie," Nat said, "you have that French accent, all right. You won't miss them if they come prowling around, will you?"

Charlie smiled, and bent his head to wipe his wrist over one cheek. In the moonlight Nat could see the youngster's tear-stained face. Poor tad, he was homesick.

"Charlie, I wonder if you could do something for me?"

"Aye, aye, sir!"

"I'm working on a problem in navigation. I'd like to explain it to you. If I can make you understand, I'll know I've got it."

"Aye, aye, sir! Anything to help!"

They walked the deck while Nat explained. Charlie was quick. He got the explanation much faster than grown men generally did.

"Thank you, Charlie. That's helped."

"Thank you, Mr. Bowditch, sir. You don't know, but you helped me, too!" Charlie grinned and went below, still muttering his words with the misplaced accent.

One morning during their second week in Cadiz, when Nat was in Prince's cabin, Charlie came to them, goggle-eyed. "We've got him, sir! A French spy! I can tell by the way he talks!"

Captain Prince's mouth twitched. "Come, Mr. Bowditch." They went on deck. Charlie was right. The erect, soldiery-looking man did have a French accent.

He was Count Mallevant, he told them—once of the French navy. He had fled to Spain during the French Revolution. Nat knew that Charlie's sigh of disappointment came from his heels.

Count Mallevant said, "I understand there is a scholar aboard this American ship—who is interested in astronomy. A very great scholar who has discovered a new way to work lunars."

Prince nodded toward Nat. "There's your very great scholar —Nathaniel Bowditch."

Mallevant invited Nat to visit the new observatory at Cadiz.

When the count had gone, Prince bowed solemnly. "How-do-you-do, scholar."

Nat laughed, but he felt the same warm flood of happiness he had felt when Dr. Holyoke called him an astronomer. He couldn't explain how he felt to a grown man, though—what it was to remember when he was twelve and found he'd never go to school again. *Nathaniel Bowditch—indentured.* He shrugged off the memory.

That night, when he stood in the observatory, he wished that he could tell Elizabeth what it was like to be there—looking through the telescope that seemed to bring the moon and stars close enough to touch. It was late when he returned to the *Astrea,* but he wrote to her. "You seemed very near when I looked at the moon. Because I knew you could see it, too." He smiled at that sentence, pleased. Maybe he'd learn to say things the way he wanted to some day!

ASTREA
SALEM

"All hands on deck!" He heard the yell and jumped to his feet. Dimly he realized he'd been hearing the boom of cannon in the distance. He hurried topside. The gunfire was coming from the British fleet. What had happened? Was Napoleon attacking? He was supposed to be somewhere in the Mediterranean.

The deck of the *Astrea* was alive with action—men running to secure battle lanterns—to loosen the guns. Presently a boat approached them and a British officer came on board. He was smiling and almost too excited to talk.

"Nelson has trounced Napoleon's fleet! In the mouth of the Nile! We've got him now! Bottled up in Africa!"

So it was just a celebration. Tom Owens growled, "Secure your guns!" Nat smiled at the words. Tom sounded as disgusted as Lem Harvey would have been.

The Englishman said again, "Bottled up in Africa! No more trouble with Napoleon . . . I hope."

"What about the French privateers in the Mediterranean?" Prince asked. "We're standing out of Cadiz for Alicante soon."

"Into the Mediterranean? You'll be safer in convoy with our fleet."

So the *Astrea,* and some four hundred other vessels, started in a vast convoy, guarded by British warships. It was not long before the lookout on the *Astrea* saw three small vessels dropping astern.

Collins leveled his glass. The lagging vessels were American. "What are the fools up to?" he muttered.

Prince studied them, too. "They're too heavy laden to keep up. Scuppers under—the lot of them. Serve them right if . . ." Then he said, "Bring her about, Mr. Collins."

"Aye, aye, sir."

There was no hesitation from the first mate, or from any of the crew as they fell to with a will, to bring the *Astrea* about. They left the protection of the convoy and headed back toward the floundering little vessels. When the *Astrea* was close enough to speak the ships, Captain Prince hailed them. The *Astrea,* he told them, had nineteen guns, and a crew that could use them. Cheers rose from the little ships.

Tom Owens swaggered and grinned. "One-man convoy! That's what we are!" Nat smiled to himself. Lem Harvey wasn't the only man "born for a fight."

For two days the *Astrea* trimmed sail to the speed of the floundering vessels. Tom began muttering under his breath. What was the use, he wanted to know, wallowing along with fools who didn't know how to sail? "They couldn't make six knots in a trade wind!" he grumbled. "They don't deserve—"

The lookout's singsong, "Sail ho-o-o-o-o-o!" froze every man in his tracks.

Then, with a glad bellow, Tom leaped for the guns.

Captain Prince came on deck and leveled his glass. "Three of them," he said, "and flying French colors."

There was no doubt about the colors—or the intentions—of the three ships. They were altering their course, bearing straight down on the *Astrea.* When the decks were cleared, the guns bowsed out, Prince went below with Nat.

Prince opened the logbook and picked up a quill. "Better note this now," he said dryly. "May be a little rushed later." He made the entry and dusted the ink with sand. "We'll need someone in the powder room when things start," he said.

Nat sat down and pulled off his shoes. He knew the danger

of a scuffed nail's striking a spark and setting off the powder. "I can take care of the powder room."

Prince frowned and started to speak. Then he shrugged. "Why not? I was going to say we can't risk having our navigator blown to bits. You know, if the powder room gets a direct hit—it goes. But if the powder room's blown to bits, the *Astrea* won't need a navigator, will she? Carry on, Mr. Bowditch." He went topside.

Nat went to the powder room, blinking in the gloom. The only light there came from a small round window into the next cabin. For a moment Nat was disappointed. He'd thought of getting a little work done while he waited. He'd forgotten they couldn't risk candles or lanterns near the kegs and bags of powder.

Johnny was there, sloshing down the floor with water. "They say it helps some. Of course, if that tier of kegs got a direct hit . . ." He shrugged and grinned. "Good luck, Mr. Bowditch, sir!"

Nat's eyes grew accustomed to the dim glow. It really wasn't too dark, he decided. And no use just sitting there twiddling his thumbs till they needed him to hand up powder. He went to his cabin and got his slate and pencil.

The next thing he heard was Prince's bellow. He started and jumped to his feet. "Aye, aye, sir! You ready for powder?"

Prince said, "The Frenchies didn't like our guns. They got close enough for a good look, then crowded sail and cleared out. Tom's disgusted. Sorry I forgot about you and left you down here so long."

"Long?"

"Great guns, man, you've been here three hours!"

"You're sure, sir?"

Prince broke out in a roar of laughter that brought Collins below. Prince told him the joke. "I give up! I've been through a lot in my day, but I never before saw a man huddle on a powder keg and forget where he was for three hours. That's one for your letter to Elizabeth!"

Nat shook his head. "She might worry, sir."

"Take my advice and tell her," Collins said. "You're married a long time, you know. And women always hear everything, sooner or later. If you skip anything, some kind friend is sure to say, 'Did your husband ever tell you about the time . . .' So you tell her first—the way you want her to hear it."

Your husband . . . Nat smiled at the sound of that. He closed the powder room and dogged shut the door, and went for his shoes. In his cabin, he returned to his work. Nothing for him to do now until Alicante.

They had been off Alicante about a week when a ship flying the American flag anchored near them—the *Ember,* from Salem, Captain Gorman commanding. Nat hadn't realized how glad he'd be to see someone from home until Captain Gorman came on board the *Astrea.*

Captain Gorman did not seem half so glad to see Nat. He nodded abruptly and said, "Captain Prince, I'd like to see you below."

Nat felt his temper rising, but he shrugged off his anger. Captain Gorman probably had something on his mind. He'd be in a better mood after he had talked to Captain Prince.

Charlie came to him, frowning with importance. "The captain's compliments, Mr. Bowditch. He'll see you below."

When Nat entered the cabin, Prince said, "Sit down, Nat, sit down, boy."

Captain Gorman sat with head bowed, his elbows on his knees, staring at nothing. Prince strode up and down the cabin a few turns. "I'm—I'm not going to stand off and on about this, Nat. Elizabeth—your wife—is dead."

Captain Gorman said, "That's all I know, Mr. Bowditch. A ship passed me that had left Salem later than we had. They gave me the word."

Nat didn't know when they went out. He realized finally that he was alone and the cabin was growing dark. Eight bells sounded. He had offered to take the anchor watch. He went topside.

Mr. Collins said, "You've been relieved, Mr. Bowditch."

Nat thanked him and went forward to the bow. For a long time he stood there, staring at the sky. The moon rose and made a glittering path on the water. Nat found himself staring down into the water. How deep was it, he wondered . . .

Charlie Waldo spoke at his elbow. "Mr. Bowditch, sir?"

Nat stiffened. "Yes? What is it?"

"I need you, sir. Could you help me, please? This navigation I'm trying to learn . . ."

"Of course, Charlie. Come along to my cabin." For an hour he worked with Charlie over the problem that had stumped him—explaining this way and that, until the boy understood.

"I have it now, sir! Thank you!"

"Thank you, Charlie Waldo. You may not know, but you've helped me, too."

He went topside again, and found Mr. Collins. "I'll stand the next anchor watch," he said. "I don't seem particularly sleepy."

Collins nodded. "Right, Mr. Bowditch." He was silent for a moment; then he went on quietly, "I remember when I lost my wife. Work helped."

ELIZABETH BARRETT BROWNING

The Meeting

BY FRANCES WINWAR

The love story of Elizabeth Barrett (1806-1861) and Robert Browning (1812-1889) is more romantic than any of their poems. When Robert met Elizabeth after their first exchange of letters, his dynamic personality took her from her invalid's couch and her father's domination into a rich and happy marriage.

ELIZABETH had been for some time in that uneasy state which follows the publication of a book. *Poems* was so far her most important work, by which she would stand or fall. How would the critics deal with it? Would they try to show how much more clever they were than the author, or would they take her poems for what they were? And what were they?

She herself had given the answer in a letter written on September 9, 1844, to her friend Lady Margaret Somerset, whose country seat, Eastnor Castle, had been near Hope End. "I also wish you to have the books before the reviews put any evil ideas into your head (unawares) about them,—and I do protest so against the notion which one or two papers have taken about '*schools*,' feeling so conscious to the heart of my heart, that what I have written has been written of no 'school' but my own verity and experience as a thinking and feeling human being. . . ."

It was that very quality of humanity in her writings which appealed to her readers. Although she lived apart from the world, there was nothing that happened outside her four walls which did not reach her. During the agitation over the Corn Laws, which threatened so many with poverty, she took sides with the poor. When she heard through Mr. Horne of the dreadful conditions under which little children were made to labor in mines and factories, she took up her pen and wrote, with protest in her heart and tears in her eyes.

After it appeared in *Blackwood's Magazine* her "Cry of the Children" stirred up more public feeling than even Lord Shaftesbury's speech in Parliament. Mothers blessed her for it. Clergymen read it from the pulpit. In the schools, children learned it by heart to plead for their unfortunate fellows.

Do ye hear the children weeping, O my brothers
  Ere the sorrow comes with years?
They are leaning their young heads against their mothers,
  And *that* cannot stop their tears.
The young lambs are bleating in the meadows,
  The young birds are chirping in the nest,
The young fawns are playing with the shadows,
  The young flowers are blowing toward the west—
But the young, young children, O my brothers,
  They are weeping bitterly!
They are weeping in the playtime of the others,
  In the country of the free. . . .

It was a heartfelt poem—direct, brave and human—written simply for all to read. It reached people outside of England and moved them to sympathy. In America, Edgar Allan Poe found in it "a horror sublime in its simplicity." In his admiration of the poet he dedicated a volume of his tales to her.

Elizabeth need not have feared being connected with any fad or school. She had succeeded in speaking in her own voice. It sprang from the heart, and that language was understood all over the world.

"Now that I come down to reading as my chief occupation," she went on in her letter to Lady Margaret, "you can scarcely fancy (or perhaps you *can*) what a very stale and flat occupation it comparatively seems to me. There is so much of active *life* in writing, that the passive reception of the ideas of other persons is tame and uninteresting after it—and like drinking water after wine . . . I have felt my imprisonment

BETTMANN ARCHIVE

Robert Browning, as painted by Field Talfourd in 1859

more than usual since the printing has been completed and feel restless in my cage. . . ."

It was in this state, made worse by the coming of winter, which meant sealing up the sickroom windows even against fresh air, that Robert Browning's letter found her. The maid had brought it on a tray with the rest of Miss Barrett's mail. It looked like any other letter, but the handwriting seemed unfamiliar.

By the light of the lamp—for it was already night, the night of January 10, 1845—Miss Barrett read the opening and started, her heart beating itself almost to pieces, as it did at every unusual happening.

"I love your verses with all my heart, dear Miss Barrett—and this is no off-hand complimentary letter that I shall write . . . Since the day . . . when I first read your poems, I quite laugh to remember how I have been turning and turning again in my mind what I should be able to tell you of their effect upon me . . . —but nothing comes of it all—so into me has it gone, and part of me has it become, this great living poetry of yours, not a flower of which but took root and grew . . ."

The rush of the words caught her breath. It was as if a great gust had thrown open the windows and cleansed the room of all illness and pain. A forceful man, Mr. Robert Browning! Surely she must have glanced at that strong profile of his, hanging on the wall among the other poets, before she continued reading. What generosity in the praise he gave her own poor reveries—he, whom a critic had called the Prince of Poets, whom Wordsworth had toasted at a banquet!

"Now, talking with whoever is worthy," she read on, "I can give a reason for my faith in one and another excellence, the fresh strange music . . . and true new brave thought . . . but in this addressing myself to you—your own self, and for the first time, my feeling rises altogether. I do, as I say, love these books with all my heart—and I love you too."

Somehow this sudden declaration of love in the first letter she had ever received from Browning did not come as too great a shock. This fact in itself amazed her. But then, his picture on the wall and the many references Mr. Kenyon had made to him, together with the curiosity they had aroused in her, had helped to prepare her. Still, as she continued reading, her pulses raced in a way that would have alarmed Dr. Chambers.

At one point her breath caught as he told her of the time he had come to call on her with Mr. Kenyon. It was, he said, as if he had been "close, so close, to some world's-wonder . . . but there was some . . . slight and just sufficient bar to admission, and the half-opened door shut, and I went home my thousands of miles, and the sight was never to be?" The question mark held a glimmer of hope in it that some day that door would open. "Well, these Poems were to be," he declared in closing, "and this true thankful joy and pride with which I feel myself, Yours ever faithfully, Robert Browning."

Yours ever faithfully. It was the conventional ending of a letter. Yet those ordinary words somehow took on a personal meaning. That night Elizabeth found it hard to fall asleep. She could not get Browning's letter out of her thoughts. Next morning she was still full of the wonder of it and, like all lonely people, she immediately felt the need to tell someone about it.

As usual, after breakfast, which Flush also shared, although he had had his own, she began answering her mail. "I had a letter from Browning, the poet, last night which threw me into ecstasies," she wrote boldly and truthfully. "Browning, the author of *Paracelsus* and king of the mystics," she added to her correspondent, after much feminine nonsense. That "king of the mystics" made Browning sound unapproachable and prevented the reader from having any foolish notions about the matter.

The letter to Browning which she also wrote that eleventh of January, had little of her usual gay bubbling, mingled with her seriousness. Indeed, her opening sounded stiff with its "I thank you, dear Mr. Browning, from the bottom of my heart." But as she went on she gradually lost her self-consciousness. "Sympathy is dear—very dear to me": she confessed. "But the sympathy of a poet, and of such a poet . . . Will you take back my gratitude for it?"

As her hand flew across the page, her true feelings found release, and she did what she had never done of her own free will—she offered a half-invitation that he come to see her. "Is it indeed true that I was so near to the pleasure and honour of making your acquaintance? . . . I would rather hope (as I do) that what I lost by one chance I may recover by some future one. Winters shut me up as they do dormouse's eyes; in the spring, *we shall see . . .*"

We shall see. That promise made up to the eager Browning for Miss Barrett's failure to comment on his "—and I love you too." He had not written those words lightly, for it was not in his nature to treat such an emotion lightly. So far—he was thirty-three—he had not known love, except for what he had taken for love when he wrote *Pauline*. To him love was the noblest gift that one human being could offer another. It was the gift of heart, soul, feeling, and imagination. It was also a need to find and complete oneself in another. He had described his own nature and others like himself in his hero, Sordello, when he said, "They would belong to what they worship." When such beings gave their love it was for ever.

Carefully Browning read and reread the pages to find meanings that were not in the words. It was a very friendly letter. But would Miss Barrett ever write with more than friendship? For the moment he was grateful for it. In the spring *we shall see*. Then, perhaps, the solid door of 50 Wimpole Street might open just wide enough for him to slip through.

Because he was a poet writing to a poet, much of his reply was taken up with their work. His poetry, he insisted, could not mean as much to her as hers to him. "For you *do* what I always wanted, hoped to do, and only seem now likely to do for the first time. You speak out, *you*,—I only make men and women speak . . .'" But to her he spoke for himself, and boldly, "I will joyfully wait for the delight of your friendship, and the spring . . . ! "

As Elizabeth read, the tears welled up. Outside it was still January, in spite of the painted transparent blind with its imitation of sunlight and green woods. Whatever sunlight entered fell in a strip upon the floor, a strip so narrow that when Flush laid his nose along it, basking in the warmth, his long ears lay in shadow. The sight would always make Elizabeth feel sorry for him and for herself. She had so little sunlight in her own life.

Whenever the little creature would come and snuggle close to her she was grateful. Grateful that he preferred staying with her to joining the noisy life downstairs. She was grateful, for that matter, to her own family for not showing that she was a burden.

Yet how everything had changed since Browning's first letter! With every new one that she received, that strip of sunshine in her life seemed to widen. As for Browning, he counted the days. He listened for the first song of the white-throat. He rejoiced on the twenty-sixth of February that spring would soon come. "Real warm Spring, dear Miss Barrett . . . and in Spring I shall see you, surely see you. . . ."

"Yes, but, dear Mr. Browning, I want the spring according to the new 'style' (mine), and not the old one of you and the rest of the poets. . . . But," she added, ". . . that spring will really come some day I hope and believe."

They bridged the passing weeks by writing to each other of the things closest to their hearts and minds—poetry, life, ideas, and their own works. Whenever the learned Miss Barrett strayed too far afield he would pull her back to what mattered to him most. "Always when you write . . . put me in, *always*, a little official bulletin-line that shall say 'I am better' or 'still better,' will you?"

The Barretts of course knew that Ba had a new correspondent in Mr. Browning. How could they help knowing, with all those letters going back and forth between Wimpole Street and New Cross? As it was, Ba had told her father. It would have been odd to have kept Mr. Browning from him when she had let him know about everyone else.

"Ah, the Pomegranate Man," Mr. Barrett would say, referring to the poet. He was proud, however, that his daughter should have a literary friendship with such a notable poet. Still, there was something slyly insulting in the name he gave him. It was one thing to associate the poet with his *Bells and Pomegranates;* it was another to make him sound like a fruit seller. It was no doubt Mr. Barrett's jealous little revenge that Ba had another admirer.

He was not really worried, however. Ba was imprisoned by her illness. At her age his sensible, loving, obedient daughter could not possibly harbor any foolish ideas about the Pomegranate Man. Besides, Mr. Barrett was sure of her devotion. He had only to open the first volume of *Poems* to have that faith confirmed in this latest of Ba's dedications:

"When your eyes fall upon this page . . . and you start to see to whom it is inscribed, your first thought will be of the time, far off, when I was a child, and wrote verses . . . Somewhat more fainthearted than I used to be, it is my fancy thus to seem to return to a visible personal dependence on you, as if indeed I were a child again; to conjure up your beloved image between myself and the public, so as to be sure of one smile. . . ."

Not even the most jealous of gods could have desired more. Therefore, certain of the complete affection of his genius daughter, Mr. Barrett let Elizabeth indulge her fancy for endless letter writing.

As spring came and the door on Wimpole Street showed no sign of opening, Browning became impatient. He was seriously worried about Elizabeth's health, although she assured him she was better. If so, why then did she not keep her promise? The dormouse had long since opened its eyes. "Do you think I shall see you in two months, three months?" he inquired, adding slyly, "I may travel, perhaps."

Elizabeth was in a panic, as he had hoped. "If you think that I shall not *like* to see you, you are wrong, for all your learning," she chided him. Then, after describing again her lonely invalid life, she mentioned something that she wished had not been so. It was the thing that had made her hesitate to invite him. "There are few of the youngest women in the world who have not seen more . . . of society, than I, who am scarcely to be called young now."

There, she had written it. It had pained her to have to refer to the fact that by Victorian standards she was no longer young, but he must know. Well, if he meant to travel, she would have to miss him, she added. But did he really mean it? This time she closed the letter with "Ever and truly yours."

Browning admired her all the more for speaking out. He was already deeply in love with her, and the fact that she was a few years older than he made no difference. The soul has no age, and he loved her, heart and soul. Since she still hesitated about having him call, he respected her wishes. "Yesterday I had occasion to go your way," he wrote her wistfully. "Past, that is, Wimpole Street, the end of it,—and, do you know, I did not seem to have leave from you to go down it yet."

At last it came, that leave. As she wrote, setting the date

for Tuesday afternoon, the twentieth of May, 1845, the tears streamed down her face. "There is nothing to see in me; nor to hear in me—I never learnt to talk as you do in London . . . Come then. There will be truth and simplicity for you in any case; and a friend."

The coming visit was no secret to the family, for in a moment of panic, Elizabeth had taken down Browning's picture and hidden it away. So that her action would not betray her, she had also removed the portrait of Tennyson who, as a person, meant nothing to her. When her brothers paid her their usual visit they noticed the blank spaces on the wall and pretended to make a great to-do, searching all over the house for the vanished portraits. Flush twitched his long ears, puzzled at this unusual excitement. Only Mr. Barrett calmly went about his business. His daughter was having a caller that afternoon. Very well. Mr. Browning was just another literary person coming to admire the family genius.

In the course of the morning Henrietta and Arabel took turns going up to Ba's room to see how she was doing. Henrietta was particularly interested for reasons of her own. She was in love with Captain Surtees Cook, a good-looking young man who seemed even more attractive in his uniform. For two years he had been courting her, coming to see her with such regularity that the family called him Perseverance. Everyone knew about him except Papa.

When Henrietta finally got up enough courage to confess her love to Papa, Mr. Barrett flew into a fearful rage. What? One of his daughters talking of love? Of marriage? Outrageous! He made such a scene that Henrietta had to be carried out of the room in hysterics while Elizabeth, who had got up to help her, fell to the floor in a faint.

Perseverance lived up to his name, however. Every morning he would wait at the corner of Wimpole Street, at a safe distance from Number Fifty. The moment he saw the stiff form of Mr. Barrett vanish down the street the captain would sprint happily to ring the doorbell. Would Papa ever change? Henrietta wondered. What if Ba should fall in love? Would Papa be different? Henrietta clung hopefully to such a possibility.

Somehow, on the day of the appointment, the morning of waiting passed for Elizabeth. She was in such a state that she did not know whether being alone with her beating heart was better than listening to the well-meant chatter of her sisters. As three o'clock, the time set for Mr. Browning's call, approached they left her alone—except for Flush and the maid, Wilson.

Ba liked Elizabeth Wilson, or Lily, as they sometimes called her. She was a good, simple girl from Sheffield, with as few words as Flush—a great virtue in Miss Barrett's eyes. For Wilson, Wimpole Street represented the height of respectability and the Barrett family its finest flower. Vaguely she felt there was something special about Miss Barrett. It made her proud to serve as the personal maid to so important a lady, whose name appeared in the papers.

Punctually at three the doorbell rang. Feeling as if she would faint, Miss Barrett waved Wilson out of the room. A few seconds later she heard steps on the stairs—Henrietta's, accompanied by the rustle of her taffetas and—how Ba's heart beat!—a firm, running pace. Henrietta came in, waited briefly as Mr. Browning went with energetic step toward Ba's sofa, and quickly left, closing the door behind her.

Flush alone was present at that first interview. Since he could not speak, much less write, no one knows what words were spoken. It is recorded, however, that Browning stayed exactly an hour and a half, for when he returned home he made that note on the envelope of the latest letter he had had from Miss Barrett.

If there was no witness to take down their words, they wrote enough to each other to tell what happened. First of all, Browning was worried that he might have talked too loudly in the stillness of that room. He apologized, saying he had formed that habit from having to talk to a deaf relative. "Indeed there was nothing wrong—how could there be?" Elizabeth reassured him. "And there was everything right—as how should there not be?"

How right everything had been she showed by her willingness to have him continue calling on her, from time to time.

At his first sight of her, Browning had been struck by the

BROWN BROTHERS

Elizabeth Barrett

beauty of her eyes. Where had he seen those eyes, dark eyes, earnest and still? Suddenly he knew. They were the eyes of his Andromeda, with whom he had been in love since early boyhood.

As for Elizabeth, she could not get Browning out of her mind. "When you came, you never went away," she confessed, when she could allow herself to tell him. She compared him with his portrait. How flat and lifeless she now found it! How unlike him, the real man, whose vitality seemed to communicate life to her. Only the eyes and forehead had been caught by the artist. But what brush could ever have captured that play of thought in his manly face?

All night long she could not sleep. "It is most extraordinary how the idea of Mr. Browning does beset me!" she said to her father the following morning, when he inquired about the visit. "I suppose it is not being used to strangers, in some degree—but it haunts me. It is a persecution."

Was Ba being her truthful self or was she trying to quiet any suspicion her father might have had? Mr. Barrett surprised her by a lofty generosity. "It is not grateful to your friend to use such a word," he said.

Her friend? Ba thrilled at the word. Yes, Robert Browning was a friend, and she would always endeavor to keep him so.

Suddenly, just three days after Browning's visit, she had a letter from him that set her pulses galloping. He loved her, and he told her so. This time he did not mention her verses or her books jointly with his love, but poured out his feelings in a wild rush that terrified her. The sight of her, so much more enchanting than his imagination had led him to expect, her sweet gravity and her sudden arch humor had so overwhelmed him that, throwing aside all convention, he spoke from his very heart.

Elizabeth almost fainted, but she controlled herself. Taking a supply of sharpened quills, she settled down to write. But the words she wanted would not come. Rather, too many came, mingled with too many emotions, for her to put them into any kind of order.

She knew she loved him, had loved him even before their meeting. For that very reason she must discourage his generous impulse. He was young and a genius, with his life and work still before him. She was no longer young. Had she not bravely told him so? She knew she looked much younger than her years. Dear Miss Mitford would often say that she, Ba, with her curls and her long lashes, had the appearance of a girl about to be brought out.

Even so, was she not an invalid, shut up in her room, beyond all hope of living a normal woman's life? Browning loved her. He poured out his love with that princely bounty that was so much a part of him. But she could not accept that offer of his hand and heart, of his youth and his future. Her hand dropped and her pen with it. Despite all the languages and all the words she knew, she found none to express what she felt.

All of that night was torture. She did not dare fall asleep in her feverish state for fear of betraying herself to Arabel, who slept in the same room. Not until the following evening could she pull herself together to write to Browning. Even then the letter was full of dots and dashes and heavy lines, revealing her state of mind. He must never again say, or *unsay*, such things as he had said, she told him. He must *forget them at once and for ever.* So they would "die out between *you and me alone*, like a misprint between you and the printer. . . . if there should be one word of answer attempted . . . *I will not see you again.*"

She knew that by writing such words she ran the risk of losing the one great light that had ever come into her life. But to save Browning against his own generosity she must speak out.

He was so badly frightened by her letter, especially by the threat of her never seeing him again, that he became as rash in taking back his words as he had been in writing them. Why, she had completely misunderstood him, he wrote back, unaware of his lack of gallantry. He had only tried to point out to her his own inferiority. The sentence Miss Barrett had mistaken for a declaration of love had only been an expression of praise.

Knowing himself to be in the wrong, he got deeper and deeper into trouble the more he argued his case. She must realize he had his faults, he said. For every wreck of a Vesuvius in his little world, he warned her, "there are huge layers of ice and pits of black cold water . . ." Would it not be better, he suggested, if she sent back his letter? Unless, of course, she had already destroyed it. "When Mephistopheles last came to see us in this world outside here, he counselled . . . 'never to write a letter,—and never to burn one.' "

Elizabeth was quick to accept his apology, even though her womanly feelings had been hurt. It was awkward to be told that one had seen a declaration of love where there had been

COURTESY OF PARKE-BERNET GALLERIES

Robert and Elizabeth Barrett Browning

nothing of the sort. It was a blow to one's vanity. Perhaps she had been wrong in coming to such a conclusion, she wrote back. But there *had* been *something* in his letter that had led her to it. Was it possible she did not know him, as he implied? "I was certainly innocent of the 'ice and cold water,'" she said, ". . . and am only just shaking my head, as

Flush would, after a first wholesome plunge." As for the letter that had caused all the mischief, she returned it. "Burn it at once," she said, ". . . and never mind Mephistopheles."

The much-worried Browning leapt for joy when she forgave him and made an appointment for his next visit. "Enter R. B.," he wrote back, ". . . as boldly as he suspects people do just after they have been soundly frightened!"

He was a model of behavior when he saw her again. He spoke softly, controlling his actions and even his expressions before Miss Barrett's powerful fascination. He was in love with her. Yet he was bound by his promise, after his foolish letter, never to speak on that subject again. No doubt as a reward for his good behavior Elizabeth allowed him to call her Ba. To his great joy she also let him come to see her twice a week. For her those were exciting days, when she would listen for the doorbell and then for his rapid step upon the stairs. Her heart would beat so hard that she had to press her hands against it.

The door would burst open. He would walk quickly to her, take her hand and kiss it. Flush would twitch his ears, not quite trusting such vigor in that room where so little ever happened. Now that the New Cross gardens were in bloom, Robert would bring flowers which Elizabeth insisted on arranging herself. Strange, she would tell him, how much longer his flowers lasted than any others.

Browning did not forget the favorite, either. To get into Flush's good graces he often brought him cookies baked by Sarianna. The dog would eat them with the air of doing him a favor. But while Browning sat in his armchair facing Elizabeth on the sofa, Flush's golden eyes would be fixed upon him, and he would start up ready to defend his mistress whenever Browning's voice would suddenly ring out in enthusiasm. Browning himself had eyes only for Ba. She looked so frail, with her vast brow leaning on her small hand. And so ethereal. And so beautiful! But he must not betray his emotions. He had promised.

They talked about everything in the wide range of their learning. But even if they had said nothing, they would have been happy. For they loved each other. They knew it without the need of words, and they let their love grow like a plant in the depths of their being. The time would come when its blossoming could no longer be hidden.

Meanwhile Browning had been doing for Elizabeth what Dr. Chambers and the rest of the medical profession had not been able to accomplish. Why must she be constantly lying on her sofa? See, the sun is shining. Rise—you can do it! Stand here, beside the sofa, in this patch of sunlight. Reach out—wash your hands in it. I knew you could do it. You feel weak? Your hands. Let me hold your hands. Come—only a few steps to the window. The back gardens are all in bloom. And there are the chimney pots. Don't you love the chimney pots of London?

"Flush! Flush! Be a good dog! Mr. Browning is only trying to help me! Flush!"

Little by little Elizabeth managed to walk to the window by herself. Later she even ventured to take little journeys about the room. Never had Browning known such pleasure as when he saw her walk across the room to the bookshelves, to look up something about Shelley.

One day she informed him, "Yesterday I went downstairs—or rather was carried—and am not the worse." Eventually she was able to make the stairs on her own feet.

The first time one of her brothers saw her coming into the parlor, all bundled up in her cloak, he was so startled that he cried, "So glad to see you!" as if she had been a stranger.

Because Browning did not trust the drug which the doctors prescribed, Elizabeth learned to rely on it less. "That you should care so much!" she exclaimed in astonishment. "Then *I* must care . . . It would be dangerous to leave off the calming remedy, the doctor says, except very slowly and gradually. But slowly and gradually something may be done."

"Slowly and gradually what may *not* be done!" he encouraged her joyfully.

MOSES

The Pillar of Cloud and the Pillar of Fire

BY KATHERINE B. SHIPPEN

Illustrations by Lili Cassel

The Jewish people were slaves in Egypt when Moses, their leader, vowed to lead them to freedom. His petition to the Pharaoh had been rejected and the misery of his people was greater than before. Moses alone continued to believe that God would lead the Jewish people out of bondage.

NOW, by Pharaoh's decree, the slaves labored double in the brickyards. Faster and faster they were driven, and heavier and heavier were the loads they carried. And Moses saw this with mounting grief, so that sorrow and pity filled all his days.

Had he been the cause of all this suffering? Had he brought this misery upon them—he who had wanted so to help them? What could he do against the entrenched power of Pharaoh, directed now toward the Hebrew slaves?

He could not bear to watch the slaves working. He could not linger in the neighborhood of the brickyards. If his way took him there, he hurried past and tried not to look.

Yet as the days went by it seemed to him incredible that this could be the end of their struggle against Pharaoh. Had he not called on Jehovah? Was Jehovah not more powerful than Pharaoh? He would not go back to the peaceful life of Midian. Perhaps, after all, some way would be found.

So day followed day, and season followed season, and Moses was still in Egypt, waiting. In the spring the Nile waters rose and filled the irrigation ditches and flooded the fields, and later the farmers plowed and sowed their seed and harvested their crops, and still Moses waited.

In the markets the people bartered onions for oil, oil for honey, honey for wheat, wheat for necklaces. And the dust stirred up by the hoofs of the donkeys covered all with a white powder, and the flies buzzed and droned. And still Moses was there.

Only now the work of the people was heavier than it had been before. The tax collectors on their rounds were demanding larger amounts of barley or of linen, the overseers were exacting heavier labor. And Merneptah's tomb in the cliffs west of the city was slowly rising to colossal proportions, for it was the custom of every Pharaoh to build his tomb and have it ready against the day when his own mummy should be put into it.

There was little complaint among the people now. They accepted the lot life brought them hopelessly. Of what use was it to complain? Would it bring you more to eat? Yet Moses was never resigned. Surely Jehovah would not tolerate injustice, he kept saying to himself. Surely He would send some sign. And Moses was right; for soon strange things began to happen.

One day Moses was sitting on a low stone wall at the edge of the Nile watching the river craft that went back and forth and up and down the stream. Some of them were cabin boats bearing loads of grain and jars of oil, or animals for the temple sacrifice. Some of the boats carried striped sails, but since there was little breeze, most of the sails were furled and the rowers were bending over painted oars. Now and again the pleasure boat of some nobleman passed him, its painted stern curved up and carved like a lotus flower. The procession on the river was like a pageant passing by, bright and beautiful for anyone who did not look beyond it and see the suffering that was there.

Moses had watched the river for some time when he observed an unusual commotion. A great barge loaded with heavy dark red blocks of building stone was moving slowly toward him. It had brought the stone from the mountains, far up the Nile, to be used in Merneptah's tomb. Since the stone was so heavy that it weighed the barge down almost to the gunwales, it was necessary to use as many as a dozen small row boats to pull it.

With shouts from the overseers and creaking and splashing

of the oars, the barge slowly made its way to the place where Moses sat. Then the small boats threw off the ropes, and the barge was made fast to the wall.

The master of the barge, a short squat man with a shaven head and a strong muscular frame, sat down beside Moses on the wall.

"There's another piece of the tomb delivered," he said. "Or almost delivered, that is. It takes a long time and much sweat to make a mountain into a tomb."

"How was the trip?" Moses asked him. "Did you have fair winds to help you down the river?"

"The winds were fair enough," the master said. "I have no complaint of them. But there is a queer thing up the river. I never saw anything like it in all the years that I have been going up and down. The water is almost red up there—it looks more like blood than water."

"What makes it red?" Moses asked.

"I don't know what it is," the master said. "It's queer enough, anyway."

"Is there some sort of insect in it, or some sort of plant?" Moses asked him.

"It looks more like blood," said the master.

Their talk was interrupted then, for preparations for unloading the barge were complete, and the master wanted to supervise the moving of the building blocks.

The blocks were extremely large and heavy, and moving them was a very slow process. When each one was lowered to the ground, it was slid along on a drag. Rollers were placed under the drag, and slaves were harnessed to it to pull it across the ground toward the site of the tomb. One block was much heavier than the others. The slaves who were harnessed to it could not budge it, even under the crack of the overseer's whip. So more and more slaves were brought, and when finally it moved, very slowly and very grudgingly, there were a hundred slaves throwing their weight against the weight of the block. Moses felt cold and sick as he watched them.

They dragged the great block on until it came to a hollow, and it moved slowly and heavily down the incline. It seemed as if no force on earth could have stopped it as it rolled heavily downward, but the slaves were kept in harness, so that they could pull it up the other side of the hollow again.

There was one slave, a Hebrew, slighter and younger than the rest. Moses could not see his face, but he noticed that his shoulders were sagging, and that his breath came in sharp gasps. His place was behind the other slaves, nearest to the drag and its weight of stone. When the stone started to move down the incline, the overseer cried out and the slaves ran forward, but the young slave that Moses was watching suddenly crumpled and fell. He lay still while the great block moved slowly toward him.

Moses sprang forward. Quickly he pulled the boy to one side, while the drag with its great weight of stone moved on.

He drew the boy's limp body to the shadow of a wall, and called to a passerby to bring a cup of water. After a while the slave stirred into consciousness, and Moses saw the suffering and sorrow of all the world in his dark eyes. Bending close over him Moses heard him speak.

"Why did you save me?" he whispered. "I didn't want to live."

But Moses' hand was cool and firm on his shoulder, and his voice was clear and definite in his ear.

"You have to live," he said. "You and I have to live, and fight."

Moses had good reason for hopefulness now, for though no change had been made in Pharaoh's harsh decree, there were certain portents which seemed to him to have meaning. Plagues of frogs and flies and lice followed each other along the valley of the Nile in swift succession. Such plagues had been known in Egypt before, of course, but never had they come so fast, one after another. And now a murrain fell upon the cattle, and violent hailstorms destroyed the crops just before harvest time.

All these things were of the utmost annoyance to Pharaoh, who was accustomed to commanding what he wished. If plagues like these were repeated often they might result in serious shortages and make large tax collections impossible. He consulted his astrologers and magicians, but they could suggest no remedy. They were in fact extremely nervous and frightened, and their fright took on new proportions when the sun was shut away by the clouds for three whole days —a strange occurrence indeed in that land of cloudless skies.

But if Pharaoh and his astrologers were worried by the strange phenomena, Moses found them filled with a possible meaning for the Hebrew people.

"Jehovah is helping us," he said one day to Aaron. "We must be ready. Some day there will be a final, culminating event. I cannot tell what it will be, but we must be ready. When the final blow comes to Pharaoh, he will let us go— if no sign comes, we will go anyway."

So for more than a year he worked and planned, that the people might be ready when the time came. He decided to talk with every Hebrew in Heliopolis, and he visited their houses, one after another, paying his visits when the work in quarry, mine, or field had stopped because of darkness. Many were the stories of evil he heard as he talked to the workmen and shared their chunks of bread and mugs of beer. Every night he spoke of an end of their sufferings, and of freedom. But they were tired and discouraged with their struggling and paid little heed to him.

One night he stopped at the house of a man named Nun and, sitting in the doorway, talked to him of the people's apathy.

"How can we rouse them," Moses kept saying. "What can we do to stir them?"

But Nun could only bow his head. Finally he spoke:

"What does a man know of freedom who was born a slave?" he said. "A man who has worked as a slave from one year's end to the next, does not know what freedom is."

There was a long silence. Joshua, the son of Nun, had been sitting in a corner of the room, polishing a cane that he had carved. He was a strong, well-built youth of about twenty with a handsome face and curly black hair. He rose from the stool where he had been sitting, and stood before Moses and his father now.

"Can't we tell them again?" he said. "Can't we go to see them all a second time? . . . I will go with you."

"Come, Joshua," Nun said sharply. "What impertinence is this. You, a mere youth, advising Moses what to do? I beg you to forgive his lack of manners," he said, turning to Moses.

But Moses put his hands on the lad's shoulder.

"I think that Joshua is right," he said. "Will you help me, Joshua?"

So night after night, Moses continued to talk to the people, and often Joshua was with him. Moses grew very fond of him.

"Do you want your children to work as you have worked?" Moses asked the people whom he visited. "What right has any man to strike you with a whip? Are you a beast?"

Gradually the light of understanding came to eyes that had too long been dulled. And slowly one after another they began to grasp what it might mean to be free. Slowly then a great plan began to take shape, and the Hebrew people knew that they would stir themselves to a harder effort than any they had ever made.

"By the night of the spring solstice we should be ready," Moses said. "But we must not go until we have made the spring sacrifice. Each one who has a flock must choose his most perfect lamb, and smear its blood on the lintel, and roast its flesh in the fire. Even though the feast is quickly prepared, and the bread we eat with it is quickly baked without leaven, we must not neglect to make the sacrifice as our fathers have always done. After the sacrifice has been made this year, we will leave Egypt. Pharaoh will rage; it may be some of us will die at his hand; but life means nothing to us as we are; we must go in spite of him."

These were the plans that Moses made, repeating them over and over as he went from house to house.

When the night of the spring solstice finally came, not a Hebrew slept. Those who were slaves, and those who had some small possession of flocks or herds—all lay awake. In every house the people whispered together as they made their hushed preparations. Bundles were packed and donkeys harnessed with heavy saddlebags. In the outlying districts of the city, flocks of sheep and goats waited behind their bars. In every house a lamb's blood was smeared on the lintels and the doorposts with prayers to Jehovah, and a lamb's flesh was baked in the fire. And in every house men and women, girded and shod, with staves in their hands, stood ready to depart.

They had no way of knowing that events were already beginning to occur in Pharaoh's palace which were to help them in their exodus.

A faint, faint moan stirred through the dark of Pharaoh's palace. It was soft almost as a whisper, yet it was sorrowful as death. Pharaoh, lying restless on his couch, heard it. He rose and made his way through the dark to his son's chamber. He put his hand down on the boy's body—and knew that he was dead.

"Awake! Awake!" he cried to any that could hear him. "Awake! Bring lights! Bring lights! My son!"

Suddenly the palace blazed into light. From every court, from every room, servants and princes, men and boys, women and children, came running. They crowded into the bedchamber with lamps and torches and candles, until the darkness was turned into a flaming light. But the young prince, Pharaoh's son, lay still and dead upon his couch.

The physicians came with ointments and drugs, the magicians brought their spells and incantations, but the young prince did not stir.

"Not the prince only, but the chief steward's son is stricken. And the baker's son. Woe! Woe!" they cried.

"The sickness is spreading through the city. There is none that is safe now. No, not Pharaoh's son himself."

"Where is the high priest?" someone said. "Send for the high priest of Amen."

A slave was despatched to the temple, and soon the high priest of Amen, who was known as "The Great Seer," appeared at the door of the bed chamber.

There was a hush among the people who crowded the room, as he made his way slowly toward the bed and stood looking down at the Pharaoh's dead son. The gold light of the torches and the candles shone down on his shaven head and on his rich embroidered robes.

"It is the work of the Hebrews," he said, with authority. "Their god, Jehovah, is very powerful. First the Nile ran red as blood, then came the frogs, the flies, the lice, the murrain on the cattle, and the hail that destroyed the crops. Then the darkness when Amen absented himself from his people for three full days. Now this. Moses has said many times that he would call again upon Jehovah. He has called upon Him now."

"What can we do?" Pharaoh asked him, his voice dull with his sorrow. "What can we do? Can we make sacrifice to Jehovah?"

The chief priest of Amen shrugged his shoulders.

"Amen's people cannot worship a Hebrew god," he said. "The only thing to do is to send the Hebrews out of Egypt. Have them go at once. Tonight."

"Tell them to leave tonight! At once! Tonight!" the people cried when they had heard the chief priest speak.

Pharaoh heard, and bowed his head lower. The people in the room waited, to see what Pharaoh would do.

At that moment the door opened, and a new figure entered. The vizier, whose palace was at some distance from Pharaoh's, had been hastily summoned. He had thrown on a mantle of wine-colored cloth and had hastened to Pharaoh's palace by the light of a flaming torch. Pharaoh, broken and uncertain in his grief, turned to him now.

"What shall we do?" he asked.

The vizier was a man of decision.

"I will go to tell the Hebrews to leave the city," he said, and turning to a slave, "Have the chariot prepared," he said.

The people pressed round him, trying to hear.

"He's going to tell them to leave," one woman said, relief and excitement in her voice. And then she turned to the vizier. "Take them this ring," she said, slipping a jewel from her finger. "Only let them take it and go—tonight."

"Do they want gold?" another asked. "Take them this." She had gone to another room and brought back a heavy bag of gold dust.

"Give them these bracelets," another said, pulling from her arms two bands of gold richly crusted with jewels.

Another brought her earrings, and another a single great emerald. The pile of jewels began to mount at the vizier's feet.

Soon the slave who had been sent to the royal stables, brought back the great black horses, quivering and blinking

FRATELLI ALINARI

Moses, as sculpted by Michelangelo for the tomb of Julius II

in the light, and these were harnessed to the vizier's chariot. A second chariot also was brought so that the chief steward might bring the treasure of gold and jewels that was to persuade the Hebrews to go quickly.

Down the long avenue the chariots raced, down the dark streets of the city, past the brickyard, past the vineyard, until they came at last to the house where Moses and Aaron lived. A light streamed out into the darkness from the window of the house.

The vizier raised his hand, and knocked on the wooden panel. Inside Moses and the others were standing, their staves in their hands, their shoes on their feet, and their robes drawn round them, as if they were prepared for a journey.

"I have come to urge you to go in haste," the vizier said, his eyes moving about the room and its occupants.

"We are ready to go now," Moses answered, taking up a bundle that lay on a table near him. But then he paused, and looked narrowly at the vizier.

"There is only one thing we ask before we go," he said.

"What is it?" the vizier answered. "Ask anything you will."

"Will you swear that these Hebrews who were slaves, are henceforth free?" Moses asked.

"I will swear anything," the vizier answered. "I swear by Amen. And by Osiris. And by Ptah. And by the spirit of my father. And by the spirit of my grandfather."

"That is enough," said Moses.

The Egyptians who stood behind the vizier pressed forward offering golden chains, and rings, and bracelets.

"Swear it again," they said. "Swear it again. Only tell them to make haste."

Without further words Moses stepped out through the door, thrusting the Egyptians aside. Up and down the streets other doors were opening, and other men and women and children were pouring into the road.

More and more they came, pressing up from every forlorn and miserable quarter of the city. There were men and women in little groups bringing their sleepy children, and old men tapping their canes unsteadily as they walked with uncertain steps. Some of the people carried bundles of clothing and others drove donkeys loaded down with bags of grain, or goatskins filled with water. Some carried young lambs in their arms, thinking them not yet strong enough for so long a journey. Others drove flocks of sheep and goats before them, calling to them from time to time to keep them together. But for the most part their voices were quiet. The only sound among them was the slow shuffle of thousands of feet as they moved like a slow drab army out of the city, toward the eastern road that leads into the desert.

When they had finally left the city behind them, the sun came up, lighting the way that they must go. Seeing it, someone near the front of the procession began to chant an old song. And one after another their voices took up the chant until it swelled from thousands of throats, and beat out the time for thousands of shuffling feet:

The Lord is my light and my salvation;
Whom shall I fear?
The Lord is the strength of my life;
Of whom shall I be afraid?

So chanting, the Hebrews left Egypt and slavery behind them.

The great mass of people with their animals and baggage moved slowly toward the East, over a dry rocky land. Moses could have led them a much shorter way to the fertile country that he had planned for them, but he wanted them to go by way of Sinai, to sacrifice at the holy mountain where he had first seen God.

"The journey is a hard one," he said, looking down at a thin tired woman who walked beside her husband and led a little child by the hand.

"True," the woman answered, "we shall be tired. But what does it matter? My husband was a brickmaker for Pharaoh, and Reuben and I had seldom enough to eat. It can't be worse than that."

"The land ahead is green and fertile," Moses told her. "There will be food aplenty for us all when we get there. And green pastures for your sheep too, if only you can manage the journey," he said, looking down at her tired face.

She smiled and made no answer, but there was no lagging in her pace.

"Can you keep your flock together, then," he said to a shepherd who drove his big-tailed sheep before him.

"I can do it," said the shepherd. "But it's not easy. They wander this way and that in search of a green twig or a bit of grass. I follow after them to bring them back. The crowd moves on. And the first thing I know, I've almost lost you. . . . I shouldn't want to keep my flock, and find that I had lost all Israel and was alone in the desert."

"That wouldn't do," Moses agreed. "Try to keep an eye on the main group."

Although he spoke confidently, the man's words troubled Moses. He looked across at the moving hosts of people with their flocks and their herds, that stretched as far as he could see.

"We must find some way of keeping together," he said. "Some kind of guide that all can see, even if they have strayed away a little. Some kind of banner," he said then. "But they couldn't see a banner at night."

He kept thinking about it all day as they plodded on. At last toward evening he thought of a fire as a beacon.

"A fire would do," he thought. "If we could make a fire that moved along before us."

They made a fire then, and put it in a big brazier, and the brazier they hung on a tall pole, and carried it swinging at the front of the crowd.

Now from the brazier the smoke mounted in a soft white column, clear and plain against the sky, and at night the fire blazed up into the darkness with a golden light that could be seen a mile away.

"It makes me feel content to watch it," the tired woman said. "It seems to show the way so plain."

"Come on," the shepherd called, flicking at his sheep with his crook. "Can't you see the fire's turning toward the right? You don't want to get separated, do you?"

So in the hot noonday under the clear blue sky, the white pillar of smoke led them on, and at night, when the dark

sky was embroidered with its stars, the fire burned on before them.

Three days and nights they journeyed thus, with brief pauses for rest. Then on the third morning they came suddenly to a narrow arm of the Red Sea.

They stopped at the shore to watch the blue water with the sea gulls wheeling over it. On the bank opposite them a mountain with bleak rocky sides rose up sharply, its summit lost in clouds.

They paused, and putting down their burdens, looked back over the way that they had come.

"Look, there," said one of them, pointing. "That looks like a puff of smoke back there, just where the earth meets the sky."

"It's smoke, or dust," another said.

They watched while the puff of smoke or dust seemed to grow bigger.

"There's movement in it. It looks like a horse," said another.

And then they knew. "They are horses!" they said.

"It's the Egyptians! It's Pharaoh! He's coming after us!"

Pharaoh's black horses, three of them harnessed to each chariot, were racing toward them, swift as light. They were flying over the ground toward the Hebrews like fire racing through a field of stubble, like lightning ready to strike them down.

"It's Pharaoh!" the people cried again and again in terror. "Fly! Fly!"

But whither could they fly? Behind them Pharaoh was approaching faster and faster. Before them the deep water lay, and the forbidding mountain.

"What can we do," they cried. "Where can we go? Call Moses! Moses!"

They could see the Egyptians plainly now. The plumes on the horses' heads blew back in the wind. The men stood, their knees braced against the chariots' sides, their golden breastplates gleaming. The chariots swayed from side to side. The chariot wheels threw up a cloud of dust as they spun round and round.

"Moses! Moses!" the people cried in terror.

They were crowded on the narrow strip of sandy beach—sheep and goats, men and women, donkeys and tired children. Before them the waves lapped and the sea gulls flew over with a moaning cry. The mountain on the opposite shore stood bleak and forbidding, its summit wrapped in cloud.

"And if we die, it is Moses that has brought us here," someone cried out.

"Were there not graves enough in Egypt, that you must bring us here to die?" another shouted. "It would have been better to serve the Egyptians than to die in the wilderness."

So they turned upon Moses since they did not know what else to do.

"Stand still," Moses answered them quietly. "Take up stones. Take your staffs if you have them. Stand close together. Put the women and the children back of you. We are here to fight, if need be. Who talks of graves?"

Quietly the men drew together and waited. Pharaoh's six hundred chariots drew nearer.

Just then they heard a rumbling noise. It was deeper and louder far than the rumble of the chariot wheels. It shook the earth. The people on the shore felt the land sway and move beneath their feet. They turned toward the mountain, and saw a stream of fire shoot up through the cloud on its summit. Then, while they watched in fascination, thick darkness settled around them, lighted only by the blaze and burst of fire at the mountain's crest. And the earth rocked and swayed under their feet.

Then suddenly, a wave washed up on the shore. So great a wave it was, that they who had been standing on dry land found themselves with the water swirling around their knees. And just as suddenly the water seemed to turn and flow in the other direction, washing and swirling as it went. It flowed so fast that it was like a high wall of water moving away from them. Behind the high wave the rocks of the sea's floor were bare, for the water had washed away from them, and they were pushed up from the bed of the sea.

The Hebrews standing on the shore with their children and their flocks, were frozen with terror as they watched the strange spectacle. It seemed as if all time had stopped in wonder and in awe.

Moses was the first to recover himself. He ran forward, down to the barren path that the tidal wave had left. "Come on!" he called to the people behind him, as he began to run through the sea.

The people hesitated uncertainly. Then Aaron followed Moses. "Come on!" Aaron called. "Come on! Come on!"

One after another they came. The women and children ran with the men. They hurried the sheep and the goats across. They scrambled up the bank on the opposite shore.

The Egyptians too had been terrified at the spectacle of the flaming mountain and the tidal wave. But when they saw the Hebrews making their way across the sea, they started after them again. With shouts and cracks of their long whips they drove their horses on, down to the shore of the sea, down where the rocks of the sea's floor lay bare behind the great receding wave.

But just as they had reached the very middle of the sea, just as the terrified Hebrews saw them coming on, the mountain shuddered, shooting blazing coals into the dark sky. The earth swayed, and the great wave of water turned and came swirling back upon them.

For a few minutes the dark water was filled with struggling movement, while horses and men were rolled over and over by the might of the water's strength. Man and beast cried out and struggled for a moment before they were buried in the depth of the sea. Where they had been, there was nothing. The Hebrews might have dreamed that they had been pursued.

Moses turned to the people. "Give thanks to God!" he cried. "Give thanks to God!"

Then everywhere throughout the throng the people echoed the words that Moses said, until what he said was like a great song that burst forth from a hundred throats.

> *I will sing unto the Lord, for He hath triumphed gloriously: the horse and his rider hath He thrown into the midst of the sea.*

Again and again they sang it.

> *The Lord is my strength and my song, and He is become my salvation.*
>
> *The Lord is a man of war; the Lord is His name.*
>
> *Pharaoh's chariots and his host hath He cast into the sea; his chosen captains also are drowned in the Red Sea.*
>
> *The depths have covered them: they sank into the bottom as a stone.*
>
> *Thy right hand, O Lord, is become glorious in power: Thy right hand, O Lord, hath dashed in pieces the enemy.*

Again and again they sang it, for no one slept all the night through.

And at last Miriam, the sister of Moses, took a timbrel in her hand and began to dance, and other women of the camp danced with her.

> "Sing ye to the Lord, for He hath triumphed gloriously," she cried.

They danced until the morning sent long fingers of light across the eastern sky.

MICHELANGELO BUONAROTTI

Years of Agony

BY ELIZABETH RIPLEY

The great genius of the Renaissance, Michelangelo (1475-1564) was only twenty-five when he completed his famous sculptured group, the Pietà. Painter, sculptor, architect, he lived with his magnificent visions for eighty-nine years, creating many masterpieces.

WHEN Gallo saw the statue of Bacchus he decided that Michelangelo was the greatest sculptor in Rome; so he persuaded a well known French cardinal to give a commission to the young Florentine.

"And I, Jacopo Gallo," he wrote in the contract he drew up for Michelangelo and the cardinal, "pledge my word to his Most Reverend Lordship that it shall be the finest work in marble which Rome today can show." Gallo described the subject of the statue. It would be "the Virgin Mary clothed, with the dead Christ in her arms, of the size of a proper man." The subject was a popular one at the time and it was called a "Pietà."

Michelangelo was tired of the pagan gods, and was glad that now at last he was able to tell a story from the Bible. Furiously he began to chip away pieces from the pure white block of marble he had chosen in the quarries of Carrara. He hardly slept at all. Sleep gave him pains in the head and stomach, he wrote to his father, and he ate only a piece of bread when he was hungry.

Ludovico Buonarotti worried about his son in Rome. In his letters he urged Michelangelo to take care of himself. He must keep his head moderately warm, he wrote, have himself rubbed down, but never wash. He recommended for headaches a dish made of herbs and split peas.

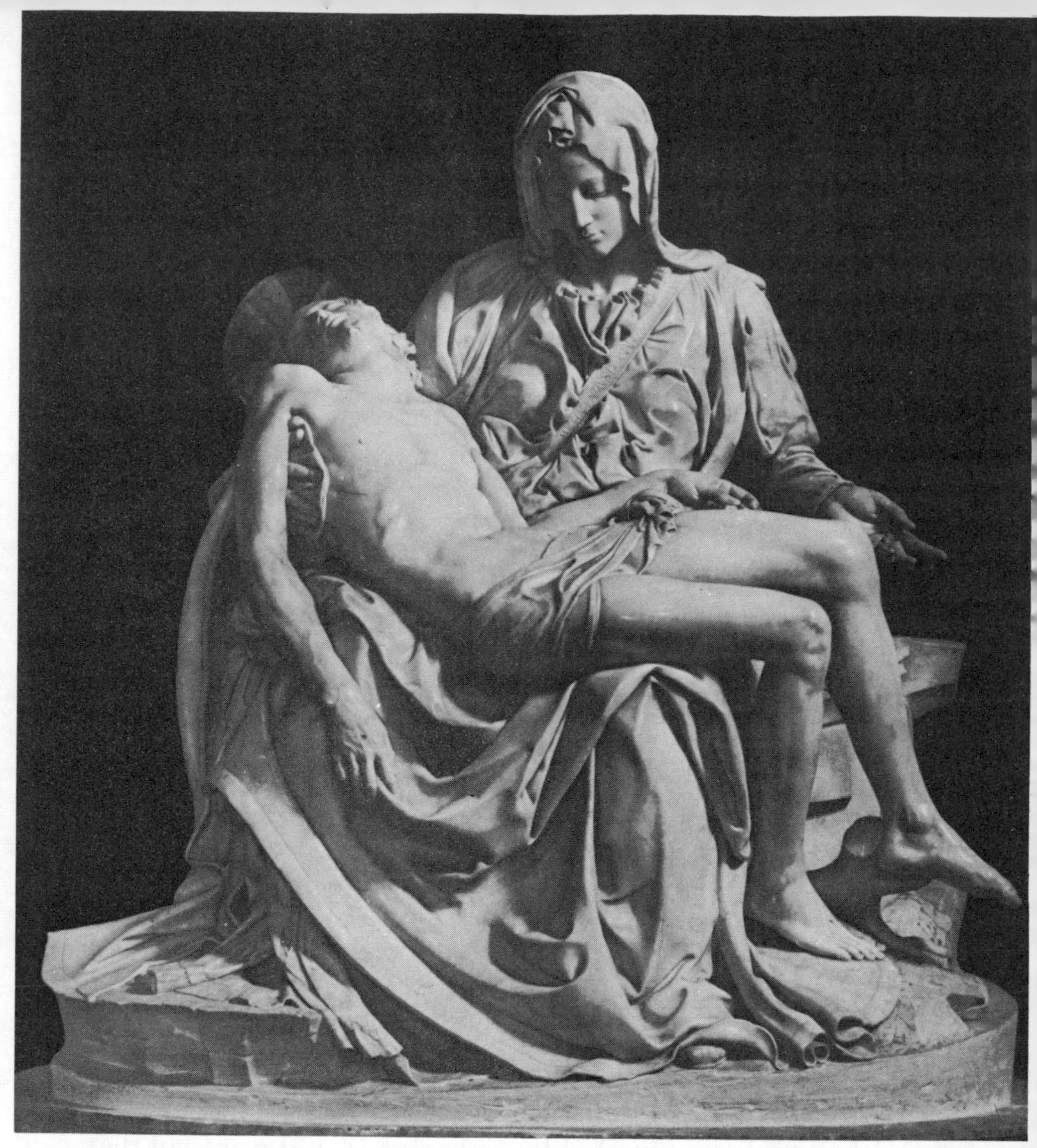

FRATELLI ALINARI

The Pietà in Saint Peter's by Michelangelo

Michelangelo paid little attention to his father's advice and worked for a whole year without stopping. Then one day the Pietà was placed in Saint Peter's Church for everyone to see. People were overwhelmed by its beauty. Tenderly the Virgin holds her dead son in her lap, and on her face is an expression of deep sorrow. Some people were surprised that the Mother of Christ had the face of a young girl, but Michelangelo explained that Christ's Mother was eternally young and pure.

Michelangelo was only twenty-five when he finished the Pietà, but he was fomous. He knew that he had created a statue of great beauty, so he carved in clear-cut letters the name of MICHELANGELO BUONAROTTI on the broad ribbon which runs across the Virgin's breast.

"Also I remind you," Ludovico Buonarotti wrote to his son in Rome, "that you must make every effort to return as soon as possible, and be assured that when you are here there will be work for you to do."

The Pietà was finished, Michelangelo was famous, and he had made money while he was in Rome. He knew that his family would welcome him now; so, early in the year 1501, Michelangelo returned to Florence.

The city had prospered while he had been away. The streets were filled with richly dressed ladies and gentlemen. Michelangelo, who hated luxuries, looked conspicuous in his dark tunic and cloak and worn boots. But everyone knew that he was the greatest sculptor in Italy. He set himself up in a studio and began to work.

Two prosperous business men from the northern country of Flanders asked him to carve a Madonna and Child for their church in Bruges. When it was finished the merchants shipped it to Flanders and proudly placed it in the church, where it may be seen today.

There is a dreamy look on the face of the stately Madonna. She does not look at the child who leans against her knee. Ten years before Michelangelo had carved the Madonna of the Stairs, and she, too, looks sadly away from the child in her lap. Perhaps Michelangelo thought of his own mother, who had died when he was very little, and expressed in the sad but tender faces of his Madonnas the grief of a mother who must soon leave her son.

In the yard of Florence's City Hall lay a long narrow block of marble. Many years before some sculptor had tried to make it into a statue. The governors of Florence refused to give it away, but when Michelangelo asked to use it the City Council gladly gave it to him.

"Worthy Master Michelangelo," they announced, "has been chosen to fashion . . . that male statue called the Giant."

When the huge block was set on end it was three times

as high as Michelangelo. As he studied the tall narrow shape he could almost feel the giant form which lived inside it. He would carve the figure of David, the brave boy who had killed Goliath. He seized his mallet and chisel and went to work.

A shed was built around the block so that no one could see Michelangelo working. Day and night Florentines heard the ring of chisel on stone as the sculptor feverishly chipped away. He worked steadily for two years. Then one day the David was finished. The city governors sent a committee of artists to look at the Giant and decide where it should be placed, but they could not agree on a suitable spot. Finally they decided to ask the opinion of the sculptor himself. Without hesitation Michelangelo said that David should stand at the entrance to one of the palaces in Florence.

With great care David was placed on a cart and pulled slowly through the streets of Florence. People watched, fascinated, as the Giant swayed back and forth in the frame which held it upright. His handsome face stared severely into second-story windows as it passed by. For three days Michelangelo anxiously followed David's progress. At night the government appointed a guard to watch over the statue so that no harm should come to it.

On the fourth day a great crowd gathered in front of the palace. The church bells rang out joyously as David was placed on his pedestal. All day the people of Florence celebrated with parades and dancing. The youthful figure of David looked victoriously over the crowd. The Giant had come to life and Michelangelo, like David, had triumphed.

Michelangelo was now the most famous sculptor in Italy, but the best known painter was Leonardo da Vinci, who was almost twenty years older. Leonardo was tall and handsome. He had exquisite taste, and a polished manner which irritated the younger artist. While Michelangelo was working on the Giant, Leonardo was decorating one of the walls of Florence's council chamber. Everyone discussed Leonardo's magnificent battle scene, and Michelangelo was jealous.

When the David was finished the City Council asked

Michelangelo to decorate a wall of the chamber. The sculptor was elated, for he felt sure he could paint a finer picture than Leonardo's.

He plunged into the work furiously. He, too, chose a battle scene, but it would not look like Leonardo's picture, which was a maze of frenzied horses and screaming warriors. He chose to paint an incident in a battle between the cities of Florence and Pisa, when on one hot summer day the Florentine soldiers had been swimming in a river near Cascina and the Pisan soldiers had attacked them. Michelangelo made a drawing which showed a tangle of nude soldiers hurrying desperately to get into their armor. So beautifully did he draw the figures that they seemed to be carved rather than painted.

Artists from all over Italy came to watch the two painters. Many preferred Leonardo's scene of blood and fury. Others liked Michelangelo's powerful nude figures in violent action.

The contest between the two artists continued furiously. Leonardo had transferred his drawing to the wall and was painting it in glowing oil colors. Michelangelo's drawing was ready for the wall, too, when suddenly he was told to stop. Pope Julius had an important job for him and ordered him to come to Rome immediately. He could not refuse so great an honor. Even the famous Leonardo had never been offered a commission from a Pope. So once again Michelangelo set out for the city of Rome.

Michelangelo's drawing of the Battle of Cascina was never transferred to the council chamber wall, and some years later the sketch disappeared. Today we have only a copy to remind us of the exciting picture which had been discussed so fiercely.

Pope Julius II had great energy and ambition. He wished to be remembered as the most glorious ruler of Christendom, so he ordered Italy's greatest sculptor to design for him a magnificent tomb. Michelangelo drew a picture of a majestic tower of marble. It had eight stories and was decorated with forty gigantic statues.

"When it is finished it will be the most beautiful in the world," he wrote to a friend. Julius was delighted with the design and ordered Michelangelo to hurry to Carrara to choose

BROWN BROTHERS

Michelangelo self-portrait

the marble. The great white blocks were shipped to Rome and piled in the square in front of the cathedral. In a nearby studio Michelangelo started to work.

Julius followed the progress of the tomb excitedly. He had a secret corridor built by which he could visit the sculptor's studio without being seen.

Out of one of the blocks of marble, Michelangelo carved a statue of Moses.* The majestic bearded figure is not supposed to be a portrait of Julius, but in the angry gaze of the great leader the sculptor expressed his idea of the fiery and ambitious Pope.

A year went by and Julius began to lose interest in the tomb. The corridor wasn't used any more, and the Pope refused to send Michelangelo any money. Enraged, the sculptor went to see him, but was turned away. Burning with the insult he rushed home and wrote a letter.

* See photograph on page 322.

"Most Blessed Father," it said, "I have today been driven out of the palace by orders of your Holiness, wherefore I am informing you that if you wish to see me you must look for me elsewhere than in Rome." Then he sold everything in his house, packed up his sketches, and set out on horseback for Florence.

That night five horsemen galloped full speed out of Rome. A few hours later they caught up with Michelangelo and handed him a letter from Julius. "When you have seen this," it said, "return to Rome under penalty of our displeasure."

Angrily Michelangelo shouted at the Pope's messengers that he would never return to Rome, and turning his horse in the direction of Florence he galloped off into the night.

As soon as Michelangelo arrived in Florence he began once more to work on his battle scene. He paid no attention to the pleading letters from Julius urging him to return to Rome. Six months later, however, the Pope arrived in the nearby city of Bologna and Michelangelo agreed to meet him. He took with him a letter from the governor of Florence. "Michelangelo is an excellent young man," it said. "We cannot recommend him too highly. One has to show him love and treat him kindly and he will perform things that will make the whole world wonder."

When Julius read the letter he decided to pardon his favorite sculptor. He gave Michelangelo his blessing and ordered him to start work on an enormous bronze statue. It was supposed to be the figure of Pope Julius for one of the churches of Bologna. Michelangelo worked on it for a year. When the figure was finished it was placed over the entrance of the church. Julius was delighted and ordered his sculptor to come to Rome immediately. Michelangelo thought of the great blocks of marble piled high in his studio waiting to be carved into statues for the tomb, and decided to obey the Pope's orders.

But Julius had lost interest in his tomb. Anxiously he awaited Michelangelo's arrival in Rome, for he had decided to have the sculptor paint pictures on the ceiling of his private chapel. Michelangelo was downcast when the Pope told him the plan. "Painting is not my trade," he said, but Julius paid no at-

Figure of God the Creator from the Sistine Chapel Ceiling

FRATELLI ALINARI

tention. Reluctantly Michelangelo consented to decorate the ceiling.

Michelangelo studied the chapel vaulting high above him. Suddenly there flashed into his mind a terrifying and magnificent plan. He would cover the whole surface with stories from the Bible. The pictures would tell the history of mankind from the creation of the universe to the birth of Christ.

Julius was excited when he saw Michelangelo's sketches and ordered him to start work immediately. One summer day in 1508 Michelangelo climbed the scaffolding of the Sistine Chapel with a roll of sketches under his arm. When he reached the platform under the ceiling he lay on his back and began to paint. For Michelangelo this was the beginning of four long years of torture.

The blazing summer sun beat through the chapel ceiling onto the platform where Michelangelo lay painting. "I am suffering greater hardships than any man endured, ill and with overwhelming labor," he wrote once to his brother in Florence. Paint dropped from his brush into his eyes. His back was arched awkwardly on the hard platform, and his feet hung loosely over the edge. When it grew dark he worked by candle light. He had a mattress brought up to the platform and often he slept there.

"I have no friend of any kind and I do not want any," he wrote, for only in quiet solitude could he bring to life the story of the creation. Occasionally the silence was broken by the sharp ring of a stick on the stone floor. Looking down, Michelangelo could see the white bearded figure of Julius pounding his cane impatiently. Aching in every limb he climbed down the scaffolding. When would the work be finished, Julius wanted to know, and Michelangelo shouted angrily that it would never be finished if the Pope interrupted him all the time. One day in answer to Julius's question the artist snapped back, "When I am able!" Julius was enraged.

"When I am able! When I am able!" he shouted furiously and brought his cane down sharply on Michelangelo's head.

Infuriated, Michelangelo rushed home and started to pack his belongings. But Julius sent a messenger to his house who persuaded him to return to the chapel.

For two years Michelangelo endured the agonies of the scaffolding, but still the ceiling was not finished. Then one day Julius demanded to see the work. In a burst of rage Michelangelo had the scaffolding torn down, and the Pope gazed in wonder at the gigantic paintings high above him. The nine central panels of the vaulted ceiling were filled with magnificent pictures which told the Bible story of the creation, and so beautifully were they painted that the figures seemed to be actually alive.

The side panels of the ceiling were still empty, however, so once more the scaffolding was put up and Michelangelo, ill from overwork, climbed to the platform and started to paint.

Through two more stifling summers and two dark winters Michelangelo lay on his back and painted. He filled some of the side panels of the ceiling with figures of the prophets. Their terrifying warnings must have reminded him of the fiery sermons of the monk, Savonarola, which had made such a deep impression on him when he was young.

Michelangelo read his Bible often and was moved by the thundering words of the prophet Ezekiel, who had said to his people: "So will I send upon you famine and evil beasts and they shall bereave thee: I, the Lord, have spoken it."

All the righteous anger which inspired these words seems to be expressed in the dynamic figure which Michelangelo painted.

A fourth summer passed, fall came, and still Michelangelo lay on his back in the Sistine Chapel. His only companions were the great figures he was bringing to life on the ceiling.

For days he ate only stale bread, which he kept on the platform with him. Often he slept with his boots on, and when he removed them his skin fell off in flakes. He had terrible cramps in his legs and he was almost blind from eyestrain.

In the panels between each prophet he painted magnificent draped figures of the women who were the prophets of ancient Greece. They were called sibyls. One of the loveliest is the Delphic Sibyl, whose beautiful face is full of anguish as if she were predicting a tragic future for mankind.

"I have been here a thousand years, I am more exhausted than man ever was," Michelangelo wrote to his father. But his family showed little sympathy for the tortured artist. They continually asked him to send them money. Their letters were full of complaints of every kind.

Exasperated, Michelangelo wrote to his brother in Florence: "I live here in great distress and the utmost physical fatigue. I have no friends and seek none, I have not even time enough to eat what I require; therefor do not put any more burdens upon me, for I could not bear another ounce."

But in spite of the four years of agony, Michelangelo continued to work. Between each prophet and sibyl he painted great pillars. On top of each he placed a magnificent nude figure. The figures do not tell a story. They are not people from the Bible or from the Greek and Roman myths. Michelangelo used them as a kind of ornament because he believed that there was no more beautiful decoration than the human form.

"I have finished the chapel which I have been painting. The Pope is very satisfied," Michelangelo wrote to his father in the fall of 1512.

Michelangelo was only thirty-seven, but he felt like a very old man. Four years of agonizing labor had made him almost blind. He had lain so long on his back that when he wanted to read he had to hold his book over his head. But he had finished the chapel at last.

The scaffolding was removed and the people of Rome came to gaze at the ceiling. When they saw Michelangelo's gigantic pictures high above them they gasped in amazement. There were no gorgeous costumes, no bright colors or rich decoration as in the paintings they had seen before. Michelangelo had told his story with three hundred and forty-three magnificent human figures, and so beautifully were they painted that they looked as if they had been carved. Even the best known painters were staggered by the colossal work.

He had toiled alone for four and one half years and had few friends, but he had proved to the world that the great sculptor Michelangelo was also the finest painter alive.

FRATELLI ALINARI

The Sistine Chapel

LOUISA MAY ALCOTT

Running in the Wind

BY CORNELIA MEIGS

When Louisa May Alcott (1832-1888) was asked by her publisher to write a book for girls, she answered, "I don't know anything about girls, except just ourselves." And that was exactly what she wrote about. Nearly every character in Little Women *is a character from Louisa's life. The family in* Little Women *is Louisa's family, Mrs. March is her mother, Abba; Meg, Beth, Jo, and Amy are the four Alcott girls.*

THE ancient red house, which had stood silent so long, was now, suddenly, full of life and bustle where there had been so much of shadows and silence before. A great adventure was just beginning, and strange, bright hopes were darting and lifting everywhere, just as the swallows had so long been darting and soaring about the eaves and above the great chimney. Louisa, standing on the doorstone, had only one feeling about this new place to which they had so surprisingly come. It would make a glorious playground.

Those unbroken fields, sloping to the river, how she was going to run and race across them! Concord had seemed to give her freedom but it was nothing to what she would have here. Even before she left Boston, she had become something of a champion in the way of hoop-rolling, and at the age of six she could drive her hoop all the way around the Common without a stop. In Concord, she had developed that art to so great a height that one day she ran and trundled to the foot of Hardy's Hill, a mile from home, then turned about without stopping and rolled the hoop back again. There were greater feats before her now, however, so that hoop-rolling seemed a very distant and a very tame enterprise alongside of what she would find to do here. She was well grown for a girl of eleven, with legs beginning to be very long, like a colt's, and which felt frisky, as a colt's do. They always skipped a little, all of themselves, as she walked along. Even after the long day of travel, they could have skipped and run, but she must go in, for her mother was calling her to supper. The twilight creeping up the valley, the misty vision of the mountains, both were beautiful to watch. But better still was the blaze and crackle of the fire in the huge chimney place. All of the travelers were thoroughly ready for supper of brown bread and roasted potatoes, served on tin plates, since as yet no china had arrived.

Louisa watched her father, thin-faced and clear-eyed, as he sat with the rosy light shining upon his mild countenance. She saw him partaking of his share quietly, solemnly, as though he were under a spell. The very food before him seemed to be a mark of the beginning of the great experiment, the undertaking which, according to his belief, was to make the world a different and a finer place in which to dwell. They were to live the perfect life here and to show others that life could be lived perfectly. He ate as though he were in a dream.

Abba moved here and there, intent only on the fact that they had actually arrived, with bundles and kettles and blankets in confusion all about them. The eyes of the children were falling shut from weariness and from a whole day of driving in the fresh, clean air. The baby—they called May the baby still, although she was actually three years old—was already asleep. Elizabeth, plump and eight, was very nearly so. The big, dark eyes of Anna were drooping. Louisa's, for a little longer, were still wide-awake and alert. Her father got up, put away his plate, and spoke. He was embarking upon one of those earnest conversations which were to be such a great part of the life in this new place, the discussion of all things under the sun. He began a little fable which was to appeal to the small members of the household and yet carry a meaning to every one there.

Louisa never heard the final message of that tale. The long day in the open air brought its expected end at last, and she was led away, blind with sudden sleepiness, to her bed. The tired mother, who had thought of everything, had managed, somehow, that there were beds of a sort, made up on the floor, into which she could tuck the children just as she had tucked them in the cottage in Concord, which now seemed left so far behind.

As we follow the daily life of this odd company through the weeks and months, we may be tempted to think with a smile of the ideas which were the foundation of this new life. We must remember, however, that Bronson and his friends, wise in some ways, mistaken in others, had the courage to find out, by the only possible means, where they were right and where they were wrong. There is only one method of testing a system of living; that is by living it. The year 1843 was at the end of a period very like that which has become all too familiar to us ninety years later. Long wars, involving both Europe and America, had brought their slowly arriving results of poverty, unemployment and bewildered suffering. Something was very wrong with the world, every one said. Here and there, a few were trying to organize totally new schemes of living. So many were tried then that we do not have to try them over again to-day.

This company at Fruitlands thought that private property was wrong and that everything must be owned in common. They followed the principle that animals must not be killed for men's subsistance, and must not even be forced to labor for man. They got up at the first light, bathed in cold water, and ate the same food they had partaken of in Concord; vegetables, bread, fruit and grain porridge. Breakfast was apt to be hurried and lunch eaten in weary silence; but there was a carefully observed rule that, as they dined in the evening, there must be talk of higher things. The men wore linen smocks, since wool robbed the sheep and cotton was produced by slave labor. They made their firmest stand of all against slavery.

There was much laughter in the old place; since four growing little girls can make it impossible for even a company of philosophers to be entirely solemn. There was in every corner that bright content that comes to a place when people are happy. All through the summer, Louisa spent glorious days, waking when the first red showed above the mountains, and running out into the sparkle of sunshine on dewy fields. As the fresh, morning wind would come down from the hills, she would turn so that it was behind her and go racing down the long slopes, feeling

The Alcott home at Fruitlands

so well, so light and so fleet that it was as though the wind could go no faster than she. Sometimes she sat in the shadow of a great clump of pines and heard the breezes sing, deep-voiced, in the branches. She would come in from these excursions, bright-eyed and rosy, to work beside quiet, industrious Anna at the tasks of the house.

Here was all the pleasure and excitement which comes to every young person who spends a summer on a farm. The animals—it was necessary at last to bring in the aid of oxen to break the stubborn hill acres—the miracle of the growing seeds and dark furrows turning green, the black crows flapping overhead, the smell of blueberries with sun on them, the solemn-faced woodchucks sitting upright amongst the stones,—all these were a new and continued delight to the girls. Louisa and Anna had the feeling, not merely that this was an alluring life, but that there was the zest of a strange adventure combined with the ordinary round of labor. They understood that the undertaking was unlike anything that had ever happened before and that somehow they, the two girls, had an actual part in it. They carried on their own share of the work in the farmhouse, Anna with a good deal of skill for a girl of twelve, Louisa still eagerly and awkwardly, both of them determined to be of help to their mother.

What they did was an odd mixture of pleasure and toil. Anna could bake bread and she and Louisa could get a meal without older help. Anna would go for a walk in the woods and come home with a shining face, unable to speak of all the beautiful things which she had seen. "My favorite word is 'beautiful'," she wrote in her diary. Both the elder children would help with the washing and ironing and then would go out to gather blueberries and blackberries in the thickets on the rocky slopes above them. Anna gave lessons to her sisters, but she was also not too old to play fairies with them, in the mossy clearings of the pine wood, or to gather oak leaves and flowers to make wreaths for every one in the household.

At the end of the day, both little girls would write in their journals, Anna filling hers with quiet, pleasant reflections and a record of the work she had done, Louisa covering her blotted pages with accounts of her turbulent thoughts, of her glorious runs on the hill, with the wind all about her, and, alas, of her quarrels with Anna, of their reconciliations and of her grief over the bad temper which would not be controlled. She was to find very early and was to know until very late that it is hard to be good. Abba Alcott, tired and hard pressed, did not always know how to calm the sudden storms. Bronson almost always could. No matter what had been the small differences, the day always ended in peace and with an unbroken knowledge between the two girls of how much they loved each other. They went to bed in the little room under the roof listening to the sounds above, to the wind sliding by overhead or stirring in the tall elm trees, or to the steady rain on the shingles so close above their heads. Louisa was excitable and sometimes was so full of the events of the day that she would lie in the dark, broad awake. She would recite poetry to herself, until presently the rhymes and rhythms would mix with the rustling of leaves or the patter of rain, and she would be asleep.

They would walk to the mill and watch the water go splashing over the dripping wheel, and see the smooth stream slide quietly over the dam and plunge, white and glittering in the sun, into the pool below. They would help rake the hay and carry it to the waiting cart; they would go up to the wood and build bowers of twigs and ferns for their dolls. On rainy days, they would both curl up in the big kitchen and read endlessly. In the evening, Bronson would not be too tired to get out the beloved book and read aloud in the light of the bayberry candles, the story of which Louisa spoke in her diary as "dear Pilgrim's Progress." Then at last, when it was bedtime again, he would put down the book, look about with his mild, radiant smile and ask,

"What is God's noblest work?"

They must all answer, the older philosophers, Charles Lane and Abram Wood and Joseph Palmer, and also the children, Anna reflectively, Louisa impulsively, sweet, round little Elizabeth sleepily. Abba Alcott, who had toiled without ceasing for a moment since daylight, would be sitting by the single lamp, sewing as though her life depended upon it. She was the only woman there, and hers was the only really able pair of hands for the tasks of preparing food, sweeping, washing, and keeping all this household clothed. The questions went round from one to another, but she did not answer. It was agreed that she was to be excused, that she had other things of which to think.

Louisa was growing so rapidly that she was beginning not to know at all what to do with her long arms and legs. She still thought that running on the hill was the most glorious thing in the world, and yet—it was strangely beautiful to sit longer and longer at the edge of the woods, looking down on Fruitlands and wondering—wondering—not as to what was God's noblest work or what was the nature of Man, not about any of the things talked of by the philosophers before the fire, but wondering and wondering still.

There is a certain incident, belonging to Louisa's early years, which it is very difficult to place in regard to time. It made so deep an impression upon her, and she spoke of it so often afterward, that it cannot be omitted from any account of her life, even though there is no record of just when it happened. It shall be told here.

One day, as she stood in the kitchen, she heard a strange sound in the brick oven. Before cooking stoves came into use and when open fires were still the only means for preparing food, it was usual, where there was a large chimney, to take the space next to the fire for a bricked-in oven, with an iron door. Wonderful cooking was possible in those old ovens; there are, indeed, certain kinds of bread which cannot be baked successfully in any other way. Louisa knew that no such noise was appropriate to the baking of bread; curiosity possessed her and she opened the door and peeped in. A face looked out at her, a black face, gaunt, and as wild and desperate as a hunted animal's. She jumped back, slammed the door and ran to her mother.

Abba told her in a whisper that there was a man hidden in the oven, a contraband. Louisa was to say nothing of what she had seen, since even the people in the house who knew of such a presence did not talk of it to one another, for fear of being overheard. Contraband was the name given to those runaway slaves who managed to slip away from the plantations of the South and make their way to the freedom which they could win by getting to Canada. People who sympathized were always willing to hide the fugitives and to pass them from one place to another until they came within reach of safety. If they were caught, they were carried back to chains and floggings, while their benefactors were liable under the law for concealing them.

Few laws have been so often broken. Long before the actual climax of the slavery quarrel, the matter of fugitive slaves was a sore point between the North and the South. When, in the white heat of final fury, South Carolina led her sister States out of the Union, she declared that the North had been the first to break the original compact by habitually giving shelter to runaway slaves. Abba and Bronson Alcott were amongst that great number who gave aid and shelter to the contrabands and thus aided, by one more instance, the growth of the tremendous quarrel which became the Civil War.

Louisa Alcott spoke several times in the record of her life of that moment when she saw what slavery really was. Her family think that perhaps the incident took place in Germantown, where the house at Pine Place had a big, farmhouse kitchen and a brick oven. The brick oven at Wyck was enormous. It is certain that Reuben Haines and his Quaker friends were strongly against slavery and that various old houses in the town have hiding places still pointed out as the refuge of runaway slaves. But Louisa was only two when she left Germantown; and she speaks always of the affair as something which she recollected so vividly that it seems scarcely possible it happened when she was so small. It could not have been in Boston and almost surely was not in Concord. Fruitlands was somewhat out of the ordinary line of travel for the escaping contrabands; yet all through New England there are places, as at Germantown, where they have been hidden. We cannot be sure where and when she saw that terrified face in the darkness, but we do know that she never forgot it and that it helped to bring her to a great resolve in later years. Even when she was only eleven, it was about slavery as well as about many other great and small things, that she wondered as she sat on the hillside above Fruitlands.

The grain was tall in the sloping fields, growing even more rapidly than young Louisa; the apples were swelling on the trees; summer was passing. So many questions had been asked about the new experiment that the philosophers found themselves too often called from their work to explain their ideas and principles to others. It was beginning to be time for the harvest; every one was anxious to make sure of the barley which was to be the chief crop of the newly broken fields. What they had to put in the barn for the winter might make for either the life or the death of the enterprise. Just as the grain was ripe, however, just after it had been cut and stacked to dry, there came a summons to a conference which Bronson and his friends could not put aside. The barley could wait for a little, they were sure; and here was another harvest which they felt was more pressing.

They trudged away and left Abba, the four girls and young William Lane to take care of the farm. One day passed calmly, but by the next trouble began to threaten. The merciless warning of a northeast storm was in the sky; dark clouds were rolling up. Wind and lightning showed among the thunderheads; rain was evidently upon them. The children ran out, bringing baskets

BETTMANN ARCHIVE

Louisa May Alcott in 1860

and bags, anything in which grain could be carried. Abba snatched from the pine chest her Russia linen sheets and ran after the others. The sheets were spread upon the ground; the little crew of harvesters worked like ants; they carried their loads to the barn, then rushed back, panting. The big sheaves almost upset the smaller workers, the grain spilled down their necks and the stubble was harsh and sharp beneath their running feet. But by the time the storm broke, the bulk of the crop was safe under the big barn roof. There was something, at least, put away for the winter.

There was corn to harvest later, and again the children helped, this time with the husking, which went on into the night, lit by lamps in the barn. It was beginning to grow cold now; searching winds swept down from the highlands and played at will through the draughty old house. The band of philosophers had dwindled; hard work had quenched the enthusiasm of some; cold and discomfort hastened the going of others. Charles Lane and his son would not give up, nor would Bronson Alcott. But he and Lane would have long talks in the little study away from the main room. The girls, passing the door, would hear such unaccustomed words spoken as money, crops, income.

Louisa never knew just when it was that she began to feel the stirring of change in the air and realized that a chill cloud of desperate trouble was slowly settling down upon them all. Her father had worked like a dozen men upon the farm, in the relentless determination to make it produce enough to feed them all. He was always tired; but it was not weariness which shadowed his countenance now. Abba Alcott's deep eyes followed him wherever he went about the house. She herself was worn to the verge of exhaustion, but she toiled unfalteringly at her daily work. The look on her own strong face was not one of mere anxiety. It was terror.

They had celebrated Elizabeth's birthday in June, in perfect fashion, with a little tree in the woods, decked with presents, with a procession winding up the path, singing as it went, to the music of Charles Lane's violin. William Lane and the girls had lessons with their father and instruction in music from Lane. They shared all the tasks together, the children and Abba sometimes helping to rake hay in the fields, Bronson often doing the cooking, Lane having been known to assist with the washing. It was all very gay at first; then it was gay no longer. Louisa's birthday came and her father's, both on the twenty-ninth of November, but the snowy day was little more than barely noticed as a festival.

"Our way has gone wrong," Bronson was heard to voice his despair at last, as he and his friend sat in the study. Lane, apparently not so much disturbed as his companion, answered in an eager stream of talk, through which one phrase sounded plainly again and again.

"The Shakers, the Shaker Community, has succeeded where we have failed."

Across the river, on the slope of the hill opposite, stood the Shaker village with its plain houses, its spreading orchards and broad, well-tilled fields. They were a body of people who also owned all property in common and did their work by sharing the tasks. The men lived in one building and the women in another, for they did not believe in marriage and thought there should be no such things as wives and husbands and households with children. The Government turned over to their care the orphans and foundlings which, to-day, are brought up in state homes. These children lived all together in common nurseries. They had good food and sensible training, but, so Louisa and Anna must have wondered, as they looked at those gray buildings beyond the hill, did they have enough love? Did the babies ever cry for some one to rock them; did the older girls ever long for a person so near and so dear as to be almost a part of oneself—a person like Mother?

Life at Fruitlands was strange and hard, but the little Alcott girls did not know it. So surrounded were they by love and watchfulness that the discomforts and privations which crept more and more into their days did not seem to matter. What did matter was that these two beloved ones who were their whole world were growing day by day more sorrowful and desperate. Often and then oftener, Bronson Alcott and Charles Lane would walk away over the hill to the Shaker village, and Abba Alcott, the girls' mother, would watch them from the window.

One night Louisa, slipping into bed with her sister, felt Anna's firm body suddenly shaken with sobs. The two clung together, weeping wildly in fully admitted terror.

"What is it?" Louisa questioned desperately.

It was something about Mr. Lane, Anna explained. She had got an inkling of the truth,—that Lane thought they ought not to be there, Abba, Anna, Louisa and the little girls. He was trying to persuade Bronson to give them up, to live as the Shakers did, and to forget that he had any children or that they ever were a family.

Louisa's heart stood still at the very thought. Few children loved their parents and each other as did the little Alcotts. They had so little else; but they at least had one another! Louisa's strong, warm nature held passionately to her dreaming father, to her devoted, toil-driven mother, to the two smaller ones, gentle-spirited Elizabeth and May of the vigorous will. She had the feeling that she wanted to protect them as well as to love them. She knew, even in her child's mind, that her mild, visionary father, with his great ideas, needed them all to help him keep safely in the path of ordinary life. Charles Lane might insist that, for the sake of a tremendous purpose, a man ought to give up such small things as family love, loyalty and devotion to one's own. He did not know that it is upon such things that the very structure of life is built. It was in those dark and desperate days that Louisa learned to know the truth of what family life should be, learned it and never forgot.

Did the support of the "dear Pilgrim's Progress" help them then? I think that it must have, that each one of them thought of that immortal ordeal and gathered some courage from it. There is a glorious passage when Christina, the mother of the family, goes down into the river, without fear or hesitation, to reach the beauty of the life beyond. Abba must have felt that she was crossing some such river of doubt and terror now, must have felt the water very cold about her knees as she girded her fortitude and waited. No discussion of the matter passed between her and the older girls, but they all three understood one another—everything in Louisa's after life shows how fully she understood what was threatening them then.

One thing Bronson Alcott believed, in which he was right seventy years before other people began to see the same truth. He maintained that children had minds and hearts and spirits of their own, and should have a voice in what was decided concerning them. It was a portentous moment in the history of them all, when he finally acted upon that belief.

On a certain evening, when Charles Lane was temporarily away, Bronson called a family council and laid the matter before them all. He and his wife and the two older girls faced the issue squarely; should they separate for the sake of Bronson's idea or should they keep together? There was no question of what the children thought. Anna and Louisa were able to speak their passionate desire; the smaller ones, feeling vaguely that something was wrong, merely cried and clung to their father. Abba Alcott, even now, did not say a great deal. He must do what he felt was best, she told him, but he must be sure what was best. He listened with bent head. He could make no decision even now. Next day, Charles Lane came home.

Then, suddenly, everything was settled. The children, perhaps nobody, ever knew just how it came about. Charles Lane and his son were gone, after some scene with Bronson Alcott of which, happily, there is now no record. In that bare house, with the December blasts whirling about it, the Alcotts all gathered close, fiercely close together before the hearth, safe from being torn asunder.

But something had happened to the children's father. Louisa stared at him as he sat in his chair, looking about at them with a broken smile. He was happy to be with them, but the fearful struggle had shattered him. He was worn out, he was ill unto death. He had worked so desperately on the Fruitlands farm, trying to draw from those unwilling acres a living for his family, for his companions and his idea! He was tired with this outward struggle; he was still more worn from the battle of doubt within. The children, with round eyes of terror, saw him lying on his bed finally, lying there day after day, too ill to move, to speak or to eat. It seemed as though, after all, he was going away from them.

Abba Alcott's unbroken spirit still stood firm in that house, as the days passed. From her the girls learned to see that, when all else fails, courage is the only thing left to cling to, courage and faith in God. The slow days crept by as the illness increased and then spent itself, until rest and untiring care and returning peace of mind began to accomplish their ends. Bronson Alcott was courageous too. He had seen his great experiment fail in spite of everything he dared to put into it. Although he had fallen into some errors, he had been wise enough, in the very last hours of despair, to know that he was mistaken. He had refused, finally, to wreck the lives of his beloved ones, even though he felt that he had wrecked his own. Strength and health began to come back very slowly, as little by little he was drawn away from the open door of death.

Abba's devoted and understanding brother came to her aid in this desperate situation. He had never failed to appreciate Bronson. Through the help of Samuel May, she was able to rent a house in the near-by town of Still River, a house dignified enough to boast a name of its own, "Brick Ends." As soon as Bronson was sufficiently recovered, they left the draughty, bare farmhouse and moved their few remaining possessions to the village.

It was very different from the gay arrival in June, that day when they set out on the journey away from Fruitlands. Bronson Alcott, still helplessly ill, was carried out of the house and laid, wrapped in blankets, upon a wood sledge. That was the easiest way to take him over the rough road to Still River. Anna walked beside him, his gentle, unquestioning daughter, who had wondered and suffered over all this incomprehensible affair, but who took it as it came, with no rebellion or protest of her own.

Louisa came behind, one rapid thought treading fast upon the heels of another. How was this strange adventure to end? Where were they going now and what were they to do? They were together at least, and, as long as she lived, she was going to battle against anything that might try to separate them. People who loved one another must stand together. So far she, who was barely eleven years old, had been able to do little; she had only stood by and watched the peril coming closer. But she could help soon; she must help, she would help always. Her old comrade, the wind, was sweeping and calling all across the hill, but she had no time to turn back for a last run with him. Louisa Alcott, as she trudged away over the snow, had set her face determinedly toward the real adventures of life.

The Alcott family was moving. It was not the first time, as we well know, nor yet the last; for, in the first twenty-eight years of Louisa's life, this household was to achieve the record of twenty-nine moves. Scars on the mahogany and walnut dressers bore witness, now, of perhaps a dozen upheavals through which they and the Alcotts had gone together. Louisa, standing on the threshold and watching the low-posted beds and the horsehair sofas come staggering in, was now thirteen years old.

Moving had never ceased to be an adventure with the casual Alcotts, and, with the exception of that single, heavy-hearted departure from Fruitlands, was invariably a gay occasion. The rambling brown house, which was now to be their domicile, resounded with cheery voices all along its dark passages. The corridors offered steps up and steps down, to betray unwary feet not yet used to the small individualities which every one expected in houses of the Revolutionary period. No one, however, cared about such small inconveniences. Louisa's spirit thrilled to the adventure of taking up life in a new place, in a storybook old dwelling with a pine-covered hill behind it, and with a gate opening upon the Concord-to-Lexington highroad. Down that road Paul Revere had galloped; over the pine-covered hill had marched a company of redcoats to take part in the first battle of the Revolution. The family was glad to come back to Concord, the peaceful, pleasant town with its square white houses and with its neighbors who were all friends.

Since leaving Fruitlands two years before, they had dwelt, first for eight months in Still River, later for a short time in Concord, taken into the house of a good friend who was glad to help them in their extremity. Finally they moved to Boston, where Abba as well as Bronson looked for work for the support of the family. Now, however, under the suggestion of that unfailing friend, Mr. Emerson, and with his help, they were returning to Concord, this time to reside in a house that actually belonged to them. It seemed as though at last they might be settling upon some permanent plan of living. They decided to name the house Hillside; it is now known as Wayside.

The big, wooden dwelling had been surrounded, at first, with various buildings, sheds, a wheelwright's shop, and a barn across the way. Mrs. Alcott, with vigorous enterprise, had the barn moved to their side of the road, had the shop cut in two and each half attached to an end of the house. In one of these two small wings was a little room which was to be Louisa's very own, where she could keep all her treasures, write and read, and do whatsoever she liked. It had a door into the garden, so that she could run outside, under the trees, whenever the fancy seized her. How long she had desired just this, a place of her very own!

Hillside, later called Wayside

The house had eight outside doors, so that, as they were settling to the table, or to read about the lamp in the low-ceilinged sitting room, a rap somewhere would send every member of the family flying, each one to a separate door, to admit the arriving friend. It was there, with a great deal of flurry and fluttering, that the household sat down at last, that evening of the moving-in. Anna had been busy in the kitchen; Louisa had kindled crackling fires in the numerous fireplaces. The smaller children were washed and Bronson came out from the congenial task of unpacking his books. Around the table there began a hilarious account of the adventures of the day, each person having her own joke to tell of the absurd mishaps which go with moving, of the things which were lost and broken, of the lack of things which could not be had in a household where money was still as scarce as good spirits were abundant.

In Louisa's eyes, the two great assets of the new abode were the little room in the wing and the barn. The Alcotts never kept a horse, although the girls often dreamed of galloping down the shady Concord roads, as did the more fortunate members of their acquaintance. There are, however, a hundred good uses for a roomy barn, other than those intended by the original builder. As every one knows, barns are particularly well suited for dramatic purposes. The drama, at that time, was Louisa's ruling passion. It is probable that before she slept that night, she was already busy outlining plots wherein beautiful heroines were rescued from dungeons, and princesses, disguised as slaves, won the hearts of disillusioned kings. As soon as the little room was in order, very bare and neat, with the scent of dried herbs in the closet, Louisa sat herself down to the table and fell to creating. Thus were born not only Duke Roderigo, but Duke Roderigo's boots.

Some little time later the Alcotts' Concord friends were invited to witness the first, and possibly the only performance, of a drama in three acts by Louisa Alcott, enacted, from the hero and the villain down to the page boy who brings in the cup of poison, by the four Alcott girls: stage manager and mistress of costumes, Louisa Alcott. She was good at creative dressmaking and knew just what her characters should wear. The hero was of the extravagantly noble kind, full of splendid motives and manly virtues. It was absolutely impossible to portray him without a slashed doublet, a sash, and tall, romantic boots. Louisa, with her vigorous mixture of fanciful and practical energy, made not only the hero, but the boots as well.

Somewhere she laid hands upon some skins of tanned leather and cut out crude profiles of what she imagined a nobleman's boots to be. These she sewed together, over and over, as a less enterprising young person sews patchwork. The result was truly magnificent. To walk any distance in the boots would have been quite impossible; but noblemen of Louisa's kind did not walk, fortunately; they strode a few paces to the rescue of captive maidens. Louisa trod the boards of the barn theater through her first play, in a blaze of glory. The curtain went down to applause which shook the old barn rafters. Some of the acclaim was for Anna, who was a really gifted actress, some of it was for Louisa; and a great deal of it was, deservedly, for the boots.

Excited and delighted by her first success, Louisa worked away in the little room, writing more and more dramas of the same sort. So many plots came crowding to her brain that from plays she overflowed into stories of the same grandiloquent sort. They were cut out, as the boots had been, by the pattern of what she imagined the life of the high nobility to be, and they were put together with the same industrious ingenuity.

Between the stories and plays she dreamed long dreams of the great things she hoped to do. "Am I going to be an actress," she wondered, "or a playwright, or a story writer?" She had no idea which it was to be.

Whatever it was, she was going to be it with all her might. Yet underneath her soaring fancies there lay a firm foundation of practical resolution. She saw plainly that her father, though recovered now, had very little real knowledge of the jostling world about him, that her mother was worn and worried over the problems of living. She could see that her sister Anna was as ambitious as herself, that Elizabeth was not strong, and that little May was growing up with a beauty-loving nature of passionate intensity. No children ever loved one another and their parents more than did the Alcotts. The way in which Louisa adored them all, as the years passed, could never be put into words,—the way she loved them and intended to take care of them.

There in the little room she made what she called the plan of her life and vowed to herself that she would give these beloved ones what each one needed. There was to be security for her father, peace and comfort and "a sunny room" for her mother, opportunity for Anna, care for Beth, education for May. One of the most interesting tales in the world is the record of how resolutely Louisa kept that promise and how, no matter what things went against her, she always refused to be beaten.

She was not, however, taken up continually with thoughts of the drama and of the future. She still ran in the fields and climbed the hills; she loved to sit under the pine trees on the ridge behind the house and think long, intense thoughts. Through all that first summer at Hillside she was free and happy. She would write busily in the little room, undisturbed, and would often work late into the evening. When she was tired at last, she would put down her pen and run out into the garden. The grass would be dewy and soft under her feet, the tall fruit trees would be dark against the stars. She loved to climp up into the crooked, comfortable branches and sit there, dreaming, until her thoughts had traveled far away from ordinary things. She would look back, within her memory, upon Fruitlands and all that incomprehensible incident which still cast a dark memory over their lives. She would wonder whether it was over and whether they were going to follow an ordinary existence now, to the end of their days. She hoped that they would not.

It is not certain whether she ever knew of the very last act in the curious drama of Fruitlands. Abba Alcott, whose struggle for the safety of her family had been so silent and so desperate, Abba whose will had stood against Charles Lane's and had finally won the day, seems in the end to have regretted her victory. Bronson's illness and despondency lasted so long, his heartfelt sorrow over the failure of the experiment was so great, that at last even his wife's brave determination faltered. She sat down and wrote a letter, such a letter as once she never would have dreamed that she could indite. She wrote to Charles Lane and asked him to come back, asked him to take up work once more with Bronson, so that he might be happy again. She knew what such a thing meant. But she asked Charles Lane to come.

With what agony of anxiety she must have waited for his answer. As has been said, she was a woman of most intense feeling. We know she was, for otherwise she could not have humbled her pride and put by her greatest desire for the sake of her affection for Bronson Alcott. Perhaps not even he knew of her offer; it seems scarcely possible that she told the girls of it. The reply came at last. Charles Lane had not continued with the Shakers, whom he had joined on leaving Fruitlands. Somehow that connection also had been unhappy. He was going back to England. With his departure, the shadow of his presence vanished from their lives forever. The Alcotts never saw him again.

One former member of the Fruitlands establishment, Joseph Palmer, came back to buy the abandoned land and to keep up a strange sort of idealized existence on the old place. He vowed that no traveler should ever go away hungry from his door. On one side of the farmhouse hearth stood a great iron pot of beans, on the other a similar one full of potatoes. Any one was welcome to come in and help himself. Destitute people took refuge there, sometimes staying for months or years. Joseph Palmer and his wife, Nancy, made no profession of being Transcendental philosophers; their only only system of thought was a complete overflowing of human kindness. Yet there was nothing weak and vacillating about the character of old Joseph. A farmer near him, Silas Dudley by name, disputed with Palmer the right of way across Dudley's land from the Fruitlands farm down to the high road.

Mr. Emerson recounted to the Alcotts how, when a deep snow fell, Joseph Palmer undertook to clear the drifts away from the path across the disputed land, while Silas, the owner, sallying out with his shovel, fell grimly to work to shovel it on again. Regardless of the pleas of their alarmed households, they worked against each other all day long, two old men in the bitter cold. Finally a compromise was suggested. If Mr. Emerson were called upon to decide which was right, would both agree? They said they would; Emerson's was a name to conjure with, such was every one's confidence in his justice and his impartial friendship. The dispute was decided and the tale carried home to the Alcotts. Louisa and her sisters could laugh over it, in spite of the dark memories of Fruitlands. But it is not certain whether Abba could join in their laughter.

What a friend Mr. Emerson was! Always, when things seemed difficult, when troubles were on the point of overwhelming this happy-go-lucky family, he was at hand to offer aid. Advice, belief, more substantial things, he was ready to give them all. His big, square white house was not far away, a refuge and meeting place for all of his legion of friends. Here in the parlor, sitting before the broad, white-paneled fireplace, Bronson Alcott could talk and talk of the things deepest in his heart and know that he spoke to one who would truly understand. Those red velvet, cushioned chairs, the long sofa against the wall, the crackling flames shining on Emerson's unclouded face, what a scene of peace it was for a storm-tossed philosopher! Sometimes there sat with them a very shy, young man, who did not say much, but whose ideas were like clear flame when once he gave voice to them. Henry Thoreau, so diffident that very few people ever could say they really knew him, was a warm and close friend of the Alcott and Emerson families. What talk it was, there by the fire, of the threat of war still a great way off, of the new ideas, of Transcendentalism, of regrets and wondering over Fruitlands. Fiery talk, quieted by Emerson, gloomy talk cheered by him! Wonderful talk that will not easily be matched in our hurried time!

For Abba Alcott, Mr. Emerson had practical, steadying counsel, shrewd advice concerning those money matters which perplexed her so sorely. To Louisa he gave the freedom of his library and all that went with such a privilege. She was at liberty to choose anything from those tall mahogany shelves which reached to the ceiling, to curl herself in a corner of the comfortable sofa and read to her heart's content. Her curiously varied education, got partly through her father, and a great deal of it through reading by herself, received a strong impetus here where such a wealth of wise, friendly books was ready to her hand. She could read anything she wished; but she got advice now and then, suggestions dropped gently by the owner of that hospitable library. She would slip in, see Mr. Emerson sitting at work, writing busily on a board upon his knee, for he never even owned a desk. She would take down a volume, get a quick smile from that strong, sensible, infinitely friendly face, and slip quietly out again. She would stop in one or another of the other rooms, the broad, sunny dining room, or the shabby, beloved parlor where the chairs and the carpet were so worn by the coming and going of philosophic feet. She might perhaps peep into the guest chamber, the room of honor opening from the dining room, which the Emersons, also fond of "Pilgrim's Progress", called "The Room Looking to the East." Its windows opened upon fields and stone walls, upon rows of apple trees along the road which wound up the hill and disappeared. Matthew Arnold slept there and many another distinguished guest who came from afar to seek out Ralph Waldo Emerson.

It was no wonder that Louisa, just growing into the romantic age, acting extravagant dramas and composing them, reading the great tales of romance, should have plunged, herself, into the very depths of fathomless sentiment. She found, in Mr. Emerson's library, a book which told of a little girl's adoring admiration for the great poet, Goethe. She made up her mind, at once, that she would be like Bettine, and that Mr. Emerson would be just the proper subject for such hero-worship. Little by little, she built up a dream of romantic feeling about this dear friend of them all. When she had been writing late, in the little room, she would, as has been said, slip out into the darkness of the garden, climb into the friendly arms of one of the big, hospitable cherry trees and sit there watching the moon come up over the dark hills, thinking deeply romantic thoughts. Louisa was growing up. That she was not quite grown and still a little girl, we know from the fact that the owls, swooping silently through the still night, would frighten her so much that she would run headlong into the house to bed.

She left flowers very shyly on the doorstep of her adored Mr. Emerson. She sang a serenade under his window, sang it in German and in such a small voice that nobody heard her. The object of her devotion was utterly unconscious of what was going on in her youthful heart. Years later, when Louisa was so well grown up that all this seemed like a past existence, she told their friend of the period of sentimentality concerning him, and the two laughed together over the intensity of her young feelings. She had written him letters which she never delivered. He asked for them, when he heard of them so long afterward; but he was not allowed to see them. It was probably Louisa's first act when she came to years of discretion to destroy those missives; for when Mr. Emerson finally heard of them, they had long since been burned.

In the barn were held meetings of an important organization, the Pickwick Club. Only the Alcott girls were members; but they published a paper just the same, with laboriously written numbers full of stories by all of them, sentimental tales of Anna's, dashing poems by Louisa. The sisters also maintained a post office on the hill behind the house, where a girl friend of theirs would leave her letters, flowers and books, and where the Alcotts would post their replies. The post office was a well-loved institution which lasted as long as they lived at Hillside.

Thus passed the first summer. There was a day in the autumn when Louisa had gone out for an early run and stood at the summit of a wooded ridge, to watch the day break above the

WIDE WORLD

Louisa May Alcott as a successful author

river. The maples were scarlet and the birch trees gold, all about her; the morning was absolutely still, there was a thin mist over the low meadows beyond which the sun was coming up. It was a moment of such complete and unbelievable beauty that it made her suddenly feel that she was transformed into a different person. She said afterward that she never understood God so fully as she did at that second, and that she understood Him forever after, from having realized, all at once, the beauty of the world which He had given her to dwell in. She went home with something new in her heart which she was never to lose.

From the spring that she was thirteen until the autumn of the year that she was sixteen years old, she lived at Hillside. Not much seemed to happen to her; and yet, those years were extraordinarily important in what she learned, in what she discovered, and in what friends she made. There is no doubt that they were the happiest years of her life.

For the first time she went to school, the winter that she turned fourteen. Louisa and Anna had much ado to persuade her father and mother to let them go, for it had been Bronson's pride that, although he had no other pupils now, he could at least undertake the education of his daughters. He and Abba were wise enough to see, nevertheless, that the girls needed companions of their own age and should not always study alone. Anna found the new life interesting and easy to get used to; but it was not so simple for Louisa. She was very shy and was now so tall as to be conspicuous amongst girls of her own age. She was awkwardly conscious of being oversized and always felt large and clumsy and unduly burdened with hands and feet. She was so gay and so full of good spirits, however, that she was immediately welcomed by her new comrades. As they all grew better acquainted, some of them were surprised and startled by the sudden changes of mood which so often came over her, when, instead of being the most lively company in the world, she was, all at once, silent and unresponsive, wrapped in thoughts whose strange gloom she could not explain. Then the cloud would pass, leaving Louisa as cheerful and as much in demand as before. The Alcott girls made a great addition to Mr. John Hosmer's district school. Louisa could run faster and jump higher than any other girl there, and vault over fences with long-legged ease. She was always lamenting the fact that she was not born a boy.

The girls did not go to school a second year, but had lessons with their father and Mr. Henry Thoreau. Louisa seemed so much occupied with all the delights of a girl growing up, that it hardly seemed evident to any one how deeply she had resolved to set her shoulder to the wheel of the family fortunes. When she reached sixteen, she decided it was time to begin.

The barn, scene of her first dramatic triumph, was also the setting for her first venture in the greater enterprise of helping to take care of her dear family. She organized a little school there, probably at the suggestion of Mr. Emerson; for it was his children who made up the greater number of the pupils. In spite of his great love for Bronson Alcott and his belief in his friend's ideas, Emerson chose Louisa, rather than her father, to teach his own children. Bronson had really great views upon education; but it fell to Louisa to translate those views into something which the young persons about her could truly absorb and understand.

What she had learned from her father made her a good teacher; but it could not make her love the task of instruction. Besides knowledge, she brought to the task energy and an enthusiasm for succeeding, along with that boundless friendliness which is the heart of a real teacher's success. The little girls got much from her; she in turn got much from them. There is no better way to learn how to understand the minds of children than to teach them. Louisa gave generously and taught well; but she could not learn to like her work. She was too restless and impetuous; she was too prone to find the long hours of sitting still as trying as did even the smallest of her pupils.

Determination, however, can take the place of patience, if earnestly applied. As Louisa sat at her desk, presiding over the small flock, her own thoughts, still busy with romance, flitted far above their labors, just as the steel-blue swallows were flitting high above, amongst the rafters, or skimming out through the open door into the sunshine. Little Ellen Emerson loved Louisa and was often at Hillside, in just the same way that Louisa ran in and out of the big, white Emerson house. For her,

Louisa began to write some stories, very different from those of her usual melodramatic style. They were about flowers and birds and fields, little fables which were the natural flowering, in her own mind, of what she had learned while teaching the school. After reading them to Ellen, she tossed them aside amongst the plays and the tales of counts and nobles, which she so loved to compose. As yet few eyes besides her own had seen any of the scribbled manuscripts.

It may be guessed that the proceeds from this scholastic undertaking were not very great and were of far less value than the experience which came out of the summer's work. In the autumn certain questions became acute in the Alcott family. They had a roof over their heads, it was true. But with so little income, it was impossible for Abba Alcott to see that the six members of the household were properly clothed and fed. Bronson Alcott must not be misjudged. He was untiringly industrious, and anxious, above everything in the world, to do what he could for his family. Yet it was impossible for him to find employment of any sort which would support them. He could not, by the labor of his hands, do enough work to supply all their wants. He knew much of farming, but it had been proved at Fruitlands that his ideals and theories interfered with success, even in that form of occupation. For commercial work he had no talent at all and could not be of any practical use in a counting house or in any pursuit of buying and selling. He was beloved by all who knew him and looked up to with admiration by every one who understood what he had to offer. He gave lectures on Transcendental philosophy and on many others of the deep subjects being studied in that day. He was an excellent speaker, an exceedingly indifferent writer, a profound thinker and a devoted friend. As a practical support for his family, he was always striving, but in the eyes of the world, never successful. He was to come into his own, at last, but it was not now.

As they had done at Fruitlands, the family held council over ways and means, an unhappy depressed council, for it was evident that the pleasant life they were leading at Hillside must come to an end. Mrs. Alcott had been offered employment in Boston, as an official visitor to the poor, and a brother had offered the family his house in which to live. It seemed that the necessities of food and raiment came before the affection they all had for friendly, happy Concord and the nearness of their guide, philosopher and friend. The decision was made; they moved to town and once more entered upon a new era.

Louisa's experience with teaching gave her enough confidence to start bravely with the same sort of work in Boston. For two years she taught here and there, helped her mother, took care of small children as a nursery-governess, sewed, did anything to which she could turn her hand. The family fortunes did not prosper very greatly, so that there were often difficult times in those various dwellings in which they lived, one after another. There was never depression or discouragement, however, for something ridiculous was always to be seen in every misadventure, something to call forth mirth and become the basis for a treasured family joke. Every evening they would gather about the lamp on the table and each one tell of the occurrences of the day, always making a good story of it, to the great entertainment of the rest. Anna was teaching, Louisa was doing a dozen things, May was going to school. When the record of their doings was complete, Mrs. Alcott would read to them or tell them ever-new tales of her own childhood and girlhood. One of her audience, at least, never forgot any of those stories.

INDEX of Authors and Titles

ACKNOWLEDGMENTS

The publishers wish to express their appreciation to the following publishers, agents, authors, and artists who have granted permission to use material appearing in this book. Any errors or omissions are unintentional and will be corrected in future printings if notice is sent to The Crowell-Collier Publishing Company.

THOMAS Y. CROWELL COMPANY "God's Troubadour," from *God's Troubadour, The Story of St. Francis of Assisi,* by Sophie Jewett, copyright 1910, 1940, 1957 by Thomas Y. Crowell Company.

DODD, MEAD AND COMPANY, INC. "Growing Pains," from *Young Edgar Allan Poe,* by Laura Benet, illustrated by George Whitney and by photographs, copyright 1941 by Dodd, Mead and Company, Inc.

DOUBLEDAY & COMPANY, INC. "The Discovery of Radium," from *Madame Curie,* by Eve Curie, translated by Vincent Sheean, copyright 1937 by Doubleday & Company, Inc.; "Out of Darkness," from *The Story of My Life,* by Helen Keller, copyright 1902, 1903, 1905 by Helen Keller; reprinted by permission of Doubleday & Company, Inc.

FOLLETT PUBLISHING COMPANY "A Lawyer's Oath," from *Mr. Justice Holmes,* by Clara Ingram Judson, illustrated by Robert Todd, copyright 1956 by Clara Ingram Judson; reprinted by permission of Follett Publishing Company, Chicago.

FRATI MINORI COVENTUALI Illustrations "Brother Francis Gives His Cloak to the Poor Man" and "Brother Francis Giving Up His Worldly Goods," by Giotto; reproduced from the Basilica Patriarcale e Sacra Convento di S. Francesco, Assisi, by permission of Frati Minori Conventuali.

HARPER & BROTHERS "The First Tom Sawyer," from *The Autobiography of Mark Twain,* edited by Charles Neider, copyright 1959 by The Mark Twain Company; "The Pillar of Cloud and the Pillar of Fire," from *Moses* by Katherine B. Shippen, illustrated by Lili Cassel, copyright 1949 by Katherine B. Shippen; "The Traveling Newspaper Office," from *The Boys' Life of Edison,* by William H. Meadowcroft, copyright 1911, 1921 by Harper & Brothers, copyright 1939, 1949 by William H. Meadowcroft and Charles H. Meadowcroft; reprinted by permission of Harper & Brothers.

HOUGHTON MIFFLIN COMPANY "A Soldier Is Made," from *America's Robert E. Lee,* by Henry Steele Commager, illustrated by Lynd Ward, copyright 1951 by Henry Commager and Lynd Ward; "The Astrea to the Rescue," from *Carry On, Mr. Bowditch,* by Jean Lee Latham, illustrated by John O'Hara Cosgrave II, copyright 1955 by Jean Lee Latham and John O'Hara Cosgrave II; reprinted by permission of Houghton Mifflin Company.

ALFRED A. KNOPF, INC. "The Dream of Freedom," from *Mozart,* by Manuel Komroff, copyright 1956 by Manuel Komroff; "Greek and a Toothbrush," from *Mary McLeod Bethune,* by Emma Gelders Sterne, illustrated by Raymond Lufkin, copyright 1957 by Emma Gelders Sterne; reprinted by permission of Alfred A. Knopf, Inc.

MRS. HENRI LABOUISSE (Eve Curie) Photographs for "The Discovery of Radium," from *Madame Curie,* courtesy Mrs. Henri Labouisse.

JEAN LEE LATHAM Permission to reprint "The Astrea to the Rescue," from *Carry On, Mr. Bowditch,* published by Houghton Mifflin Company.

LITTLE, BROWN & COMPANY "Running in the Wind," from *Invincible Louisa,* by Cornelia Meigs, copyright 1933 by Cornelia Meigs; reprinted by permission of Little, Brown & Company.

McGRAW-HILL BOOK COMPANY, INC. "Lonely Crusader," from *Lonely Crusader: The Life of Florence Nightingale,* by Cecil Woodham-Smith, copyright 1951 by Cecil Woodham-Smith; reprinted with permission of Whittlesey House, a division of the McGraw-Hill Book Company, Inc.

McINTOSH AND OTIS, INC. "The Pillar of Cloud and the Pillar of Fire," from *Moses,* by Katherine B. Shippen; reprinted by permission of McIntosh and Otis, Inc.

JULIAN MESSNER, INC. "Dancing Star," from *Dancing Star: The Story of Anna Pavlova,* by Gladys Malvern, illustrated by Susanne Suba, copyright 1942 by Gladys Malvern; reprinted by permission of Julian Messner, Inc.

WILLIAM MORROW AND COMPANY, INC. "The Boy with the Horn," from *Trumpeter's Tale: The Story of Young Louis Armstrong,* by Jeanette Eaton, illustrated by Elton C. Fox, copyright 1955 by Jeanette Eaton; "Fighter Without a Sword," from *Gandhi: Fighter Without a Sword,* by Jeanette Eaton, illustrated by Ralph Ray, copyright 1950 by William Morrow and Company, Inc.; by permission of William Morrow and Company, Inc.

G. P. PUTNAM'S SONS "The Boy at Wrigley Field," from *Lou Gehrig: A Quiet Hero,* by Frank Graham, copyright 1942 by Frank Graham; reprinted by permission of G. P. Putnam's Sons, publishers.

THE VIKING PRESS, INC. "The Great Adventure," from *Nansen,* by Anna Gertrude Hall, illustrated by Boris Artzybasheff, copyright 1940 by Anna Gertrude Hall and Boris Artzybasheff; reprinted by permission of The Viking Press, Inc.

HENRY Z. WALCK, INC. "Years of Agony," from Michelangelo, by Elizabeth Ripley, published and copyright 1953 by Oxford University Press, Inc.; reprinted by permission of Henry Z. Walck, Inc., and Oxford University Press.

THE WORLD PUBLISHING COMPANY "The Meeting," from *Elizabeth: The Romantic Story of Elizabeth Barrett Browning,* by Frances Winwar, copyright 1957 by Frances Winwar; reproduced by permission of The World Publishing Company, Cleveland and New York.